From Toxic Institut
Therapeutic Environments

Residential settings
in mental health services

Edited by Penelope Campling,

Steffan Davies and Graeme Farquharson

Gaskell

© The Royal College of Psychiatrists 2004

Gaskell is an imprint of the Royal College of Psychiatrists, 17 Belgrave Square,
London SW1X 8PG, UK
http://www.rcpsych.ac.uk

British Library Cataloguing-in-Publication Data.
A catalogue record for this book is available from the British Library.
ISBN 1-904671-07-1

Distributed in North America by Balogh International Inc.

The views presented in this book do not necessarily reflect those of the Royal College of
Psychiatrists, and the publishers are not responsible for any error of omission or fact.

The Royal College of Psychiatrists is a registered charity (no. 228636).
Printed by Bell & Bain Limited, Glasgow, UK.

Contents

Tables, boxes and figures

Contributors

Dinesh Bhugra, Professor of Mental Health and Cultural Diversity, PO 25, HSRD, Institute of Psychiatry, London SE5 8AF

Heather Boardman, member of Francis Dixon Lodge Therapeutic Community, Leicestershire Partnership NHS Trust

Anthony Bree, Lead Nurse, Outreach Team, Francis Dixon Lodge Therapeutic Community, Leicestershire Partnership NHS Trust

Lin Burton, Department of Occupational Therapy, Mental Health Services for Older People, Leicestershire Partnership NHS Trust

Penelope Campling, Consultant Psychiatrist in Psychotherapy, Francis Dixon Lodge Therapeutic Community, Leicestershire Partnership NHS Trust, Gipsy Lane, Leicester LE5 6FA

Mick Collins, Research Nurse, Rampton Hospital, Nottinghamshire Healthcare NHS Trust, Retford, Nottinghamshire ON22 0PD and Honorary Research Fellow at the University of Sheffield

Sarah Davenport, Lead Consultant for Women's Secure Services, Guild Lodge, Guild Park, Whittingham, Preston PR3 2AZ, and Chair, Rehabilitation and Social Psychiatry Section, Royal College of Psychiatrists

Steffan Davies, Senior Lecturer in Forensic Psychiatry, University of Leicester, and Honorary Consultant Forensic Psychiatrist with a Special Interest in Rehabilitation, Rampton Hospital, Nottinghamshire Healthcare NHS Trust, Retford, Nottinghamshire ON22 0PD

Graeme Farquharson, Director, Relationships at Work Ltd, Ripon, North Yorkshire HG4 2DD

Justine Faulkner, Associate Director of Training and Development, Avon and Wiltshire Partnership Mental Health NHS Trust, previously Programme Lead for Acute Inpatient Care, Sainsbury Centre for Mental Health, 134–138 Borough High Street, London SE1 1LB

Wendy Ferguson, Department of Occupational Therapy, Mental Health Services for Older People, Leicestershire Partnership NHS Trust, South Charnwood CMHT, Bridge Park Plaza, Bridge Park Road, Thurmaston, Leicestershire LE4 8PQ

Wilson Firth, Consultant Psychiatrist for Adults of Working Age, Leicestershire Partnership NHS Trust, and Honorary Senior Lecturer, Leicester/Warwick Medical School, Brandon Unit, Leicester General Hospital, Leicester LE5 4PW

Rex Haigh, Consultant Psychiatrist in Psychotherapy, Winterbourne Therapeutic Community, Winterbourne House, 53–55 Argyle Road, Reading RG1 7YL; Chair of the Association of Therapeutic Communities and Personality Disorder, and Development Consultant for NIMHE South East

Shelley Hammersley, Department of Occupational Therapy, Mental Health Services for Older People, Leicestershire Partnership NHS Trust

Judith Hill, member of Francis Dixon Lodge Therapeutic Community, Leicestershire Partnership NHS Trust

Sheila Hollins, Professor of Psychiatry of Disability, St George's Hospital Medical School, Psychotherapist, Vice-President of the Royal College of Psychiatrists, and Vice-President of the Institute of Psychotherapy and Disability

Jeremy Holmes, Consultant Psychotherapist, North Devon District Hospital, Barnstaple, Devon EX31 4JB, and Senior Clinical Research Fellow, Department of Mental Health, Penninsular Medical School, Exeter

John Howat, Consultant Rehabilitation Psychiatrist, Nottinghamshire Healthcare NHS Trust, Westminster House, 598 The Wells Road, Nottingham NG3 3AA

Nick Humphreys, Adult Psychotherapist, Francis Dixon Lodge, Gipsy Lane, Leicester LE5 6FA

Kathleen Jones, Emeritus Professor of Social Policy, University of York. Correspondence: 44 West Moor Lane, Heslington, York YO10 5ER

Sandra Kelly, Lead Nurse, Francis Dixon Lodge Therapeutic Community, Leicestershire Partnership NHS Trust

Peter Kinderman, Reader in Clinical Psychology, University of Liverpool, Liverpool L69 3GB

Paul Lelliott, Director, College Research Unit, Royal College of Psychiatrists, London

Joel McCann, Counties Outreach Services, Suite B, The Point, Granite Way, Mountsorrel LE12 7TZ

Rudolf H. Moos, Senior Research Career Scientist and Emeritus Director of the Centre for Health Care Evaluation in the Department of Veterans' Affairs Health Care System, and Professor in the Department of Psychiatry and Behavioral Sciences at Stanford University in Palo Alto, California, USA

Paul Munroe, Clinical Risk Coordinator and Instructor in the Management of Violence and Aggression, Rampton Hospital, Nottinghamshire Healthcare NHS Trust

Ian Overton, Staff Nurse, Francis Dixon Lodge Therapeutic Community, Leicestershire Partnership NHS Trust

Sarah Paget, Training Services Manager, Community Housing and Therapy, Bishop Creighton House, 378 Lillie Road, London SW6 7PH

Alan Quirk, Research Fellow, College Research Unit, Royal College of Psychiatrists, 83 Victoria Street, London SW1H 0HW

Jim Rose, Director, The Nurture Group Network, 18 Ash Green, Billericay, Essex CM11 2LR, and former Professional Advisor to the Home Office on the placement and management of young people sentenced to long-term custody for serious offences

Peter Ruane, Rethink, Chelmsford and Mid-Essex Rethink Carers' Support Group. Correspondence c/o Steffan Davies

Valerie Sinason, Child Psychotherapist, Adult Psychoanalyst, Director of the Clinic for Dissociative Studies, 815 Finchley Road, London NW11 8AJ, and President of the Institute for Psychotherapy and Disability

Leela Thampy, Senior House Officer, Department of Psychological Medicine, King's College Hospital, London

Christine Timko, Research Career Scientist and Associate Director of the Centre for Health Care Evaluation at the Department of Veterans' Affairs Health Care System, and Consulting Professor in the Department of Psychiatry and Behavioral Sciences at Stanford University in Palo Alto, California. Correspondence: 795 Willow Road (152-MPD), Menlo Park, CA 94025, USA

Teresa von Sommaruga Howard, Architect, Organisational Consultant and Group Analytic Psychotherapist, 9 Westrow, Putney, London SW15 6RH

Terry White, Project Manager, Community Housing and Therapy, Eastbourne, East Sussex

Acknowledgements

The Editors thank Bethan Ashton, Anna Kaczmar, Theresa Maddon and Louise Weston, for administrative support and the Staff of Rampton Hospital Library.

Preparation of Chapter 14 was supported by the Department of Veterans' Affairs Office of Research and Development (Health Services Research and Development Service) and by NIAAA Grant AA12718.

Foreword

John Cox

This refreshing book is forged out of the therapeutic community movement energised initially by the reform of large mental hospitals but now tempered by a modern mental health service. The editors have nevertheless challenged simplistic ideas that privacy and personal space are always necessary in a therapeutic milieu, and that gender separation in admission wards is always appropriate.

Penelope Campling, Steffan Davies and Graham Farquharson are innovative in their approach and have successfully brought together other experienced authors who are also motivated by humanistic values. Maintaining a therapeutic environment in a modern mental health service is indeed a core skill and is consistent with the search for a personalised health service that includes biosocial and psycho-spiritual approaches.

This book is a wake-up call for trainers and trainees. Neglect supervised experience in large and small groups, neglect the discipline of the community meeting, cease to regard patients as people, and mental health services will become increasingly impoverished.

The therapeutic community approach to mental health is derived from a variety of ethical imperatives. This thoughtful book begins to spell them out and to stimulate an international reader to think about contrasting values and to develop further the evidence base for the effectiveness of these key social therapies.

John Cox
Professor Emeritus, Keele University
Secretary General, World Psychiatric Association
Past President, Royal College of Psychiatrists

Foreword

Anthony Sheehan

Mental health is close to my heart. I started out as a mental health nurse some 22 years ago and eventually found myself at the heart of policy-making.

During these years I have seen at first hand the shabby conditions and poor standards of care that some mental health service users have experienced. More recently, the Government has realised that mental health services are in dire need of modernisation and has tried to take notice of the 600 000 service users who expect and deserve a 21st-century mental health care system. The National Service Framework, followed by the National Health Service (NHS) Plan, identified mental health as one of the three top clinical priorities across the whole of the NHS.

What is clear is that many areas have endorsed the principles of the National Service Framework for Mental Health overall, but have not applied these principles to the design or delivery of their in-patient services. They plan a community-oriented service and provide a hospital often remote from key connections, with little thought, usually based on historical services rather than patient need. In too many places in-patient services have been relatively exempt from socially inclusive thinking and continue to overemphasise containment and segregation, unwittingly colluding with and reinforcing the public's negative stereotypes about mental illness.

The design and physical appearance of a unit and ward need to act as a tangible statement of value to service users, carers, staff and public. (Chapter 7 includes photographs of what can be done with care and imagination). Inclusive mainstream settings positively influence public perception of mental illness and diminish stigma and discrimination. We need to use our buildings to create positive awareness of mental health's place in the everyday reality of community life. Local user-friendly provision makes seeking help a less threatening experience for people and diminishes risk to individuals and communities.

Environments must also be opportunities for people to gain access to accurate information and meaningful dialogue. People who feel vulnerable or powerless can increase their self-confidence, personal effectiveness and resilience by being informed and sharing their experiences with people who listen with understanding and respect. Having a voice in developing services and influencing policies should be encouraged as much as possible.

Choice, information, positive role models, a sense of being heard and opportunities for developing skills and improving one's life should be the main features of a human, interactive and enabling environment. The contributors to this book are steeped in the experience of taking up these challenges and working through their inherent difficulties in a wide range of settings. I was particularly pleased to read perspectives from users (Chapters 15 and 25) and carers (Chapter 16) and also research evidence speaking of users' experiences (Chapter 5).

Residential units are home to the most vulnerable people in society, whereas acute in-patient areas are where people go during the most distressing and vulnerable stage of their illness, when they are in greatest need of support, help and understanding. If we are to move from a custodial ethos to a therapeutic one, we must have environments that reflect their purpose.

It is important for everyone who works in mental health care to understand that a new age is upon us. As part of this transformation, this book has an important role in raising awareness of what goes wrong when an environment become dehumanised and, conversely, what can be done to enhance and humanise an environment so that it can fulfil its therapeutic potential.

Anthony Sheehan
Director of Care Services
Department of Health

Preface

This book is about creating therapeutic environments for people in mental health settings. In our view, the idea of how you establish and protect a therapeutic environment has become lost in recent times. We would argue that the need for this knowledge and skill is timeless and, its having been lost, there is an urgency to reassert what this means and what is involved, particularly in the context of current knowledge, practice and evidence. For this reason, we have aimed to produce an introductory text accessible to all staff, including students and the newly qualified across the disciplines. In this way, we entertain the hope of influencing a new generation of practitioners – to encourage, to excite and to prevent them having to reinvent the wheel.

With the emphasis on community care in psychiatry, and fostering and adoption in child care, residential environments have been neglected over the past three decades. One result has been that only the most unwell and disturbed are admitted to residential settings, making the task of creating something therapeutic even more difficult. Residential settings have become known for their dilapidated buildings, shocking overcrowding, demoralised, underpaid workforce and paucity of creative thinking. There have been examples of bad practice in all sectors, with adverse media coverage of psychiatric hospitals and children's homes ridden with scandals. The response has often been to divert more money away from in-patient/residential settings and a more pervasive cynicism about their therapeutic potential. The naïve assumption is that community treatment or foster care are less risky or even risk free, when in fact, in all likelihood, the risk is unchanged but less visible.

There is evidence, however, that the tide is beginning to turn, with renewed interest and concern and some good things happening. For example, the Department of Health has recently published a policy implementation guide on acute in-patient care (Department of Health, 2002), the Association of Therapeutic communities has set up a quality network (http://www.therapeuticcommunities.org/quality-network.htm) and the Charterhouse Group of Childcare Services has supplemented the Care Standards Act 2000 with its own Standards and Criteria for Therapeutic Community Childcare, Health and Education (http://www.charterhousegroup.org.uk/standards.htm). At the very least, there is pragmatic acceptance that residential units for people with mental health problems will continue to be needed – however good the quality of community care.

This is most obvious in forensic areas, where provision of secure settings both for adults and for children is a growth area. But more generally, admission to a residential setting should be seen as one of a range of options to meet individual needs and not necessarily as a last resort when everything else has failed. The concepts of 'asylum' and 'sanctuary' – so obvious to laypeople – need to be rediscovered by mental health professionals. Otherwise, patients are forced to get worse before they receive the respite they need; and staff neglect the importance of psychological containment in their zeal to intervene and move things on. Of course, this is not straightforward, as the same environment may be facilitative and healing for one person and generate disabling dependency and regression in another. The dangers inherent in residential environments need to be acknowledged, with investment in appropriate resources, particularly staff training and supervision. Building up an appropriate level of expertise within the workforce will take years and there is a danger that short-term solutions may lead to long-term problems. It is vital that expectations are realistic if history is not to repeat itself.

At their best, therapeutic environments should provide a living–learning experience for all involved. This means that mistakes will be made and there needs to be a firm commitment to maximising the learning potential within the culture and minimising the temptation to blame and humiliate when things go wrong. Our first responsibility is 'to do no harm'. Nevertheless, environments do not categorise in a black-and-white fashion into good or bad, therapeutic or toxic. We work with a foot on both sides of the line and know that all the ingredients present for malignant practice are inherent in the work. The importance of protected thinking time, supervision and reflective practice cannot be overstated. Where these are present, there is opportunity for environments to recover quickly; others will slip into bad practice.

The book is divided into four parts. Part 1 explores the problems and what goes wrong; Part 2 attempts to establish some basic principles for maintaining successful therapeutic environments; Part 3 tackles the particular problem of acute wards; and Part 4 considers specific specialist settings and client groups. Although we have encouraged authors to approach the subject in a practical manner, anybody looking for a simplistic formula or procedure will be disappointed; for therapeutic environments are about the struggle to form human relationships and cannot be short cut or manualised. As editors, we do not necessarily agree with everything written, and some of the chapters approach the same topic from conflicting perspectives. But we wanted to convey a sense of realistic tension and the potential for creative dialogue. We hope the diversity in perspective and style gives colour and richness, but we have also tried to establish some sense of continuity by introducing each chapter. We have deliberately invited a wide range of chapter authors, representing different disciplines and including academics, clinicians, front-line staff and users. All are experts in terms of their experience but of necessity provide only an introduction to their subject, hopefully whetting your appetite for further reading. Inevitably, we have left out topics and authors who deserve to be included.

All emphasise the importance of relatedness, whether it is in the arrangement of furniture, a sensitive understanding of different cultures, protecting the boundaries of a staff support group or encouraging group activities. Another common theme is the importance of history: an institution with a memory; a staff team with an understanding of why things are as they are; how decisions were made and why; a coherent narrative of the unit and how it developed. Related to this is a focus on the relationship between the internal world of the unit and the external world: how the particular therapeutic environment fits into the system at large; how it manages difficult transitions – joining and leaving, for example; how it relates to people on the boundary, such as carers; how it manages interface issues with other teams and agencies; and how it relates to managers, commissioners and stakeholders. Perhaps most often mentioned is the importance of reflective practice: a protected space to step back and reflect on the work and our involvement in it. This attitude should permeate the system and include external authorities who need to understand the complexities of the task if they are to avoid the disruptive effect of seesaw decision-making.

As editors, we have all worked in therapeutic communities and have a wide range of interests and engagements with therapeutic environments of all sorts, spanning the worlds of prisons, forensic and rehabilitation psychiatry, adolescent and child care, and psychotherapy. Although we have an eclectic background of models to apply to the understanding of problems in mental health and institutions, we share the belief that human beings are interdependent and that healthy individuals and healthy environments are directly connected. We are all creatures of our environment and of each other: developing our sense of identity; learning patterns of relating; developing a repertoire of emotional responses in the context of a matrix of social relationships. It follows that a humane society should be prepared to invest heavily in caring environments in all sorts of different settings, but most obviously for those who are particularly vulnerable – children and adults with mental health and severe learning problems.

Contrary to the prevalent sense of demoralisation in this area, we know that working in residential environments can be a particularly enriching, energising, exciting experience for staff as well as residents, with infinite opportunities for learning and developing ourselves, not just as professionals, but as partners, parents and friends. Most importantly, we have seen first hand how the experience within a therapeutic environment can nurture, heal, empower and literally provide a lifeline for some very frightened, hurt, confused and despairing individuals.

Department of Health (2002) *Mental Health Policy Implementation Guide: Adult Inpatient Care Provision*. London: Department of Health.

Penelope Campling,
Steffan Davies and Graeme Farquharson

Part I

Understanding the problems

CHAPTER 1

The historical context of therapeutic environments

Kathleen Jones

Editors' introduction   Kathleen Jones, Emeritus Professor of Social Policy at the University of York, has had a long and distinguished academic career in social sciences that started in the 1950s, when she lived in a large mental hospital and wrote her doctoral thesis on the history of such hospitals. She is renowned for her astute analysis of institutional and community care. In this chapter, she outlines various historical influences on therapeutic environments.

Simon Schama calls history 'a hairy beast', and so it is. It needs to be handled very gingerly, with much circumspection; but history is all we have to learn from: for the present is gone in a flash, and we cannot see the future, although we try to shape it. The history of therapeutic environments for mentally ill people does not support any simplistic idea of 'progress'. Although the creation of support networks for those who are vulnerable and confused is plain common sense and simple humanity, it has proved surprisingly difficult to achieve on anything more than a local scale.

The optimistic view of the history of the mental health services is that we have moved from a period of superstition and denial (when mental illness was not recognised and 'lunatics' were subject to scapegoating and witch hunts), through one of intimidation, when the only treatments advocated by the medical profession consisted of purging, bleeding and physical restraint, followed by one of routinisation, when patients became lost in great depersonalising asylums, to one of acceptance and support, when they are treated without stigma in the community (Box 1.1). But few now pretend that it is that simple.

Box 1.1   Phases of development in attitudes to mentally ill people

- Superstition and denial (e.g. witch hunts)
- Intimidation (e.g. physical restraint, purging)
- Routinisation (e.g. left and forgotten in large asylums)
- Acceptance and support (e.g. living as normally as possible in the community)

Unfortunately, many of the old attitudes are still around

The older attitudes are still very much alive, and can recur in unexpected places; and there are new kinds of depersonalisation inherent in the procedures of control by information technology and psychopharmacology. Maintaining human values and face-to-face interaction is still of crucial importance, and more difficult than ever.

Small therapeutic environments may well have a long history, but it is largely undocumented. The Retreat at York, founded in 1792, was a step forward in the 'Dark Ages' of the history of mental health services, a small institution run on principles of human respect and kindness. But it is necessary to remember that it opened with only 30 patients, and they were all members of the Society of Friends, or Quakers: comfortably middle-class people of peaceable ways. Attempts to apply this system to the industrial poor who filled the county asylums of the 19th century soon failed: the asylums simply could not cope with the stark human need and the increasing pressure of numbers.

The individual in a social context

Dynamic group psychotherapy as we now understand it has developed since the Second World War. However, it was given a stimulus by the battle casualties from two world wars. The First World War produced a concern for the men suffering from the condition then known as 'shell shock'. Between the wars, the work of London's Tavistock Clinic in using group discussion and group support as therapeutic tools was outstanding.

During the Second World War, Prime Minister Winston Churchill, who was always capable of surprising his critics, agreed to the appointment to a new Army psychiatric unit of a small group of psychiatrists and social psychologists led by Dr J. R. Rees of the Tavistock Clinic and including both members of Rees's own staff and psychiatrists from London's Maudsley Hospital. Dr Rees became the unit's director, with the rank of brigadier, and other members of the team became lieutenant-colonels, with sufficient rank to put their largely unorthodox ideas into practice. They developed new methods of officer training; they advised on man-management and morale-building; and at the end of the war, they worked with men suffering from the trauma of battle and those, such as prisoners of war and concentration camp victims, who had been damaged by institutional pressures. They learned a good deal about institutional pathology, and most of them did not much like the Army. They shared with their patients a profound hatred of formal regulations, arbitrary orders, stereotyped relationships and compulsion; and they developed ideas on the positive potential of group interaction and group support.

A small number of pioneers of group therapy (Box 1.2) attracted much interest both in psychiatry and in the social sciences. Their

> **Box 1.2**   Pioneers of group support as therapy
>
> - J.R. Rees and Wilfred Bion, Tavistock Clinic, London
> - G.R. Hargreaves, World Health Organization
> - T. F. Main, Cassel Hospital, London
> - Maxwell Jones, Belmont Social Rehabilitation Unit (later renamed Henderson Hospital), London

principles were the replacement of formal roles by genuine human interaction; democratic decision-making rather than autocracy; and group support as the principal means of therapy. Group therapy principles could be applied in the community as well as in the hospital, and as community services began to expand, there was a halcyon period in which the new methods looked like the way forward for some of the most difficult patients of the mental health services. The intensive method involved 'reality confrontation', 'acting out' and 'collapsing the authority pyramid'. Robert Rapoport, who applied an analytical socio-logical eye to work at the Henderson, found that it worked best with young male patients who were inadequately socialised; but in a less intensive form, group therapy became widely used in both hospital and community services as a means of challenging older, rigid systems of management, and giving patients a new freedom of expression. The model was much admired on the international circuit, reported at conferences and copied in many other countries, including the community mental health centres that developed in the USA in the 1960s.

Disillusion

So what went wrong? How did it happen that, by the mid-1970s, psychotherapy was no longer a formal specialism of psychiatry and that such a promising movement was gradually pushed back into a few specialist centres? The answer seems to be that, although small is beautiful, the law of nature is that the large fish will always gobble up the little fish: larger and more powerful movements were to destroy much of its potential. Some of these movements led to positive achievements in mental health care, some did not. The cumulative effect on residential group psychotherapy was devastating. Nobody actually attacked the group approach, or stated that it was in any way harmful. It simply suffered by default.

The first of these movements was the discovery of the phenothiazine derivatives in 1953: new ranges of drugs that offered the possibility of suppressing many of the distressing symptoms of mental illness. These drugs made it possible for some patients to remain in the community without the need for hospitalisation, and for others to be discharged earlier. Patients who were previously inaccessible to rational debate were freed from distressing hallucinations or behavioural problems. The new pharmaceutical treatments were so successful that frank, uncontrolled psychosis is now comparatively rarely, and then only briefly, seen in Western mental health services. The inevitable effect of these new discoveries was that the drug companies became rich and powerful, dominating the research field. If the companies sometimes exaggerated the efficacy of their products in advertisements, and ignored long-term side-effects, they were telling governments the world over what they wanted to hear: that money was better spent on medication than on long-term incarceration in out-dated institutions; and that supporting mere talk (which is always difficult to evaluate) was a waste of time when controlled drug trials could provide hard statistical proof of the efficacy of pills.

The next movement came from sociology – now a comparatively minor part of the social sciences, but, in the 1960s, an expanding discipline in British universities and the cherished hope of those who looked for a better society. The rise of the associated movements of labelling theory and deviance theory started from the admirable premise that some labels – 'lunatic', 'cripple' and 'fallen woman', for example – were hurtful to the people so labelled, and exaggerated one aspect of their situation while ignoring others. A holistic view demanded that every human being should be accorded respect, and those with social problems should not be cursorily dismissed as second-class citizens. This movement sometimes ran to extremes and developed its own rigidities, particularly in the fields of gender studies and race relations; but the overall effect was to produce a new and much-needed sensitivity in the use of language. Although there are still groups in society who dismiss labelling theory as 'political correctness', the point has been made that classifications such as 'Black', 'disabled' or 'schizophrenic' should be used very sparingly, because they do not tell the whole truth about human personalities and human capabilities.

Deviance theory took labelling theory into the fields of psychiatry and criminology, with the argument that the labelling process caused 'deviancy amplification': people labelled as 'mentally ill' or 'criminal' were classified as members of a stigmatised class, and became more deviant as a result. In anti-psychiatry (notably in the work of R. D. Laing and David Cooper), and in radical criminology, the argument that mental hospitals and prisons served as mechanisms of social control rather than agencies of treatment and reform was persuasively put. The fault lay with 'society' and not with the individual defined as deviant. Unfortunately, the process of replacing the old specific labels by the new and undiscriminating label of 'deviants' produced a new kind of stigma, which if anything was worse.

In the mental health field, these movements coalesced into a 'literature of protest' in the 1960s and 1970s – in the work of writers who assumed (wrongly) that their predecessors were a conformist generation and that the patients whom they saw in mental hospitals (by this time medicated and behaving 'normally') had no need to be there. The earliest of these writers was Erving Goffman, whose *Asylums* (1961) was a scholarly and thoughtful text on the pathology of large institutions. Goffman had proposed to follow *Asylums* with another book on good institutional care, but he never wrote it. He died in the early 1970s. His successors were less balanced. Michel Foucault's 1961 *Histoire de la Folie* – a mesmerising Gallic tirade based on long-outdated French sources – was published in English in 1965 as *Madness and Civilization*, with the message that all institutions were Bastilles and agencies of oppression. Thomas Szasz, an American professor of psychiatry, produced a whole stream of very lively and readable books alleging that psychiatric investigation is a new version of the Inquisition or the 17th-century witch-hunts, and that psychiatry does not exist: all that patients really suffer from are 'problems in living'. Few readers noticed his subtext, which was an attempt to kill off the developing American community mental health programmes in the interests of fee-paying private practice. A series of sensational books followed, notably from Andrew Scull in California and Roy Porter in London. These made much play of terms like 'mad-doctors' and 'madhouses', and were lavishly illustrated with pictures of manacles, leg-locks and straitjackets.

Very little of the literature of protest referred to the situation in Britain, where, in comparison with the USA, mental hospitals were small and relatively humanely administered within the National Health Service. Britain never had 10 000-bed hospitals surrounded by electrified fences. One of the more ingenious devices of Foucault and Szasz was the 'diachronic' method by which material from any period of history and any country could be pulled out of context and aired as though it were currently universally applicable. Much of the literature of protest was of very poor academic quality, designed to sell books rather than to help mentally ill people, and it created a new kind of stigma.

The move away from therapeutic institutions

A public outburst of paranoia against mental hospitals followed. In the late 1960s and early 1970s, mental hospital scandals were hot news in the British tabloid press. Hardly a mental hospital escaped dramatic allegations, newspaper headlines and public inquiry. Good, bad and indifferent, they were all tarred with the same brush; and their days were numbered because, again, this was what governments wanted to hear (see Chapters 17 and 26 for different perspectives on this).

In the 1980s, the economic climate changed, and there was a drastic reduction in public expenditure. The Thatcher administrations adopted the extreme right-wing economic analyses of Milton Friedman and F. A. von Hayek. Their message was the overwhelming importance of the development of global capitalism, wealth creation and a specious formulation known as the 'trickle-down theory', which held that if the rich became richer, some of their prosperity might eventually reach the poor. These right-wing economic theories were immensely influential in a period when public spending was ruthlessly slashed, greed and self-seeking were exalted as virtues, and hospitals, like schools and universities, became desperate for cash. Meanwhile, one more intellectual movement had developed with very shady academic credentials, but enormous political mileage: normalisation or 'mainstreaming'. This started in the field of what was then called mental handicap (another label that has disappeared), starting from the perfectly acceptable premise that if young people with learning difficulties were given the same opportunities and advantages as other young people of their age, they could often profit from them. The idea was extended to the field of mental illness, and soon twisted from an argument for upgrading services for a group with special needs to a denial that they had special needs, with the contention that people with psychiatric problems do not require any services other than those available to the rest of the population. This of course was music to the ears of health service administrators.

Asset-stripping had become a popular sport. Hard-pressed administrators saw the destruction of the mental hospitals as a positive social duty as well as an obvious source of financial saving, and one after the other these solid old Victorian institutions bit the dust (Box 1.3). They were not as isolated as their detractors had alleged. Most of them were in the suburbs of large cities or towns, and the land was valuable. Much of it was sold to developers for luxury homes, leisure centres or shopping malls. There were vague promises about developing community care, and some political gestures were made towards 'ring-fencing' the necessary funds; but these did not last very long. Nobody really knew how community care should be structured, and nobody in

---

Box 1.3 Factors influencing the closure of the asylums

- More effective drug treatments
- Mental hospital scandals
- Reductions in public expenditure
- The concept of normalisation (evolving from labelling theory and deviance theory)
- Civil liberties campaigners, evolving from the anti-psychiatry movement and the literature of protest

authority really wanted to find out. Marjorie Wallace (now director of the mental health charity SANE) wrote a series of searing articles for *The Times* in 1985 and 1986 on the plight of thousands of long-term mentally ill people who were simply discharged from closing hospitals and sent to bed-and-breakfast accommodation, or left to sleep on the streets. This was the time when 'Cardboard City' developed within a stone's throw of the Houses of Parliament in London, but despite much pressure from social reformers, no government action was taken. Research proposals aimed at developing new principles of community care were shrugged aside, because they would reveal needs and cost money. Local authorities were hard-pressed, too, their funds reduced so drastically that some of them had to sell their town halls and lease them back. They were closing community facilities, not opening new ones. Psychiatrists increasingly put their faith in psychopharmacology, which had the great advantage that they needed only to prescribe for patients, and did not have to spend time and effort in trying to understand them.

By this time, residential group psychotherapy had lost most of its bases, and it survived in only a few specialist units such as the Henderson Hospital in London and Peper Harrow (in Surrey), where enthusiasts kept alive the principles of humanity and social interaction.

Could things get any worse? When revision of the mental health laws was under consideration in the early 1980s, Britain was targeted by members of the American Civil Liberties Union, an association of lawyers, who raised the banner of 'civil liberties' against psychiatrists on the assumption that the only human rights issue of any importance was that of the illegal detention of individual patients. The best known of these was a young American lawyer named Larry Gostin, who acquired considerable influence in both parliamentary and mental health circles, during the framing of the Mental Health Act 1983.

Human rights issues are of two kinds: specialists on the subject distinguish between 'rights-for' (the provision of appropriate care and treatment to people in need) and 'rights-against' (illegal detention or the abuse of compulsory treatment). Both internationally and nationally, attempts were made in the immediate post-war period to establish rights-for mentally ill people. In Britain, the National Health Service Act 1944 and the (English and Welsh) Mental Health Act 1959 were both enabling documents, concerned with setting standards to which all authorities should aim, specifying the services that should be available for all mentally ill people. But by the 1970s, there was a good deal of cynicism about this approach, which tended to disappear in a cloud of wishful thinking and good intentions. It was replaced by an emphasis on specific rights-against, to be enforced by the American concept of 'due process', which means action through the courts. This was good news for the legal profession, and created many difficulties for psychiatrists. The Mental Health Act 1983, which embodied these ideas, dealt only with the personal rights-against of patients who were compulsorily detained, even though by this time such patients constituted less than 5% of all patients in hospital – and most patients were not in hospital, they were out in the community. Despite many representations to Parliament asking for a clear legal statement on patients' entitlement to community care, the provisions have continued in law on this very narrow basis. Present plans for legal revision do not redress this situation: they are concerned primarily with fresh possibilities of detention for patients considered dangerously antisocial.

The current situation

In the past few years, Government has endeavoured – yet once more – to reform the National Health Service. Ministers and their advisers have put their faith in the means of supervision and control made possible by administrative systems. Official guidelines and descriptions of 'good practice' specify most possible contingencies, but rarely if ever deal with principles. League tables based on fairly crude criteria assess hospitals as though they were football teams. Many health service workers are suffering from information overload, simply unable to absorb the waves of paper instructions that daily come down the chain of command. They cannot even remember what they were told to do last week. Good human relations and group dynamics cannot be taught by simple, impersonal prescription. The principles need to be clarified, learned, absorbed, tested, discussed in face-to-face contact and internalised if they are to result in attitude change and personal growth. To expect staff to learn these skills from rules and regulations is rather like expecting Michelangelo to paint by numbers.

Over the past 40 years, therapeutic communities have been at the mercy of intellectual controversy and economic crackdown. Ideas have been promoted, taken out of context, pulled out of shape and often pursued to the limit of logical absurdity, all in the name of progress. In the mental health field, the effect has often meant the destruction of teaching skills and research skills – to the point where many of us have despaired of preserving human values. There has been a failure of belief in the value of human relations.

If the current plans for the reform and expansion of the National Health Service come to fruition, perhaps we shall have another chance to demonstrate that the sensitive employment of human understanding and group support is a powerful tool for healing – although it cannot be evaluated by simplistic and insensitive research methods.

If Government is at last coming round to a new realisation of the value of therapeutic community principles, the issues and projects reported in this book may represent a valuable step in rallying constructive forces after a long period of attrition.

References and further reading

Foucault, M. (1961) *Histoire de la Folie á l'Age Classique*. Reprinted (1965) as *Madness and Civilization: A Hsitory of Insanity in the Age of Reason* (trans. R. Howard). London: Pantheon.

Goffman, E. (1961) *Asylums: Essays on the Social Situations of Mental Patients and Other Inmates*. London: Pelican Books.

Jones, K. (1994) *Asylums and After*. London: Athlone (now Continuum).

Jones, K. & Fowles, A. J. (1984) *Ideas on Institutions: Analysing the Literature on Long-Term Care and Custody*. London: Routledge & Kegan Paul.

Kennard, D. (1998) *Introduction to Therapeutic Communities*. London: Jessica Kingsley Publishers.

Pines, M. (ed.) (2000) *The Evolution of Group Analysis*. London: Jessica Kingsley Publishers.

Trist, E. & Murray, H. (1990) *The Social Engagement of Social Science. Vol. 1: The Socio-Psychological Perspective*. London: Free Association Books.

CHAPTER 2

How good staff become bad

Graeme Farquharson

Editors' introduction In this chapter Graeme Farquharson explores the problem of malpractice. He approaches this difficult topic by thinking about the various pressures affecting individual staff members, for example social expectations, personal 'baggage', the effects of working closely with mental disturbance, group forces and institutionalisation. He also describes some instructive, classic social psychology experiments.

In the first decade of this new century, good mental health workers are at a premium. There is a shortage of personnel in all disciplines in the fields of health and social care. Recruitment is difficult; retention no less so. It follows from this that if employers are to attract and retain good staff, there must be close attention paid to how these staff are prepared for the task and supported in it. This goes beyond simple conditions of service such as salary, holiday entitlement and training opportunities – important though these undoubtedly are. With specific reference to therapeutic institutions, several factors can be identified as being potentially harmful to or problematic for staff, and these should be borne in mind by the workers themselves and by their employers. This is particularly so when working with patients with severe psycho-pathology (e.g. psychotic conditions, personality disorder, conduct disorder) and it is that kind of background that informs this chapter.

Starting out

When workers contemplate looking for a new job, this usually reflects one or more of a number of considerations, for example dissatisfaction with or outgrowing their current role, readiness for more seniority and/or a wish for more money. Alongside this, almost inevitably, goes a certain level of idealisation of the new role and new workplace, especially if it is an innovative and/or prestigious setting. Often, this idealisation rapidly turns to disillusion. Of course it is right that workers be enthusiastic and strive for excellence. Similarly, seeking personal and career development is to be lauded. The difficulty lies in the fact that the same problems of human relations have to be worked at here as elsewhere. How people make and sustain relationships requires daily attention and the vagaries of relationships are immune to notions of newness or of prestige.

Box 2.1 Potential subgroups within a therapeutic environment

Staff:
- Different disciplines
- Night and day staff
- Senior and junior
- Gender, race, culture, religion, age, social class and educational background
- Shared affiliation and attachments (e.g. football teams)

Patients/clients/users:
- Gender, race, culture, religion, age, social class and educational background
- Shared afflictions and attachments, usually more transient than staff

Staff and patient cross-groups
- Gender, race, culture, religion, age, social class and educational background
- Similar life events and traumas
- Shared affiliations and attachments

A key aspect of group life within the institution

Within therapeutic institutions, there are two groups of people, one of which we call 'staff' and the other we call 'patients'. The naïve view is to think that the former group simply 'acts on' the latter, hopefully to benign effect. The reality is, of course, altogether more complex, for although it is true that the staff act on patients, this is no more true than saying that the patients act on the staff.

Neither group can be said to be fully rational actors in the drama, as both bring unconsciously determined material to bear on how they form relationships, react to incidents and behave in particular situations. The two groups are, in fact, made up of a number of functional subgroups (Box 2.1).

Simply by dissecting roles in this way, we see that all involved – staff and patients – have competing demands on their allegiance, some of which they will be aware of, some not. This can (and does) give rise to intra-psychic and inter-group conflict. All personnel are constantly participating in an inter-group event, which is much more complicated than may at first be recognised. The drama and intensity of relationships within a residential group setting have been capitalised on by the media in television programmes such as 'Big Brother' and 'Survivor'.

Anxiety

The patients (residents/clients) in such an environment usually have had difficulties in their early lives, often gross difficulties. Several of them will have endured some form of abuse. Frequently, they will have had little experience of living successfully with birth parents, or even substitute parents, for any length of time. At least some of them, as they have grown up, will have begun to strike back at the world in the same way as it previously struck at them, making relationships characterised by oscillations between idealisation and denigration, exploitation, excessive sexualisation and so on. Even in less extreme cases, the net effect of early life experiences will often have been some interference with the emergence of a capacity for healthy attachment, with a consequently impaired capacity to make and sustain adult relationships based on mutuality, reciprocity and interdependence. Thus is anxiety writ large within the therapeutic setting.

Nor are staff themselves always free of anxiety. In the ordinary way, our personal histories and life experiences reflect, for example, loss, sometimes abrupt and painful. Changes in modern family life are such that many have experience of disruption to parental care and of newly constituted family structures. Beyond that, there are the everyday existential considerations that beset us all, sitting alongside our individual hopes and fears. A significant minority of staff will themselves have experienced abuse in their early years. It can be courageous to use such personal trauma in the service of helping others; it can also be at considerable personal cost.

Thus, there are many different ingredients in these new therapeutic relationships. The fragility of human relationships is not well understood by most people, even in the best of circumstances. In these inauspicious situations, where suspicion and mistrust predominate, the potential for things to 'go wrong' increases exponentially. For these simple reasons, therapeutic work that emphasises the management of anxiety begins from a more realistic base. It must be noted that this does not mean ignoring or denying anxiety. Rather, it involves facing and examining its sources. Frequently, workers think that to feel anxious is somehow wrong or reflects some personal deficit. This attitude makes it clear that anxiety is inevitable and ubiquitous and is to be understood. It can be managed well and reduced, or it can be managed badly and exacerbated. It cannot be completely eliminated.

A key feature of the staff role is to 'contain' anxiety, to hold it intrapsychically and to return it to the patient in the form of 'manageable doses', so that it can be reabsorbed and integrated in such a way that it can be tolerated and need no longer be projected into others (see Chapter 4).

To state the obvious, this is demanding and sophisticated work, which can be accomplished only if, in turn, the anxiety of staff is also contained. There are many circumstances, individually and collectively, when emotion is heightened and predominates to such an extent that, in effect, it attacks one's capacity to think. Such periods are inherently dangerous in the sense that staff might react overquickly to a problem, rather than respond in a considered way, thereby making a difficult situation even worse.

The containment of staff anxiety can be achieved only by the wider organisation and key senior figures. The fundamentals of this lie in basic employment characteristics – such as secure employment, adequate remuneration, ensuring the taking of holidays – and in the appropriate infrastructure of policies and procedures, clarifying what happens in the event of a variety of foreseeable situations. Above this there must be a layer of management activity designed to assist in the understanding of the perplexing or the frightening. This will be achieved through some combination of professional supervision (internal) and consultation (external), including mentoring.

Dynamic factors that can contribute to destructive processes

Excessive concentration on the individual

This, at first sight, seems a paradoxical notion. After all, we put people in therapeutic institutions to help them as individuals and to address their specific needs. So there must be appropriate attention given to these needs and difficulties. At the same time, however, each one is a member of a living group, a social matrix wherein each will take up particular roles and will re-enact characteristic, interpersonal styles, including difficulties. Some of this will generate behaviour that requires careful managing; much of it will provide important clinical information. In addition to this, there may be problematic group phenomena such as scapegoating that require attention. And of course, within well-defined limits, staff will wish to work through the medium of the group for purposes of managing daily life, for example planning some activity or addressing interpersonal conflict.

To focus exclusively on the individual, therefore, is to miss some rich information from the wider situation, which might well impoverish the treatment response. A 'bi-focal' approach, concentrating now on the individual, now on the group, allows the individual to be seen in a social context and permits a fuller understanding of his or her relationship style.

The oscillatory pattern

Day-to-day life in most residential and in-patient facilities has a certain rhythm to it. Some situations can be anticipated, some recur depending on circumstance, and the more one can become familiar with this rhythm, the less one is at its mercy. There are various ways of conceptualising it, but an image elaborated by Rapoport (1960), who described the cycle of therapeutic community life in terms of an oscillatory pattern, is particularly useful in helping to explain phenomena that might otherwise be confusing or even frightening.

There are a number of phases of this cycle. Phase A is the stage of (relatively) greatest equilibrium and integration, i.e. most people are getting on with what they are meant to be getting on with most of the time. In this phase, consensus is fairly easily reached and the purposeful activity engenders trust.

During phase B, senior residents/patients are ready to leave the community and do so appropriately. New patients arrive to take their place and, in the processes, the group composition changes dramatically. More mature figures, who were, to a significant extent, identified with the staff and with the task, have gone and have been replaced by new people who do not yet have these identifications. So the move towards greater disorganisation begins. Anxiety mounts as new patients test the limits and some of the old patients might be lured back into more defiant, oppositional stances. At this stage, in a variety of ways, the unit might be experienced as failing.

Phase C, the stage of maximum tension, has now been reached, requiring authoritative action by staff (or sometimes patients) to regain equilibrium. Effectively, 'join us in the treatment task or leave' is the challenge to oppositional patients, and sometimes individuals will have taken such an extreme stance that there is no other option but to go. Meanwhile, others return to the focus of treatment and re-engage with the task.

The final stage of the cycle is phase D, the reorganisation phase, which sees an upsurge in reparative activity. It is as if there is a collective drawing of breath, a sigh of relief that the conflict is over, at least for now. Authority figures can step back as involvement and participation increase, with some return to purposeful activity.

Not every service will go through these stages exactly as described, but most will go through something akin to them. It is helpful to staff, particularly new staff, to have some conception of this, some preparedness for foreseeable difficulties, otherwise anxiety can become acute and border on the unmanageable. This is particularly true in the start-up phase of a new unit. As there is as yet no collective memory, when tensions rise or there is a difficult situation, there is no one who can convincingly reassure by saying 'Last time this happened, what we did was…'. As yet, there has been no 'last time' and, until there is a bank of shared experience, the staff team and the individuals within it are particularly vulnerable.

Three situational factors

In the residential/in-patient setting at least three factors should be borne in mind that contribute to rendering the treatment task especially difficult:

(a)   the severity of the psychopathology (both individually and its density within the group);

(b)   that the role distance is less (staff become much more 'known' figures than in the out-patient situation);

(c)   that the 'therapeutic hour' never ends. In the out-patient setting, people can be very difficult, but eventually they go home again. During an in-patient stay, they are 'at home'. A difficulty that emerges towards the end of a session may still have to be engaged with, an hour or so later, in the corridor (if only to underline that it will have to wait until a more appropriate time).

The problem of the 'special patient'

It has long been recognised (Stanton & Schwartz, 1954; Main, 1957) that particular patients elicit particular responses from particular staff. The idea here is that regressed patients (particularly those with borderline personality disorder) will, from time to time, evoke in their carers states of mind that broadly coincide with their own internal conflicts. Consequently, phenomena specific to the individual patient may be seen in the group, as a result of mass projection and splitting (for a fuller discussion of these, see Chapter 4).

Where this kind of understanding is not available to staff, the splits will go unrecognised and will be taken up as if 'fact'. Typically, one member of staff (or one subgroup) will be in touch only with the charming and creative aspects of a particular patient, while another will see only his or her manipulative or destructive characteristics. Commonly, this leads to staff disputes about the individual's treatability and, not infrequently, to discharge.

Social coercion

Two classic social psychology experiments – the first conducted in the early 1950s by Solomon Asch and the second more than a decade later by Stanley Milgram (see Hinshelwood, 1997) – famously demonstrated how powerful psychological forces can be brought to bear on individuals so that their capacity for independent judgement is seriously impaired.

Asch's experiment focused on perception and, in the laboratory, demonstrated how 'a minority of one' finds it extraordinarily difficult to stand up against prevailing group opinion and, more often than not, will move towards conformity with other group members, despite the evidence of his or her own eyes.

More troubling, Milgram's experiment showed how independent moral judgement may collapse in the face of authority. In this case, subjects were told that the purpose was to study 'the effects of punishment on learning'. The subjects had, apparently, to administer electric shocks to others if they made errors in a learning task. Despite their better judgement, they administered increasingly large shocks on the say-so of the experimenter, even when they had evidence of the physical 'distress' of the person they were punishing. Milgram's experiment makes very clear how easy is the descent into unethical behaviour in the presence of malignant authority.

Pathological institutional roles

In the same tradition as the above, another empirical social psychology experiment (from the early 1970s) suggested other powerful social forces at play in a residential institution. The criminologist Philip Zimbardo and colleagues (Haney *et al*, 1973) sought to examine the psychology of prison life by creating an elaborate, and carefully designed, role-play, in which 21 students were allotted the role either of guard or of inmate.

Despite the fact that any kind of interpersonal relationship was available to each individual and to each group, the participants immediately took up stereotyped interpersonal styles, and very much became 'prisoners' and 'guards' and, fairly rapidly, became 'abused' and 'abusers'. The impact was dramatic: five prisoners had to be released early, showing signs of acute emotional distress. The intention had been to run the experiment for 2 weeks, but it had to be terminated after 6 days, such was the concern for the well-being of the participants. It should be noted that, in the subsequent 'de-role-ing', the guards had not wanted the experiment to end. This reflected other notable features of the period of experiment, for example no time was lost through staff (guard) illness and guards voluntarily worked additional hours.

This experiment can be criticised from a number of points of view, but it does starkly reveal the power differentials between the two groups and how these can be enacted in extreme forms. A more recent version of Zimbardo's experiment has been shown on English television (*The Experiment*, video and manual available from the BBC, London). This time the guards were more lenient, but a group of the prisoners staged a coup and set up a regime in which the guards and the rest of the prisoners were humiliated and badly treated.

It would be a comforting thought to regard these behaviours as confined to experimental situations or to history. Sadly, the recent past has seen the uncovering of too many actual incidents of harm in all forms of residential and secure care for any comfort to be drawn.

Summary

The first task of any therapeutic institution is 'to do no harm'. In this chapter, I have tried to demonstrate that there are intrinsic situational factors and pressures likely to promote harm, and that it is the responsibility of staff to acquaint themselves with these; to manage them appropriately so that destructive possibilities are blunted and more constructive opportunities are facilitated.

It should be understood that these forces and pressures are universal and inevitable and their presence does not of itself betoken a 'bad' or mismanaged institution. Rather, it is how they are attended to, how they are managed, that is important.

References

Haney, C., Banks. C. & Zimbardo, P. (1973) Interpersonal dynamics in a simulated prison. *International Journal of Criminology and Penology*, 1, 69–97.

Hinshelwood, R. D (1997) *Therapy or Coercion? Does Psychoanalysis Differ from Brainwashing?* London : Karnac Books.

Main, T. F. (1957) The ailment. *British Journal of Medical Psychology*, 30, 129–145.

Rapoport, R. N. (1960) *Community as Doctor*. London: Tavistock Publications.

Stanton, A. & Schwartz, M. (1954) *The Mental Hospital*. New York: Basic Books.

CHAPTER 3

Toxic institutions

Steffan Davies

Editors' introduction   In this chapter Steffan Davies describes the many ways in which institutions can be damaging and the factors that contribute to this. He draws on recent inquiries, the unsettling effects of their recommendations, which swing from one priority to another, and on his own experience of a large institution.

Institutions caring for difficult, and sometimes dangerous, individuals have an extensive history of problems, and the recent inquiries into Ashworth Hospital are only the latest in a long line. This chapter reviews some of the recurring issues of such inquiries and questions what lessons we have learnt from them.

My clinical work takes place at Rampton Hospital, one of the three high-security hospitals serving England and Wales. With 400 beds and contained within a high-security perimeter fence, it is one of the few remaining large institutions in the National Health Service (NHS). The history of Rampton and the other high-security (formerly known as special) hospitals, Ashworth and Broadmoor, is littered with scandals and major inquiries. In this respect they have much in common with other large institutions such as the old asylums (for a fuller account see Martin, 1984), prisons, workhouses, hospitals for the mentally handicapped, geriatric hospitals and residential schools.

We are proud of many aspects of the care that we provide at Rampton. Our patients have some of the most severe forms of psychiatric disorder such as schizophrenia and personality disorder, often in combination. In addition, to warrant admission to high security, they must present a 'grave and immediate' danger to the public 'if at large' (Department of Health, 1989). Our work is poorly understood by the media and politicians; this creates additional pressures, compounding the difficulties of the work. This lack of understanding and clarity, also reflected at times in our own attitudes, contributes to some of the problems discussed in this chapter. That I concentrate here solely on what can go wrong should not be taken as meaning that all institutions are by definition bad. All residents within institutions are potentially vulnerable, owing to the unequal power relationship with staff, and all institutions consequently have the potential to go wrong. Understanding and guarding against this is a key task for the managers and clinical staff, which they overlook at their, and their patients', peril.

In this chapter I concentrate on psychiatric hospitals and, given their recent histories, secure hospitals. Many of the features discussed can be seen in other services such as prisons, and in smaller units such as children's homes. Recent descriptions of acute psychiatric care (see Part III of this book) show many of the characteristics of 'toxic' institutions. However, acute wards, owing to their smaller size, more open nature and less disturbed (notorious) population have not attracted the same degree of attention as the large hospitals, although many of the same failings are present.

What are institutions?

Goffman (1961), in his seminal work *Asylums*, defined 'total institutions' as possessing the following characteristics:

- a barrier to social intercourse with the outside and to departure, which is often built-in (e.g. high walls);
- all aspects of life are conducted in the same place and under a single authority;
- each member's daily activity is carried out in the company of a batch of others;
- all phases of the day's activities are tightly scheduled;
- the activities are brought together in a single rational plan purportedly designed to fulfil the official aims of the institution;
- a basic split between a large managed group (inmates) and a small supervisory staff;
- grossly restricted social mobility between the two strata;
- the staff control information, decision-making and access to the institution's hierarchy;
- being resident in an institution is incompatible with family life.

There have been efforts to overcome some aspects of the total institution, for example allowing patients access to their records and involving them in decision-making at an individual level through the care programme approach and collectively through patients' councils. Overall staff numbers in secure psychiatric services are now far in excess of patient numbers, although patients outnumber staff in day-to-day clinical situations. Most aspects of a total institution are, however, as applicable today to high-security hospitals and many other institutions as they were in 1961. Many of these features are indeed essential for the institutions to fulfil their role, and the therapeutic task is to minimise their negative consequences without jeopardising safety.

Institutions can be bad for you

There are many potentially harmful consequences of being a patient in an institution, and some of these are shown in Box 3.1. Although seemingly dramatic, all of the harmful effects shown are well documented in various inquiry reports. Some effects, such as those on physical health, are very common, whereas the more serious outcomes such as unnatural death are very rare. Here I take as examples rare but serious unnatural deaths (the starting point of many inquiries) and the more common effects of institutionalisation.

The starkest result of things going wrong in an institution is the death of a patient, visitor, member of staff or member of the public. Of these, the most common is the death of a patient. This is rarely by direct assault by other patients and even more rarely by assault by a member of staff. By far the most common cause of unnatural death within institutions is suicide. Suicide is the end product of multiple factors, including mental disorder, life experiences, external events and current care. Some suicides are not preventable, even in closely supervised settings. The concept of malignant alienation, developed by Morgan (Watts & Morgan, 1994), is useful here. This describes a process characterised by

'a progressive deterioration in [patients'] relationships with others, including loss of sympathy and support from members of staff, who tended to construe these patients' behaviour as provocative, unreasonable, or overdependent ... Such alienation between patient and others appeared to have been malignant in that it gained momentum and was associated with a fatal outcome' (Watts & Morgan, 1994).

Box 3.1 Some harmful effects of institutions

Loss of liberty Patients may not be free to leave, move around the institution, have access to their own possessions

Social isolation Difficulties for family visiting, restrictions on phone calls and letters, discouragement from staff, stigma on families, peers who may not be amenable/desirable social contacts

Institutionalisation Reduced interactions, impoverished social skills, loss of motivation, reduced communication

Deteriorating mental health Lack of stimulation, depression, hopelessness, substandard psychiatric treatment

Poor physical health Poor diet, lack of exercise, poor physical health care, smoking, side-effects of medication

Death Suicide, neglect, lack of care, murder

Patient characteristics contributing to this included psychotic withdrawal and severe character pathology, both common in secure psychiatric units. The lack of opportunity for staff to express negative feelings was another important factor. Malignant alienation was described initially in general psychiatric settings, and the potential for its occurrence is much greater in forensic settings, where in addition to psychiatric factors such as psychosis and personality disorder there is the impact of patients' offences for staff to deal with (see Conflicts in care below). Good staff support, particularly offering safe ways to express negative emotions (see Chapters 12 and 20), is important, as are more general factors such as maintaining therapeutic hope.

Other high-profile deaths in hospital are those following restraint. These are often complicated by factors such as the poor physical health of the patient and high-dose medication. Again, these deaths are often the result of multiple combinations of causes rather than a single event. More subtle causes of mortality are the effects of institutionalisation on patients' physical health. These include weight gain through poor diet and medication effects, lack of exercise and inadequate attention to physical health by psychiatric staff. These effects on physical health are common in all in-patient settings and among severely mentally ill people in the community.

The effects of an anti-therapeutic environment can be less obvious, but they are still pervasive and damaging. The 'three hospitals study' (Wing & Brown, 1970) illustrated how attention to such apparently basic aspects of a regime as access to personal possessions, having one's own living space and the availability of meaningful daytime activity can have a profound effect on behaviour and social functioning. By conducting an observational study in three mental hospitals in different stages of reform the authors were able to observe how changes in regime affect patients. A change of regime in the opposite direction even produced a regression in patients who had improved previously. The study is encouraging in demonstrating the positive effects of regime change on patients' mental health and social functioning.

Mechanisms of harm

The causes of harm resulting from staff behaviour include active malicious acts (it must be stressed that this involves only a minority); failure to protect more vulnerable patients; neglecting to carry out one's duties to a high professional standard; and working for institutional convenience rather than individual patient care (Box 3.2). This section looks at some of the factors that lead to clinical practice falling below acceptable standards (see also Chapter 2).

A particular problem for large institutions is their tendency to become inward-looking and to not question their own practices.

Box 3.2   Mechanisms of harm

Consequences of poor practice
Institutional needs taking precedence over patient care
Insufficient quantity and quality of care
Well-intentioned but misguided care
Neglect
Direct, malicious assault

Geographically isolated institutions in particular have difficulties in attracting staff and tend to recruit from the local area, thus perpetuating existing institutional practices. It can be difficult for staff to keep up to date with developments in their field and it is often hard to get institutions to adopt new ideas and techniques. This can cause practice to fall below accepted standards and to become out of date: initially acceptable practice is gradually altered and grows less effective. Consequently, care can also fall behind current standards and patients receive suboptimal and eventually unacceptable care. This might be in the form of inadequate diagnosis, inappropriate medication regimes, lack of adequate monitoring of side-effects or underutilisation of more up-to-date psychological therapies. The cumulative effect of a restricted labour pool, difficulties in recruiting and professional isolation can be a gradual deterioration in care standards, leading to poor outcomes. In combination with other factors this can contribute to disastrous outcomes such as fatalities and widespread abuse. A committee of inquiry led by Louis Blom-Cooper was set up to investigate complaints of ill treatment of patients at Ashworth Hospital, which were broadly upheld:

'The low standards of therapeutic practice have by no means been confined to nursing care and treatment. Our criticism of Ashworth in the latter half of the 1980s can be shared among three segments of the therapeutic community: a lack of commitment by some nursing staff to the proper care of the mentally ill and patients with learning disabilities; a less than adequate psychiatric service in terms of assessment and treatment of patients; a lack of clinical leadership in the medical and nursing professions, and an absence of firm hospital management, leaving a power vacuum' (Blom-Cooper, 1992: p. 253).

Many of the mechanisms of harm, including poor practice, neglect, poor-quality care, the precedence of institutional needs over patients' needs and even direct assault, are illustrated within Blom-Cooper's report. Strong clinical leadership and management are needed, with a commitment to improve clinical care, if change is to be effectively implemented. Ensuring professional, managerial and other contacts with the wider community and institutional openness to legitimate scrutiny are important in maintaining such improvements.

Conflicts in care

Institutions are usually created to deal with social problems. Their inmates, residents or patients are therefore often also economically deprived, mentally disordered, criminal, delinquent, poorly educated and poorly integrated into society. There is often a great deal of public ambivalence about these institutions and their residents (Box 3.3). One has only to reflect on the public debates on the punishment and rehabilitation of offenders to see this played out. The patients in secure hospitals have many of these characteristics: by definition they have mental disorders and are dangerous. Although by name, function and legal status hospitals, secure hospitals are often confused with prisons and criticised for treating patients too leniently. Other bodies simultaneously raise concerns about them being too restrictive and anti-therapeutic (see Policy, management and organisation below).

The public and media attitude towards psychiatric services and patients is something that we have all experienced and is the focus of this section. It is illustrated by press coverage of Rampton Hospital following the admission, as a patient for assessment, of someone accused of a particularly horrific child murder (for example, try searching under 'Soham' and 'Rampton Hospital' for the period 1 August to 31 October 2002 in the online archive of *The Independent* newspaper, at http://www.independent.co.uk). It should be remembered that at that stage the person had been charged but had not appeared in court, let alone been convicted. The media coverage forced the hospital to defend itself against accusations of being a 'holiday camp' and caused it to express concern about the detrimental effect of the publicity on the care of other patients and their chances of rehabilitation. The press reporting reached such a level as to potentially prejudice a fair trial and was described by *The Independent* as 'A terrible way to report a terrible crime: the hypocrisy and guilt of the media' (Orr, 2002).

The staff that work in these services are also members of the public, with families and friends who are exposed to the same media. Society's ambivalence about patients in their care must be reflected in their own

---

Box 3.3 Conflicts in care

Public attitudes, especially mixed messages
Punishment *v.* rehabilitation
Public safety *v.* patients rights
Empathetic therapeutic relationship *v.* disgust at crimes
Caution and safety *v.* pressure to admit and discharge
High quality *v.* cost pressures
Victims *v.* aggressors (it is not unusual to be both)

---

emotions. This was recognised in a 1995 Health Advisory Service report on Ashworth Hospital quoted in Kaye & Franey (1998: pp. 240–241):

'Maintaining open, empathic and helping yet objective relationships with people whose acts may be or have been abhorrent requires a great deal of maturity and balance from the staff if the offences are not to be dissociated from the individuals and denied or patients avoided or mismanaged. Individual members of staff can find themselves under immense emotional strain in endeavouring to maintain helping relationships while holding onto awareness of patients' behaviours, past and present.'

Policy, management and organisation

Large institutions often have complex internal management systems, form part of larger organisations (e.g. the NHS or the Prison Service) and are subject to national policy (Box 3.4). Faults within management systems and between different levels and components also contribute to problems in institutions. The high political profile of secure psychiatric services leads to a high degree of political interest and scrutiny, exacerbated by, and contributing to, frequent inquiries. Inquiries are usually set up to deal with specific issues such as abuse of patients and poor care (Blom-Cooper, 1992) or breakdowns in security (Fallon *et al*, 1999). The recommendations of such inquiries are usually accepted by government and have to be acted on by hospital managers and staff even if they have reservations about their practicality and utility. Inquiries usually make sensible recommendations, but they have a tendency to focus on their particular issue to the detriment of the wider picture. The consequences, intended and unintended, of this and the role of local management form the basis of this section, which looks at the effects of two inquiries, both concerning Ashworth Hospital, one following from the other.

The Blom-Cooper inquiry made many recommendations about liberalising patient care at Ashworth (Blom-Cooper, 1992). These were mostly introduced, not always in a well-managed way, but with many benefits to patients in all three UK high-security hospitals (Ashworth,

---

Box 3.4 Aspects of policy, management and organisation that affect institutions

Direct political intervention
Consequences of intended policy
Unintended consequences of policy, or policy misapplied
Public opinion and media pressure
Serial reorganisation
Unit or trust management, middle-management

Table 3.1 Examples of contradictory recommendations from two committees of inquiry into Ashworth Hospital

Blom-Cooper recommendations	Fallon recommendations
76: patients should have a readily accessible personal telephone system, like those available in general hospitals	4: the use of ward-based telephones must be carefully controlled and monitored to prevent misuse[1]
39: the over-restrictive regulations relating to personal and security items should be urgently reviewed	2, 3, 9, 10, 31: new rules allowing searching of staff, visitors and patients' rooms and limiting the amount of personal possessions in patients' rooms

1. One result of this recommendation was a ban on incoming calls for patients except in emergencies.

Rampton and Broadmoor); for example, patients are no longer locked in their rooms at night. The subsequent inquiry into the personality disorder unit at Ashworth (Fallon *et al*, 1999) made numerous recommendations about security procedures that were at times directly opposed to those of the earlier Blom-Cooper inquiry. Two examples of this are shown in Table 3.1.

The review of security set up in response to the Fallon inquiry (Tilt *et al*, 2000) led to the introduction of a tighter security regime in all three high-security hospitals. Consequently, the response to problems on the personality disorder unit at one hospital has had a detrimental effect on the care of patients in all high-security hospitals in England and Wales:

'We are concerned that the implementation of the Security Directions should not impose overly time-consuming and restrictive practices in hospitals at the expense of therapeutic interactions between staff and patients. These concerns are heightened by the blanket application of the directions, with a devastating result for some patients, particularly women, those undergoing rehabilitation and those who have lived in the hospitals for many years. We are particularly concerned at the depersonalising effect of some of the measures taken' (Mental Health Act Commission, 2001: pp. 57–58, para 5.25).

The two inquiries concentrated on the needs of different patient groups: people with mental illness and mental impairment (Blom-Cooper) and people with psychopathic disorder (Fallon). The liberalisations that benefited those with mental illness were often abused by those with psychopathic disorder, in part due to failures in management and clinical leadership.

Many clinicians and managers in the three hospitals feel blown in different directions by changing external forces. The mixed messages to institutions and their staff are, to my mind, best illustrated by the contradiction in making the high-security hospitals part of large mental health trusts – to integrate them into the wider NHS – while simultaneously enclosing them in higher fences and introducing search requirements for staff and visitors normally seen only in Category A prisons and international airports. At Rampton Hospital, the conference centre, which was used extensively for educational purposes, including regional and national meetings, was demolished to make way for a new control room. It has not, to date, been replaced. Regional meetings are now held 30 miles away in a venue leased from a university. Attendance by staff at Rampton, particularly nursing staff, is now more difficult and other external attendees who would previously have come to the hospital go to the new venue instead.

The conflicting recommendations of the two reports are a good example of the pendulum phenomenon often seen in relation to difficult and complex issues, with selective and polarised analyses predisposing institutions to future adverse events.

Factors in the direct care environment

There are many factors that can contribute, singularly or more often in combination, to institutions going awry; some of these are listed in Box 3.5. This section explores the example of patient mix (expanded on in Chapter 23), which has a direct impact on staff training, skills mix, resources and the type of milieu required.

The greater the variation in patient needs (for treatment, care and security), the more difficult it becomes to provide appropriate care. Patients with personality disorder generally have treatment needs very different from those of patients with mental illness. Treatments for personality disorder are predominantly psychological; patients are less disabled than those with severe mental illness and their response to and need for medication are different. Differing dependency levels, for example the need for help with everyday activities such as personal hygiene, and differing security needs also pose problems. Clinical staff have to adapt the ward environment, therapeutically, to the lowest common denominator, which in a very diverse group can be very low. The more challenging and confrontational methods appropriate for personality disorder could have a detrimental effect on mentally ill

---

Box 3.5 Factors in the direct care environment

Patient groups with differing needs (e.g. mental illness, personality disorder)
Inadequate staff skills, training and team composition
Weak clinical leadership
Lack of resources
Poor management support
Blame cultures
Poor physical environments
Demoralising culture/milieu

patients (see Chapter 20, pp. 209–210, and Chapter 23, pp. 238–239). Conversely, security needs to be pitched at the level of the highest risk. As the Fallon inquiry pointed out, the more focused the clinical task, the more opportunities are available to direct treatments and environments on specific patient groups and to develop specialist skills in the teams that can be readily put into practice:

'Such a unit [Ashworth's personality disorder unit] could facilitate the development of recognised forms of assessment, treatment and outcome measures for personality disorder; it might attract staff of all disciplines interested in their form of work; help facilitate the development of audit and research; and enable clearer distinctions to be drawn between those admitted for assessment, those undergoing treatment and those for whom treatment had failed and who required long-term humane containment on the grounds of enduring risk. Security considerations would be much higher up the agenda ... for personality disordered patients who presented the most major difficulties within the hospital' (Fallon *et al*, 1999: para. 2.13.6).

The above quotation outlines some of the possible benefits of creating a specialist personality disorder unit. These include developing assessment and treatment skills, in combination with research and audit in an area where evidence is sparse; creating differentiated subunits for different aspects of personality disorder, including assessment, ongoing treatment and long-term containment; and attracting staff to work in a difficult area. This model, supported by a large financial investment, is currently being followed in the development of 'dangerous and severe personality disorder' services, with the piloting of four high secure units at Rampton and Broadmoor hospitals and Whitemoor and Frankland prisons (for further information on the Rampton initiative see http://www.ramptondspd.org.uk).

Maintaining a healthy institution

Many factors are important to maintaining a healthy institution (Box 3.6), and some of these are exemplified in Example 3.1.

Box 3.6 Some factors important to maintaining a healthy institution

Openness to the outside world, to new ideas and external scrutiny
Political and public understanding of an institution's functions
Clarity of purpose, realistic expectations and explicit values (e.g. respect for autonomy)
Good-quality physical environment and a healthy therapeutic milieu
An ability to tolerate uncertainty and to learn from mistakes
An understanding of institutional dynamics and ability to reflect and question
Robust systems for training, development and supervision of staff

---

Example 3.1   The Secure Rehabilitation Practice Development Unit, Ashworth Hospital

The service was set up to cater for a specific patient group, men with severe enduring mental illness. The treatment model adopted was one of psycho-social intervention, which is increasingly being used in the wider NHS. The University of Manchester delivered training for all members of the multi-disciplinary team, qualified and unqualified, and including the consultant. The ward environment has been designed to provide low levels of negative expressed emotion and is monitored using the Ward Atmosphere Scale (see Chapter 14). The University of Leeds has externally accredited the unit as a practice development unit. Its work has been presented at national conferences and professional visitors are welcome.

Conclusion

Institutions of all sizes are complex organisations, often dealing with difficult people who can present major problems. There is a constant potential for things to go wrong, in a variety of ways and with a variety of adverse consequences. These primarily affect patients, but also have a negative impact on staff, their families, local communities and, at times, public confidence in aspects of public services. The mechanisms of harm are usually complex, multi-factorial and without simple solutions. Institutions are fraught with conflicts and contradictions. Acknowledging these openly and constructively and trying to minimise them is an important part of maintaining good institutions. This needs to happen on many levels, in national policy, strategic planning, local management and clinical leadership. Stable and reflective management is an important part of this. Factors that can create and maintain healthy institutions are also many, but they usually involve staff having the time, resources and opportunities to reflect on practice, keep abreast of developments in their field and maintain external links. Three things are certain: we will as a society continue to need institutions in their various forms; there will continue to be scandals and inquiries; but there will also be examples of good practice, good care and committed staff working with some of the most difficult clinical problems imaginable.

References

Blom-Cooper, L. (1992) *Report of the Committee of Inquiry into Complaints about Ashworth Hospital* (Cm 2028). London: HMSO.

Department of Health (1989) *Criteria for Admission to Special Hospital*. London: Department of Health.

Fallon, P., Bluglass, R., Edwards, B., *et al* (1999) *Report of the Committee of Inquiry into the Personality Disorder Unit, Ashworth Special Hospital* (vol. 1) (Cm 4194, II). London: Stationery Office.

Goffman, E. (1961) *Asylums*. London: Penguin Books.

Kaye, C. & Franey, A. (eds) (1998) *Managing High Security Psychiatric Care*. London: Jessica Kingsley.

Martin, J. P. (1984) *Hospitals in Trouble*. London: Basil Blackwell.

Mental Health Act Commission (2001) *The Mental Health Act Commission 9th Biennial Report 1999–2001*. London: Stationery Office.

Orr, D. (2002) A terrible way to report a terrible crime: the hypocrisy and guilt of the media. *Independent*, 20 August.

Tilt, R., Perry, B., Martin, C., *et al* (2000) *Report of the Review of Security at the High Security Hospitals*. London: Department of Health.

Watts, D. & Morgan, G. (1994) Malignant alienation. Dangers for patients who are hard to like. *British Journal of Psychiatry*, **164**, 11–15.

Wing, J. K. & Brown, G. W. (1970) *Institutionalism and Schizophrenia: A Comparative Study of Three Mental Hospitals 1960–1968*. Cambridge: Cambridge University Press.

CHAPTER 4

A psychoanalytical understanding of what goes wrong: the importance of projection

Penelope Campling

Editors' introduction Penelope Campling is fascinated by the workings of groups and institutions and how they never run smoothly. In this chapter, she tries to convey the concepts of projection and splitting, hopefully in a way that is accessible and even useful.

'The particular work that is required of psychiatric staff is 'anxiety work'. It means coping with high levels of psychological tension and it requires withstanding the intolerable. We must do first what the patient, his intimate relatives, or his friends and neighbours, and other professional helpers cannot do – that is, to bear his experiences. This is a tall order, and it faces the service with the problem that staff must face unbearable suffering' (Hinshelwood, 2001: pp. 42–43).

In this chapter, I explore why it is so difficult to provide a truly caring and therapeutic environment, an environment that values the people within and helps the healing process. In the quotation above, Hinshelwood throws some light on this question. He defines the fundamental task of mental health services as processing the 'intolerable suffering' of its patients. If this task is avoided, he goes on to say, then the institution becomes maladaptive. Here I examine how suffering affects the institution itself and discuss some common ways in which mental health environments become maladaptive.

One way of coping with suffering is to shut down bits of ourselves, so that we are not overwhelmed. Most of us do this to some extent when we hear about tragic events in the news. We put up a barrier, which protects us from the suffering we see and enables us to carry on functioning as normal.

This becomes problematic when the primary task of the organisation is to process suffering. Moreover, when levels of distress, anxiety and fear reach a critical level, the protective barrier is such that the suffering can no longer be thought about – in other words, the whole process is outside of our awareness. Psychoanalysts describe this as an unconscious defence mechanism. This process in which memories, feelings and experiences that are too painful are denied or distorted can be usefully applied to institutions as well as to individuals. A number of authors have described how supposedly caring institutions can be driven by such unconscious processes, to the extent that the task becomes neglected or, at worst, perverted and the people in need of care become dehumanised (e.g. Menzies Lyth, 1959; Obholzer & Zagier Roberts, 1994; Hinshelwood, 2001).

Unconscious mechanisms come to the fore when reality cannot be faced in its entirety and in its complexity. In turn, truth and authenticity are casualties of the maladaptive environment, with an increasing focus on unrealistic, simplistic solutions that deny the suffering of our patients and the pain that we share with them.

Mutual projection between staff and patients: the helpful and the helpless

One particular form of denial and simplification that is common in the area of mental health is to overemphasise the difference between ourselves and our patients. In order to deny our own fears of death and madness we can exaggerate the vulnerability in our patients, remaining blind to their strengths and coping mechanisms. This reinforces a separation that makes our work superficially more tolerable, but ultimately depletes all concerned. Main described the roles involved in a hospital as follows:

'Only roles of health or illness are on offer; staff to be only healthy, knowledgeable, kind, powerful and active, and patients to be only ill, suffering, ignorant, passive, obedient and grateful. In most hospitals staff are there because they seek to care for others less able than themselves, while the patients hope to find others more able than themselves. The helpful and the helpless meet and put pressures on each other to act not only in realistic, but also phantastic collusion ... the helpful will unconsciously *require* others to be helpless while the helpless will *require* others to be helpful. Staff and patients are thus inevitably to some extent creatures of each other' (Main, 1975: p. 61).

At a psychological level, this happens through a process of 'projection', in which unwanted or feared aspects of ourselves are denied and placed within someone else. Projection is a type of unconscious defence mechanism. On first reading, this might seem a rather abstract and nebulous idea – even rather absurd – but it can be an invaluable concept for understanding irrationality within relationships, particularly when interpersonal behaviour goes beyond the understanding of ordinary common sense. It is always a difficult concept to teach, so do not worry if you find it hard to understand at first. It is the type of concept that you need to live with and allow to evolve as your clinical experience develops. If you want to 'see' projection, look at a photograph of a Nazi

---

Box 4.1 Projection can be damaging

- It distorts reality
- It distorts relationships
- It stops people thinking
- It makes people ill – patients, staff, teams and institutions

---

rally or people's faces within a heckling crowd when the release of a child murderer is being discussed. In such examples, fear has been processed in a way that locates all that is hated in the other person, leaving the innocent feeling a dangerously smug and self-righteous loathing. An understanding of projection is fundamental to a psychoanalytical perspective on mental health problems and institutions. Different manifestations of projection and the related mechanism of splitting are the subject of the rest of this chapter and are summarised in Boxes 4.1 and 4.2.

In institutions, projection can be a mutual process: patients can make counterprojections. They might push their discarded more-creative aspects into the staff in their wish to be cared for and protected; or they might introject the inadequate, unwanted aspects of staff members, in the process exaggerating their own sense of being unwell and the staffs' sense of being healthy. Main (1967) described this phenomenon as patients and staff being 'creatures of each other'. Both sides, the patients and the staff, unconsciously perpetuate the stereotypes of staff as powerful, caring and helpful and patients as dependent, weak and helpless. There is something clear and comfortable about this division of roles, and the projections often hook all too easily into another's actual personality tendencies. The roles then become institutionalised and difficult to challenge.

Box 4.2 Looking out for projection

Beware of the following:

- Structures that overemphasise the helpfulness and strength of staff and the helplessness and weakness of patients
- Prejudice – it is more common than we like to admit, so keep thinking about it
- Scapegoating – it is unlikely to be just one person's fault
- Subgroups and factions, particularly if they revolve around the split perspective on a particular patient
- A 'cosy' team within a 'persecutory' environment – what would you be doing in their shoes?
- An environment in which it is difficult to think

Main was describing phenomena he had observed in the large institutions of his time. However, it could be said that the care programme approach institutionalises these dynamics in the present, with 'care' and 'responsibility' firmly placed with the professional. It is important that staff responsibility includes an understanding of the system and vigilance towards its potential for activating damaging mutual projections. More encouraging in respect of the unhelpful exaggeration of power relations by psychological processes is the development of the user movement, which gives patients a voice and encourages them to think and articulate how they see and experience the mental health settings of which they are part.

Therapeutic communities have always emphasised the idea that a therapeutic environment has to be a 'living–learning' experience for all concerned. Pullen, for example, talks about staff having therapeutic rights and residents having therapeutic duties. He writes:

'A measure of humility seems in order for the staff: Most of us have not had to cope with anything like the internal and external experiences of the residents. In a very real sense, the wisdom about living with schizophrenia is something shared by the residents' (Pullen, 1999: p. 148).

If initiatives such as user involvement, antistigma campaigns and personal development of staff are underpinned by a real respect for our patients and understanding of our own vulnerability, then the opportunity for pathogenic projections will be greatly reduced.

Institutions can have a personality disorder too

The process of projection can occur at many different levels within an institution: for example, between different subgroups and at the interface with the external world. Where projection is extreme, an institution can be thought of as having a 'paranoid personality', where everything outside the organisation is seen as bad and threatening and the cause of all that goes wrong. This is often driven by a need to deny the threats and conflict within. Caring institutions such as therapeutic communities, which have a strong ideology, are particularly vulnerable to this process, with the potential to become inward-looking and – in their efforts to protect themselves from the outside world – increasingly maladaptive and out of touch with reality. Of course, some perceived threats from outside are very real, and a great deal of reflective 'work' needs to be done in order to distinguish between reality and paranoid anxiety.

Projection and prejudice

It is much easier to project onto someone you do not know well and do not understand; and there is a natural tendency within institutions to huddle together, like with like. If one group holds a large majority or significant overt or covert power over another group, this can lead to institutionalised prejudice, for example racism or sexism. Because the process of projection is unconscious, people involved would not have the awareness to think about this in terms of prejudice. Instead, they might experience a frightened African–Carribbean male patient, for example, as aggressive, out of control and dangerous. It might be that this patient already experiences himself in this way and he might have such a history, but the danger is that the process of projection within an institution in which the patient is relatively powerless will exaggerate and worsen this man's behavioural tendencies in a destructive cycle that is difficult to stop.

Scapegoating

In mental health settings, the patients themselves complicate the picture with the impact of the mental disturbance they bring with them. Hinshelwood describes 'affect flow', in which emotions spread like an epidemic within a particular setting: 'one person passes onto another a piece of experience like a hot potato' (Hinshelwood, 2001: p. 138). Our patients are often overwhelmed by a sense of their helplessness, and if this pervading emotion cannot be adequately processed within a team, it can lead to demoralisation, cynicism and burnout. It can also be projected onto one particular member or subgroup within the team, who is then blamed, saving the rest of the team from having to face their feeling of inadequacy. For example, in a badly managed team, one person might be forced to take the blame for a particular incident or failure, so that the rest of the team are protected from looking at their part in it. When unwanted feelings in a group of people are denied and projected onto one person or a small subgroup (staff or patient) this is known as scapegoating. The process not only hurts the individual, but weakens the team, which loses the opportunity to take an honest look at itself and readapt to reality. Often the team member or subgroup chosen as the scapegoat is isolated in some way, for example the social worker in a team of nurses or the night staff working in a team predominantly doing day shifts.

Amplifying divisions

Multidisciplinary teams and staff rotating through a 24-hour rota are examples of attempts to improve communication between professions and avoid split-off subgroups. But the impact of the mental disturbance at the heart of our work continues to be channelled in various directions, for example towards 'management' or in squabbles about interface issues. It is vital that the power of this dynamic be understood;

otherwise mental health services are doomed to be continually refigured in an unconscious attempt to avoid the suffering and pain inherent in the work. This is not to say that the push to improve and modernise is wrong; but if these initiatives are to make a real difference, it is important to recognise that 'fault lines' will reappear somewhere in the structure. Such an understanding will encourage the setting up of realistic structures to pre-empt and minimise the potential damage.

The present configuration of increasingly specialised services, in which an individual patient may be passed from team to team, has fault lines at these interfaces. Much has been said about the importance of good coordination, and the care programme approach is an attempt to organise this. However, this seemingly simple and sensible idea has proved amazingly difficult to implement effectively, with inquiry after inquiry highlighting the breakdown of communication between different teams and agencies. Lack of resources fuel this, particularly in the present climate where teams bid against each other for a share of an inadequate pot of money. However, much could be gained by understanding the power of mutual projections and the particular intensity these can reach in mental health services if everyone is busy pushing their feelings of inadequacy and helplessness onto someone else – most comfortably, another team. If analysis is avoided at this level, the system is likely to become ever more bureaucratic in a futile exercise that misses the point. The cost to patients, many of whom have a profound fear of fragmentation, is enormous.

At a clinical level, patients often end up being 'overtreated', because the staff team cannot bear feeling helpless and inadequate. One thing that mental health services could usefully rethink is the need for 'asylum' admissions or some sort of sanctuary, where patients overwhelmed by distressing experiences (internal and external) can be safely contained in an environment that encourages the process of healing and where staff do not feel the need to impose labels, medication or other interventions in a superficial attempt to deny, take away or cut short the patients' suffering.

The concept of splitting

Psychoanalysts have a particular model for understanding how infants organise their experiences as emotions and relationships develop. This is based on the idea that very young infants experience love (when all is well with them) and hate (when all is not well), but existing as they do, totally in the present, they keep these experiences completely separate from each other. Melanie Klein used the terms 'good breast' and 'bad breast' for this phenomenon. Gradually, as the brain evolves, the infant develops the capacity to remember and to think about experiences in an increasingly complex and realistic fashion. For some people, however, memories and experiences are 'unthinkable' – too full of horror and fear for survival itself. This is particularly likely in children who have been abused, traumatised, deprived, severely neglected or have suffered catastrophic loss, and also in adults who experienced these traumas in childhood. Many such people find it hard to establish a coherent sense of their existence and become stuck at an early, emotionally fragmented level where good and bad, love and hate, have to be kept separate. Their emotional development is fundamentally flawed. Bringing them into a therapeutic setting offers the potential for addressing the things that go wrong, potentially providing them with a second chance to bring together parts of themselves that have become disjointed and to modify the power of the persecutory characters that inhabit their inner worlds, in some cases feeding a psychotic illness.

However, all too often the reverse occurs, and the environment is moulded into a shape that reflects the patient's inner world. Halton links this process to that of children at play, who:

'represent their different feelings through characters and animals invented or derived from children's stories: the good fairy, the wicked witch, the jealous sisters, the sly fox and so on ... By splitting emotions, children gain relief from internal conflicts. The painful conflict between love and hate for the mother, for instance, can be relieved by splitting the mother image into a good fairy and a bad witch. Projection often accompanies splitting and involves locating feelings in others rather than in oneself. Thus the child attributes slyness to the fox or jealousy to the bad sister. Through play these contradictory feelings and figures can be explored and resolved' (Halton, 1994: p. 13).

In a ward or residential setting, staff members may come to represent different, conflicting, often polarized aspects of the psychological inner world of a patient or groups of patients. The following clinical vignette illustrates how this may come about.

An example of splitting within a team

A patient, Sally, acts increasingly desperately, cutting herself with razor blades, running out of the building and provoking anger in the staff team, who eventually physically restrain her and put her in seclusion. In this way, Sally has put pressure on the staff, perhaps through the mechanism of projection and splitting, to act as her abusers had done. At some level she feels comfortable with this because it confirms what she already knows about the world – that her anger is too much for people and that people in authority cannot be trusted. The work involved to challenge these preconceptions can therefore be avoided. At another level, she feels despairing and full of hate because the environment has failed her once again and retraumatised her in the process.

The situation is complicated because a number of people are involved in Sally's care. She had a particularly good relationship with her keyworker, Rita, who was not on duty when the restraint and seclusion happened. Sally finds it easier to open up to Rita than to anyone else and has begun tentatively to talk to her about the many cruelties she suffered as a child. Because Sally finds this difficult, Rita has reassured her that she will not share this with the rest of the team. Sally is very grateful to her and tells her that she is the only person in the team who understands her.

When Rita returns to work and discovers that Sally has been put in seclusion, she feels angry with the team, which confirms her sense that she is the only person who understands Sally. She feels increasingly protective of Sally and spends as much time with her as possible, sometimes neglecting other patients, failing to complete other tasks or staying on later than necessary. The ward manager notices this and challenges her about it. Rita has a sense that other staff are giving her 'funny looks'; she confides this to Sally, reinforcing Sally's feeling that they are not to be trusted.

The situation continues to worsen. Rita becomes increasingly isolated from the rest of the team and unable to tell them about her relationship with Sally, which she is finding increasingly upsetting. Sally is on her mind most of the time and thoughts of her are even affecting her sleep. Sometimes she dreads going to work. The rest of the team are increasingly irritated by Sally and see her as manipulative. They feel that the ward would be much calmer and their jobs much easier without Sally's presence. They increasingly see Rita as having problems and wonder if these are due to her personal life. They make occasional comments to Rita about being over-involved with Sally, but this just seems to make things worse.

Discussion

This situation can usefully be understood in terms of psychological 'splitting', with one part of the team (Rita) idealising the patient (Sally) (and *vice versa*) and the other part denigrating her. The patient has a need to keep experiences separate from each other, so she projects good, loving feelings onto one part of the team (Rita, who becomes like a fairy godmother) and bad, hateful feelings on to another part (the rest, who are wicked witches whom she has to outmanoeuvre). Consequently, she acts differently in different situations, depending on who is present. Rita, therefore, sees her as a helpless abused victim, someone who is desperately trying to address her problems but is being thwarted because Rita's colleagues do not understand her. The rest of the team see Sally as destructive, deceitful and manipulative; whatever they do she continues to cut herself, often at the most inconvenient times. They know little about the cruelty she has suffered and cannot understand why she is being kept in hospital when she is so obviously not trying to get better. All involved feel they know the 'real' Sally and others have got it wrong.

Although it is easy to see why someone like Sally could be described as manipulative, it is important to understand that Sally is not conscious of what she is doing. Her experience of relationships has always been difficult: and the ward environment is simply reflecting back what she already 'knows' of the world, reinforcing the split between 'good' and 'bad' in the process. As Knowles (2001) puts it:

'If you are surrounded by abuse, violence, chaos, lack of boundaries and unpredictability before you can even think, then maybe your superego becomes redirected towards controlling the outer world ... These desperate attempts to keep yourself safe by controlling that which frightens you will, when you are an adult, be seen as manipulation, splitting, attention seeking ...'

If the environment is to be therapeutic for Sally, there needs to be an understanding within the team of the process of splitting, so that Sally's behaviour can be framed in a different way. Instead of being seen simply as manipulative, her relationship with different team members could be seen as a form of communication, conveying important information about her past experiences and inner world. Communication between team members then becomes all-important, allowing the team to think about the different parts of Sally and begin to build up the whole picture. Feeling in the team would still be intense, but there would not be the antagonism and need to dismiss the others' point of view. A different perspective could be viewed with 'interest', with some mutual listening and more open sharing of information and feelings. In time, this might allow space for feelings to shift a little, becoming a bit more mixed and complex – for example Rita might be able to acknowledge that she feels burdened by the intensity of Sally's dependence and has some anger and resentment towards Sally; and those involved in secluding Sally might be able to review the incidents that led up to this and question whether they could have handled things differently. Indeed, in retrospect they might be able to see the seclusion as an unconscious re-enactment. Sally herself might not have the capacity to engage in this work in terms of sharing in a verbal discourse, but she will benefit at a deeper pre-verbal level from being part of a more coherent environment.

Splitting between teams

The sort of splitting described within the team in the case of Sally can also occur between different teams and agencies, with the different groups holding very different, often polarised, perspectives on a particular patient. These perspectives reflect the splits within the patient, but also the mutual projections between teams – often an accumulation of misunderstandings and stereotypical beliefs going back over years. This situation can be very damaging for a patient, not just at the social level, with the risk that the patient will experience exclusion and fall through a gap between services, but also at the psychological level, reinforcing the patient's sense of internal fragmentation and alienation. Sometimes the splitting is focused on whole groups of patients: the diagnosis of borderline personality disorder or substance misuse, for example, can attract particularly polarized perspectives from different teams, with the danger that the patient can end up being treated like a football, both in the sense of being kicked around from one team to another, and also kicked in a certain direction with a view to 'scoring a goal' against the other team. Such patients have wide-ranging needs that might need input from different teams and agencies. Their situation can be made worse by an unhelpfully narrow adherence to the concept of the responsible medical officer rather than a collaborative attitude, perhaps formalised in a 'managed clinical network' (Holmes & Langmaack, 2002).

It is also helpful if staff can gently be encouraged to think about why they entered the caring professions and to extend this self-reflective questioning to their empathy (or lack of empathy) for particular groups of patients or particular settings. People are drawn to work in a certain profession or environment for unconscious as well as conscious reasons, which means that a particular setting is likely to attract staff with similar internal needs and patterns of defences – a phenomenon that Wilfred Bion described as 'valency' (Zagier Roberts, 1994). Indeed, if an individual's unconscious defences are not in tune with the collective defences of an institution, he or she is likely to leave. Insight into the collective defences of a particular setting prevent them from becoming maladaptive. This may mitigate the need to blame patients who do not 'fit' or to dismiss the perspectives of other teams.

Thinking and feeling: the importance of making links

Sally's situation described above illustrates the potential for a team to shift their thinking about a patient's problem in a way that creates links between:

- different subgroups within the team
- a patient's life experience and his or her destructive behaviour
- a patient's inner world and the group dynamic created on the ward.

There is a sense in which all mental health problems can be understood as problems of linking, whether these links be neuro-biochemical pathways, links with past experiences that unhelpfully distort the experience of the here and now (dynamic psychotherapists refer to the latter as transference) or links within the social matrix, the complex network of relationships in which we are involved, which can so affect the way we think and feel and express ourselves (see Chapter 2).

Many patients need help to think about their feelings. One way of conceptualising analytical psychotherapy is to see it as a process of creating a narrative, an opportunity for the patient to build up a coherent sense of him- or herself, a person with a meaningful life story rather than a muddle of fragmented experiences. This narrative includes an understanding of therapeutic relationships and how these link with their life story. Patients with a mental illness need to incorporate the illness and associated experiences into their narratives – a process which is movingly described in Chapter 5. This should include the experience of hospital admissions, with their inherent opportunities for gently facilitative relationships. Sadly, however, patients often experience admission to hospital wards and other residential settings as disjointed traumas, rather than an opportunity to make sense of experiences and a chance to link with parts of themselves that have become alienated.

If an environment is to be truly therapeutic and healing, then linking within the environment and at its boundaries needs to be healthy and robust. This means that there must be good communication, as well as a commitment to a reflective verbal discourse that is open and authentic. It does not mean the absence of conflict: as we have seen, conflict cannot be avoided in institutions, particularly where mental disturbance plays a prominent part. Unfortunately, many residential settings are characterised by poor communication and a lack of space for reflection. Everyone is busy, but much of the activity is reactive rather than thoughtful – indeed, it can be difficult if not impossible to think in such an environment.

The importance of thinking and linking creatively is central to any theory of organisational management. But it is psychoanalytical work that has attempted to explain why maintaining a thinking culture is so difficult. Main, for example, describes how the creative ideas of one generation become the superego-driven, rigid, unthinking rituals of the next (Main, 1967). However good the idea, ownership of the ideas and engagement in the thinking process are all-important if institution-alisation is to be avoided. Maintaining a culture of enquiry involves an ongoing process of questioning why things are done as they are. This can try the patience of longer-standing members of staff (I speak personally!), but any attempt to short-cut the process risks disempower-ing those on the front line, amplifying 'them and us' projections within the team's hierarchy, which can lead to damaging miscommunic-ations and a general loss of energy and weakening of engagement in the collaborative task.

More fundamentally, psychoanalysts believe that true relatedness can be terrifying, because it involves challenging our usual protective defences and distorting projections. Thinking about feelings and connecting in an authentic way with others are therefore deeply threatening and often experienced as unbearable or dangerous. Attempts to introduce or increase self-reflective thinking in an institution will often be resisted (e.g. with poor attendance at supervision or staff support groups) or even overtly attacked (e.g. by the denigration of the

---

Box 4.3   Dealing with maladaptive avoidance

A primary task of mental health settings is to contain and process anxiety and distress. The following may prevent maladaptive avoidance:

- A supervision structure and culture that allows staff to talk about what frightens them
- A self-reflective attitude to personal and collective defence patterns
- Formulations that clarify and focus on the task
- Thinking about possible links between the patients' inner worlds, staff feelings and team dynamics
- An understanding of the dynamics of abuse, in particular the link between childhood abuse and the potential for abuse within the institution

---

group facilitator or person making an interpretation). In a classic paper, Menzies (1960) analysed the structure of nurse training in a large London hospital and saw that the rules and rituals involved in everyday training practice were organised in such a way as to defend against the fear involved in truly relating to the patients' pain. Attempts to think about this situation were fiercely resisted, because it required staff to acknowledge their fear of being emotionally close to the experience of suffering and death.

Because self-reflective practice will always be threatening, and therefore resisted, some units have attempted to incorporate this way of thinking into their structure, with a framework or formulation that puts the patients' pain, and the thinking and linking that are an essential part of processing this, at the heart of the work (Box 4.3).

In residential settings, staff work shifts spread over 24 hours, 7 days a week and it is difficult, if not impossible, for everyone to meet together. However, a combination of staff away-days, staff sensitivity groups and focused supervision can enormously affect the culture of an environment, with a more open, reflective attitude spreading into other areas such as handovers. A self-reflective culture takes time to establish and is always vulnerable, but at its best a well-thought-out supervision structure (see Chapter 20) will provide a safe frame for staff to acknowledge and process feelings that frighten them. If they cannot do this, there is little chance that they will be able to help the patients to contain their feelings. Tranquillisers can then be resorted to too quickly, and the job becomes one of fire-fighting emotional distress rather than of psychological processing. Unfortunately, emotional distress cannot simply be snuffed out.

An environment in which people are not free or willing to think and make useful links is fertile ground for the type of divisive, unconscious projections described above; and these in turn make it even more difficult to think and communicate in a healthy way. The answer is for

---

Box 4.4 Therapy for the environment

The therapeutic environment itself needs to be the focus of an ongoing 'therapy'. The following might help this process:

- Community/ward meetings
- Staff sensitivity groups
- Staff away-days
- An external facilitator/mentor/consultant
- Supervision for team leaders/consultants
- An understanding of unconscious projective processes

---

as many people as possible to engage in thinking about the environment itself (Box 4.4). In addition to supervision, this can usefully include patients or residents in ward or community meetings and it should obviously be a focus for staff and senior management teams. There is a sense in which the therapeutic environment itself needs to be the constant focus of the therapy if it is to be robust enough to facilitate healing within and processing of the suffering inherent in the work.

References

Halton, W. (1994) Some unconscious aspects of organisational life: contributions from psychoanalysis. In *The Unconscious at Work: Individual and Organisational Stress in the Human Services* (eds A. Obholzer & V. Zagier Roberts), p. 13. London: Routledge.

Hinshelwood, R. D. (2001) *Thinking about Institutions. Milieux and Madness.* London: Jessica Kingsley.

Holmes, J. & Langmaack, C. (2002) Managed clinical networks – their relevance to mental health services. *Psychiatric Bulletin*, **26**, 161–163.

Knowles, J. (2001) Therapeutic communities – do we need to break free and think afresh? *Therapeutic Communities*, **22**, 271–285.

Main, T. F. (1967) Knowledge, learning and freedom from thought. *Australian and New Zealand Journal of Psychiatry*, **1**, 64–71. Reprinted 1990 in *Psychoanalytic Psychotherapy*, **15**, 59–74.

Main, T. F. (1975) Some psychodynamics of large groups. In *The Large Group* (ed. L. Kreeger), p. 61. London: Constable.

Menzies Lyth, I. (1959) The functioning of social systems as a defence against anxiety. *Human Relations*, **13**, 95–121. Reproduced 1988 in *Containing Anxiety in Institutions* (I. Menzies Lyth), pp. 43–85. London: Free Association Books.

Obholzer, A. & Zagier Roberts, V. (1994) *The Unconscious at Work. Individual and Organisational Stress in the Human Services.* London: Routledge.

Pullen, G. (1999) Schizophrenia: hospital communities for the severely disturbed. In *Therapeutic Communities: Past, Present and Future* (eds P. Campling & R. Haigh), p. 148. London: Jessica Kingsley.

Zagier Roberts, V. (1994) The Self-assigned Impossible Task. In *The Unconscious at Work: Individual and Organisational Stress in the Human Services* (eds A. Obholzer & V. Zagier Roberts), pp. 110–118. London: Routledge.

CHAPTER 5

Users' experiences of in-patient services

Alan Quirk and Paul Lelliott

Editors' introduction Alan Quirk (sociologist) and Paul Lelliott (professor and consultant psychiatrist) both work at the Royal College of Psychiatrist's Research Unit (as research fellow and director, respectively), where a particular interest is qualitative research into the experiences of the users and providers of mental health services. In this chapter they focus on users' experiences of in-patient services, referring to their own research, the literature on institutions and some pertinent quotations from users' literature. The experiences conveyed are relevant to many different in-patient settings.

It would be surprising if a book like this were published today without serious consideration being given to mental health service users' experiences of in-patient services. This is because:

(a) despite developments in community care, the hospital remains the hub of mental health services in the UK (a high proportion of health authorities' mental health budget is spent on in-patient services);

(b) many service users will experience some form of hospitalisation during their lives;

(c) even the shortest stay in hospital can have a dramatic influence on a person's sense of identity and social position (the label 'psychiatric patient' remains highly stigmatising);

(d) users' views on treatment and care are increasingly influential at local and national levels, and the service user/survivor movement is now a key player in National Health Service (NHS) policy development (Pilgrim & Rogers, 1999).

Representations of the 'patient's experience' of psychiatric hospital can be found in film (e.g. *One Flew over the Cuckoo's Nest* and *A Beautiful Mind*), the theatre (e.g. *Equus*) and other literary forms. Important insights can be gained from such sources. However, they are written with the explicit aim of telling a story and are not necessarily produced by people with first-hand experience of the subject matter. The main problem with such accounts is that the exceptional is portrayed as, and subsequently believed to be, quite normal.

This chapter draws on three sources of information about users' experiences of in-patient services: first, an extensive review of research literature (described more fully in Quirk & Lelliott, 2001); second, a review of first-hand accounts by former patients, in the form of testimonies and memoirs; and third, some preliminary findings from a participant observation study recently undertaken by us on three acute psychiatric wards in England. In the observation study A.Q. immersed himself in the life of three wards, staying in each for a 3-month period (for further information see Quirk & Lelliott, 2002). We do not claim to provide a comprehensive picture of users' experiences in this short chapter. Rather, we aim to identify a few issues and themes that recur, in these different sources, in order to highlight some of the counter-therapeutic aspects of in-patient psychiatric care.

The person and the environment

Personal safety

Many service users feel comparatively safe during some or all of their stay in hospital. One, Jan Holloway, for example, describes her appalling dilemma in the weeks leading up to her admission – she felt scared and vulnerable and very much wanted to be close to people, yet at the same time she found those people 'increasingly threatening' (Holloway, 1999). She then heard 'the voice' for the first time, which became louder, more intense and nastier in tone: *'She's going to kill or be killed'*. She knew that she was 'dangerous' and could see only one way out:

'I was on my own in the house and I knew I was dangerous. I was in the other world, and in the other world there were only two options. Either I would kill someone or I would die. I had to protect [my partner]; I had to protect everyone I cared about. So I decided to kill myself' (p. 42).

On being admitted to hospital a few days later, Jan immediately felt safe. One of her closest friends came to visit her the evening she was admitted: 'It was good to see her. For the first time in ages I did not feel threatened by her. In some way, in this awful place, for the first time in six months, I felt safe' (p. 44).

A risky environment

This perception of the psychiatric ward as a place of safety during a time of crisis can change during a person's stay, as they come to terms with the risks that are concentrated in this environment. There is good evidence that a ward can be a disturbing and scary place to be – for both patients and staff alike. Previous research (Quirk & Lelliott, 2001) and our own study support this (Box 5.1).

> **Box 5.1** The ward environment
>
> The ward can be a frightening place:
> - Fights can break out unexpectedly
> - Patients may be subjected to theft, bullying and sexual harassment
> - Very disturbed or floridly psychotic patients can have a massive detrimental effect on the ward atmosphere and undermine other people's sense of security

Such problems – especially the threat of violence – can feed into a vicious circle that undermines the ward as a 'therapeutic environment'. This is particularly common when mistrust and fear increase 'avoidance' between users and staff:

There were ... lots of angry young men [on the ward]. The nurses spent their time shut in the office and the door to the ward was locked most of the time. There was much overt racism among the staff. Later I found out that one of the nurses had been badly assaulted by one of the patients, and so the staff were very scared. I was scared; the nurses were scared – it could hardly be a therapeutic environment' (Holloway, 1999: p. 47).

Implications for personhood

The experience of being admitted to a psychiatric hospital has serious repercussions (Box 5.2). Many service users view being admitted to hospital as a moral failure rather than a medical event – one that can have terrible implications for their social position and identity. Sally Clay, who was first hospitalised in the USA in the 1950s, illustrates this:

When I came to, I was sitting at the corner of a grimy wooden table ... I had awakened into a nightmare, deepened by a strange, soupy grogginess that made it difficult even to open my eyes or move my head ... I knew where I was. This was a mental hospital, the bottomless pit where society's refuse was

> **Box 5.2** The in-patient experience
>
> Becoming a psychiatric in-patient means:
> - being removed from your life outside of hospital and relieved of some of the obligations that go with it
> - being deprived of many of your legal rights
> - having restricted freedom of movement
> - being placed in an environment in which your actions are likely to be interpreted in a psychopathological context
> - losing credibility by virtue of your psychiatric label

thrown. As I examined this place I realized that for the first time in my life – perhaps now for all my life – I was identified with the lowest of the low' (in Clay, 1999: p. 17).

This experience of failure can only be reinforced by the fact that mental health workers view admission as an option resorted to only when community care is failing. Today, there are no positive indicators for admitting a person to a psychiatric ward.

Much has been published on the processes involved in being admitted to psychiatric hospital and how these strip away one's previous sense of identity. The sociologist Erving Goffman has described such 'assaults on the self' of psychiatric patients in the 1950s, including 'role dispossession' (people lose the social roles they had before admission, such as their occupation); the stripping of possessions (reinforced by the failure to provide 'inmates' with lockers); the loss of 'identity equipment', which prevents patients from presenting their usual self to others, for example clothes, make-up and other status symbols; and forced interpersonal contact with other people on the ward (Goffman, 1961).

This stripping away of an individual's former identity, and its replacement by that of 'mental patient', was termed 'depersonalisation' by the social psychologist David Rosenhan (Rosenhan, 1973), and was depicted by Goffman as essentially the same process undergone by new inmates in prison or recruits in the army (Goffman, 1961). Depersonalisation is most intense in situations where there is avoidance between staff and patients (e.g. caused by mistrust and fear), a separation between their social worlds (as exemplified by staff-only areas), and where low staffing levels reduce the amount of time staff can spend with patients (Goffman, 1961; Rosenhan, 1973). Heavy reliance on psychotropic medication tacitly contributes to avoidance and depersonalisation by convincing staff that treatment is taking place and that further patient contact might not be necessary (Rosenhan, 1973).

It must be stressed that the research referred to above was conducted decades ago, when hospital stays tended to be much longer than they are today. Our research indicates that this partly explains why 'assaults on the self' of newly admitted patients now appear to be reduced. In the context of community care, hospital has become a small part in the life of many service users, who may also be managing a family, job, the social services, housing and money, and these functions have to continue while they are in hospital. A key difference for today's in-patient, then, is that in many respects he or she *remains a person* while in hospital, and is much less likely to be relieved of the obligations of personhood than were inmates of the old asylums. Even so, depersonalisation, in its diluted form, remains a source of frustration for service users we spoke to and it is as countertherapeutic as it ever was. It is probably a particular issue for those whose admission lasts longer than

> **Box 5.3** Perceptions of service users
>
> Users know that:
> - their personal story and feelings are the subject of staff discussions
> - they are under staff surveillance (although they can still be shocked to learn how much detail is recorded in their notes)
> - their everyday activities are the subject of regulations and judgements by staff
> - even the most mundane of activities, such as making a hot drink, can be disrupted through having to ask staff for permission or supplies

a few weeks. For example, one interviewee told us that she had become 'institutionalised' and 'disempowered' during her 3-month stay and feared that it would take her a couple of years to 'get back to normal'.

Powerlessness

Depersonalisation helps to explain why service users often report feeling powerless in this environment. Such 'disempowerment' is compounded by the fact that personal privacy is minimal and that their personal history and anguish are (a) available to any member of staff who chooses to read your notes and (b) discussed by staff during handovers between shifts and in other 'backstage' meetings. In addition, service users know that they are being watched, judged and regulated (Box 5.3).

Viewed from this perspective, a psychiatric ward is a difficult and bizarre place in which to live. Most importantly, it is a social context in which patients' actions and motives are at great risk of being misinterpreted and pathologised (Rosenhan, 1973). One example of this is when legitimate complaints or queries are recorded in patients' notes as being symptomatic of the illness. Stuart Sutherland, a former patient, describes this below, and sheds further light on why service users can feel that doctors and nurses are in an 'impregnable position':

'The younger doctors and nurses tended to treat patients as though they were insane, and this could be both infuriating and upsetting ... [But] none of the patients were totally out of touch with reality, and their illness only affected part of their lives. Many, for example, knew better than the nurses what pills they were supposed to be taking. However doctors sometimes wrote up the drug sheets in such a hurry that nurses could easily make mistakes. It could seem very important to be given the right drugs, but when the wrong ones were handed out any attempt to argue with the nurse would be treated as part of the patient's illness and recorded as such in the day book' (Sutherland, 1977: p. 30).

Recovery of personhood

Personal accounts have been used by researchers to study the lives of psychiatric patients who had been discharged and were now living in a town in the north of England (Barnham & Hayward, 1991). The aim of the research was to shed light on what inclusion in social life had come to mean for former patients and to explore their new identity and social position. This involved understanding the difficulties they encountered in attempting to re-establish their personhood. They continued to be lonely and marginalised and were very reluctant to re-enter the role of 'patient'. Instead, most 'simply' wanted to establish their credibility as ordinary people with rights of citizenship such as adequate employment and housing (Barnham and Hayward, 1991). However, this research referred to people discharged from an old long-stay hospital, so it might have less relevance to those who have briefer admissions today.

Recovery of personhood is a precarious process. Simon Champ, for example, describes the change to his identity resulting from his illness (Champ, 1999). Initially, when he was at his most disempowered, he *was* his illness and routinely described himself to other people as 'a schizophrenic'. But this changed:

'I was recovering my personhood and saw the illness as influencing, rather than defining me ... I began to see that, while I might not be able always to control my illness, I could control my attitude to it' (p. 119).

He thus stopped seeing himself as a 'victim' and started viewing psychosis as, in a sense, something that he does:

'I was indeed a person who happened to experience psychotic episodes, but I refused to be described as a sufferer' (p. 119).

The treatment

The centrality of medication

Forms of treatment or therapeutic activity for patients on general adult psychiatric wards include:

- medication
- weekly ward rounds by their consultant and others involved in their care
- individual sessions with the senior house officer in charge of their case
- sessions with their senior registrar from time to time
- weekly, or perhaps daily, ward meetings attended by staff and patients
- occupational therapy sessions such as art and music appreciation, and other forms of group therapy
- one-to-one behavioural therapy provided by a clinical psychologist.

Patients cannot expect to receive all of these on a regular basis, if indeed at all. For example, those expecting to have easy access to talking therapy during their stay are likely to be disappointed: service users in our research thought that the aim of face-to-face sessions with doctors was to 'check up' on them and monitor their drugs, rather than offer therapy. Previous research on acute wards found (a) little evidence of effective use of occupational therapists and psychologists, (b) that many patients are bored, and (c) that little interest is taken in them unless they are making a disturbance (Quirk & Lelliott, 2001).

Reports of the monotony of life in psychiatric hospital are by no means new (e.g. Riggall, 1929; Ward, 1947). Having spent 18 months 'cut off from friends and the outside world' in a mental hospital during the First World War, Mary Riggall wrote:

I shall never forget the awful monotony of walking around the same piece of ground all day ... No-one could possibly explain the monotony of such a life. It has to be experienced to be believed' (Riggall, 1929: p. 23).

Hospital stays tend to be much shorter these days, but boredom is still a problem for many patients, who typically fill in time sitting alone doing nothing, or looking at – though not necessarily watching – the television. Obviously there are exceptions to this. For example, patients on one of the wards we studied were offered a full timetable of groups during weekdays, and uptake and reported satisfaction were comparatively high. Nevertheless, the evidence overwhelmingly points to medication as being central to the typical in-patient's experience.

A recent survey (Rose, 2001) found that although many service users suffered from the side-effects of psychotropic drugs, most also appreciated the benefits and lessening of symptoms. They balanced the costs and benefits of medication, and coped with the former because of the latter. Resistance to medication was commonly observed during our research, but there were certainly times when patients valued their medication – even if this meant being 'well and truly doped up':

'I was given droperidol, the "don't give a fuck" drug, which calmed me down considerably. It was not that it made any of the symptoms go away – it was just that I did not care about them anymore. That, together with 650 mg chlorpromazine, ensured that I was well and truly doped up. But I felt okay. I was safe' (Holloway, 1999: p. 51).

Views on psychiatric nursing care

Service users' views on in-patient psychiatric nursing care have been explored in various research studies (reviewed in Quirk & Lelliott, 2001). Key findings are outlined in Box 5.4 and aspects of practice most often identified as being of poor quality are shown in Box 5.5.

Box 5.4   Views on psychiatric nursing care

- Users reportedly value the quality of their nursing care, but they typically have only passing relationships with nurses (the latter tend to spend most of their time in the office writing, telephoning or dealing with unexpected incidents)
- Both users and nurses find it difficult to identify which specific aspects of nursing care aid recovery from an acute crisis; however, the 'therapeutic relationship' between the patients and their named nurse is thought by both parties to be crucial
- Users value 'humane' qualities in nurses such as empathy, tolerance and respect

---

'Someone to talk to'

The lack of someone to talk to is a common complaint among users of both in-patient and community mental health services (Rose, 2001). In hospital this can largely be explained by the centrality of medication, the limited availability of talking therapy, and the passing relationships that service users have with nurses. Talking therapies are reportedly popular among the service users who have access to them, but many just seem to want a 'sympathetic ear' and a chance to talk about ordinary things (Rose, 2001). Other research shows that service users value nurses who are 'active listeners', but it is equally important that nurses know when to back off and leave people alone (see Quirk & Lelliott, 2001). Another problem arises on wards with a high turnover of staff. Not only does this make it difficult for patients to get to know staff and develop trusting relationships with them, it can also be boring for them to have to go over their stories with every change of doctor and other staff (Sutherland, 1977).

Clearly, the 'person to talk to' might be another patient. In our research we saw much social mixing between patients on different wards, for example during occupational therapy sessions, meetings of the patients' council and when patients visited other wards. Such interaction can help the development of informal support networks,

---

Box 5.5   Common examples of poor practice

- The failure of nurses to explain their actions
- Coercion and punishment on the part of nurses
- When the group behaviour of nurses negatively affects the ward atmosphere, e.g. when they congregate in the ward office for long periods, in full view of the patients

---

and indeed we saw plenty of evidence of mutual support, advice-giving and friendship among service users. Those we spoke to said that this was partly becasue they were in an environment in which they felt accepted and where allowances were made for 'bizarre' behaviour (see also Barker *et al*, 1999).

Example of 'real recovery'

Simon Champ reflects on how his experience of schizophrenic illness has profoundly challenged him to redefine his own concept of self over the years (Champ, 1999). He concludes that you do not simply 'patch up the self you were before developing schizophrenia'. Rather, you have to 're-create a concept of who you are that integrates the experience of schizophrenia'. For Champ, then, 'real recovery is far from a simple matter of accepting diagnosis and learning facts about the illness and medication'. He accepts that not everyone who experiences schizophrenia will question the concept of who they are in this way. But for him, recovery is a lifelong journey in which he values the support of mental health professionals:

'I think the best professionals involved in my care have walked alongside me, opening themselves to the mystery that is schizophrenia. They have gained my trust, sharing and supporting my inner search for meaning and understanding of self in relation to illness. We have certainly learned about medication, but we have also learned to predict stressors and avert relapse, seeing my well-being as a result of many influences on my life' (Champ, 1999: pp. 123–124).

Conclusion

It must always be borne in mind that the psychiatric hospital never was, and never will be, a place that simply provides specialist treatment and care for those who need it. It has always had three interweaving functions: (a) treatment and care; (b) social control and containment; and (c) accommodation (semi-permanent or permanent). What has changed over the years is the mix of these functions. The old asylums, for example, (arguably) blended these functions in a way that offered a 'total solution' to the social problems associated with mental abnormality (Pilgrim & Rogers, 1999). This is certainly no longer the case, in part because media 'horror stories' about the failures of community care have focused attention on containment. Yet the containment function of psychiatric hospital has been undermined by the pressure on staff to 'empty beds' for urgent new admissions, leaving the institution vulnerable to the charge that it is failing on all three fronts.

In-patient care must be designed around the wishes of the service's users – the patients themselves. To function as a therapeutic environment, the psychiatric hospital must be a place they feel safe, in which containment is done with a light touch, and where they are helped to retain their identities as people who are able make informed decisions about the therapy on offer to them.

References

Barker, P., Campbell, P. & Davidson, B. (eds) *From the Ashes of Experience: Reflections on Madness, Survival and Growth*. London: Whurr.

Barnham, P. & Hayward, R. (1991) *From the Mental Patient to the Person*. London: Routledge.

Champ, S. (1999) A most precious thread. In *From the Ashes of Experience: Reflections on Madness, Survival and Growth* (eds P. Barker, P. Campbell & B. Davidson), pp. 113–126. London: Whurr.

Clay, S. (1999) Madness and reality. In *From the Ashes of Experience: Reflections on Madness, Survival and Growth* (eds P. Barker, P. Campbell & B. Davidson), pp. 16–36. London: Whurr.

Goffman, E. (1961) *Asylums: Essays on the Social Situation of Mental Patients and Other Inmates*. London: Penguin.

Holloway, J. (1999) The other world. In *From the Ashes of Experience: Reflections on Madness, Survival and Growth* (eds P. Barker, P. Campbell & B. Davidson), pp. 37–53. London: Whurr.

Pilgrim, D. & Rogers, A. (1999) *A Sociology of Mental Health and Illness* (2nd edn). Buckingham: Open University Press.

Quirk, A. & Lelliott, P. (2001) What do we know about life on acute psychiatric wards in the UK? A review of the research evidence. *Social Science and Medicine*, **53**(12), 1–10.

Quirk, A. & Lelliott, P. (2002) A participant observation study of life on an acute psychiatric ward. *Psychiatric Bulletin*, **26**, 344–345.

Riggall, M. (1929) *Reminiscences of a Stay in a Mental Hospital*. London: A.H. Stockwell.

Rose, D. (2001) *Users' Voices: The Perspectives of Mental Health Service Users on Community and Hospital Care*. London: Sainsbury Centre for Mental Health.

Rosenhan, D. L. (1973) On being sane in insane places. *Science*, **179**, 250–258.

Sutherland, S. (1977) *Breakdown: A Personal Crisis and a Medical Dilemma*. London: Granada.

Ward. M. J. (1947) *The Snake Pit*. London: Cassell.

CHAPTER 6

Difficulties with attachment and separation: joining and leaving a therapeutic community

Nick Humphreys and Anthony Bree

Editors' introduction Joining and leaving are integral to the concept of the therapeutic environment, implying a sense of movement and reminding us that, as social and health care practitioners, we have to balance a caring response to vulnerability with our role as facilitators of independence and recovery. Problems of attachment and separation are profound and can affect therapeutic environments in all sorts of ways. This chapter is deliberately set in the context of a therapeutic community in which problems of attachment can be particularly pronounced. The principles and problems, however, should be applicable to all settings. Nick Humphreys is adult psychotherapist in the residential programme at Francis Dixon Lodge, and Anthony Bree is lead nurse in the Lodge's outreach team.

Perhaps the most difficult experience that users of a therapeutic environment have to negotiate is the process of transition: the experience of joining in the first place and then, later on, of leaving. These processes are very different for different client groups and settings – particularly for patients being kept involuntarily. But we know that patients are particularly vulnerable at these times, whatever the setting, and that the risk of suicide is high. We also know that the catastrophic despair sometimes provoked by admission or discharge can be mitigated to some degree by thoughtful care planning and careful attention to the emotional processes involved (Box 6.1). In this chapter the subject is discussed in relation to Francis Dixon Lodge, Leicester, the therapeutic community

---

Box 6.1 Attachment

- Joining and leaving tap into profound fears based on early experiences of attachment
- Some patients unconsciously re-enact early experiences of pathological attachment when they make contact with services, potentially regressing and getting worse rather than better in a supportive environment
- A sense of abandonment is sometimes associated with a profound fear of fragmentation and risk of suicide

---

where we both work. However, we hope that some of the thinking will be applicable to other settings. Most importantly, we hope that the chapter will encourage people to give more care and thought to the process of joining and leaving and be more aware of how terrifying these processes can be for some of the people with whom we work.

Assessment and consent

Assessment is usually a mutual process between assessor and patient, a collaborative dialogue that results in a decision about whether or not some time in a therapeutic community might be useful. However, difficult decisions sometimes have to be made, and the therapist is left with the responsibility for deciding whether to offer the prospective member an opportunity to join the organisation. The therapist has to bear in mind that the service on offer does not have a predetermined outcome: the new member can not only use or misuse it, but can also contribute to or detract from its efficacy.

In the process of assessment, assessors need to ask themselves two questions. Will this person be able to share information about themselves and make use of information from others? Will they be able to further this engagement to construct a secure emotional attachment and a healthy working alliance? Such capacities are usually hidden rather than obvious and their emergence has to be arranged for. In practice, this means helping the person to feel safe during the assessment. Careful boundary management that is firm but not rigid, complemented by clear, straightforward information about the assessment process, are essential starting points. This lays the foundation for an alliance with the part of the person that is healthy and will hopefully be able to think with the assessor about the part that is in trouble.

It is important to be aware of how crippling anxiety can be for the prospective new member. Without safety, distress can rapidly be experienced as boundless. Anxiety makes it difficult to think and to organise one's thinking. It can be induced by the prospect of revealing painful and embarrassing details about oneself to strangers in an interview. The very structure of this situation can arouse dormant feelings of hostility, suspicion and fear, transferred from parental authority that has proved untrustworthy or abusive. Assessment implies the possibility of rejection. Fear of rejection and abandonment on the grounds of being seen as unacceptable can lurk at the root of the person's distress. An insecure primary emotional bond with the parents can resurface at every new experience of contact. Initial contact with the service is therefore always important. A telephone call to a secretary or nurse, or an insensitive appointment letter might have contributed to fantasies about the service which assessment can either support or modify.

Box 6.2 Assessment and consent

- The first contact with the service is very important because it is likely to colour future experience
- The patient is likely to feel extremely anxious and will need help to feel safe in the assessment situation
- The concept of informed consent means that patients should be encouraged to ask questions and should be given as much useful and accessible information as possible

---

Informing the person about the service and about the nature of the therapy can further contain anxiety. Information also provides a cognitive structure that will help the person to cope more effectively with the initial culture shock of admission. Instruction about the nature of certain boundaries, such as the organisation's position in relation to confidentiality, needs to be presented clearly and sensitively. It must be explained that in some situations (such as on child protection issues) the organisation might need to communicate with other professionals. The idea of informed consent is important, although problematic in psychotherapy because an experiential process cannot be predicted. Again it is the responsibility of staff to make sure that the potential resident is as well informed as possible, with accessible written material as well as the chance to ask lots of questions (Box 6.2). However, it is perhaps more helpful to think of the patient's consent as an ongoing process: the patient invites us to continue to share in the unfolding process of the therapy, a situation that we must protect with sound ethical practice. Many potential residents over-compensate for their doubts and fears by idealising the therapeutic community, imagining it as somewhere they will at last find the unconditional love and understanding they long for. This needs to be sensitively challenged during the assessment process if catastrophic disappointment is to be avoided. The best way to do this is to encourage them to spend time with other residents.

Not all information can be readily conveyed in a one-to-one assessment. However, in a therapeutic community a peer-group assessment provides an opportunity to bring something of the experience directly to the prospective resident, a taster of what they are thinking of joining. The substance of the structure that the peer group provides is difficult to describe, but is perhaps best encapsulated by the group-analytical notion of the social matrix (Chapter 2). This term is applied to the network of communication and relationships that the new member will join and contribute to, will be revitalised by, and will eventually leave. A small group of members asking questions, talking about their own experiences or aspects of the therapy, encourages the prospective member to put together a narrative about him- or herself and implies a degree of personal agency that is often quite new. Members are in a particularly strong position to ask questions and make observations, since they can both identify with the problem and have made some headway in beginning to deal with it. These contributions prefigure the level of interest and exchange within the community. They also have a unique authority, for they cannot be refuted in the way a staff member's understanding often is: 'How can you understand? You've never been there'.

The subject of care itself is also frequently challenged by prospective community members. Fear of rejection readily produces a defensive rationale along the lines that staff are paid to care. A peer group clearly is not. They do not have to care and yet frequently do with a vigour that is disarming to the prospective member. Authenticated by their experiences, existing members can make observations that staff would need to couch more carefully. A peer group working well is characterised by a creative tension between responsibility to the individual and responsibility to the group as a whole. The group need to question whether they think they can live with the person 24 hours a day, whether they can get on – and not get on – and whether the person will be able to be openly curious with them about why.

Joining

When the new member joins the therapeutic programme, the three components of the therapeutic process previously mentioned – giving and receiving information, forming a secure attachment and building a working alliance – need to be cultivated. Securing the ground for their development is vital at this stage. The most common details of the programme's structure are frequently the most important and often the least thought about. For example, it can be destructive to the formation of a secure attachment if, in the process of admission, a new member has to pass through the administrative hands of several staff, all of whom are preoccupied with other duties. It would be similarly undermining if details of the service's expectations of the new member on the first day, or basic details of what the therapeutic programme will entail, were not explained. Some of the worst experiences new members have to face involve finding themselves alone in the midst of community activity, or being carelessly overexposed in their first group meeting. If anxiety is not moderated, the feelings of persecution that patients are so readily subject to will undermine what we are attempting to build.

A new member is not usually immediately able to harness the resources of the community. A peer-group sponsor can helpfully bridge the gap between joining and becoming involved. Practically, the sponsor is the person to take questions to. Psychologically, the sponsor's

---

Box 6.3   Joining (see also Chapter 17)

- Anxiety is likely to be high and mistrust predominant
- The peer group might be seen as less threatening than staff, and a 'patient sponsor' might be useful in helping a new patient settle in
- Information (written and verbal) about the setting, the programme and general expectations is important

---

supportive function is to moderate the all too familiar experience of marginalisation. Complementing the work of this personal relationship is the very real way in which the new member, who can too easily feel disorganised, can be 'held together' by the predictable structure of the daily programme, by the regular content of its work and by the social reality of the living situation (Box 6.3).

The important groundwork that we have sketched in is a prerequisite to the new member finding their place in the therapeutic programme. If the achievements of this early phase can then be maintained, they will form the basis from which personal growth and development proceed.

Leaving

The task of leaving requires a powerful emotional struggle. Having been strengthened and defined by the therapeutic environment, the person must now strive to emerge and separate from it. A former group member chose the prosaic image of an egg timer to reflect on his leaving. For the greater part of its journey the movement of sand at the top of the funnel is barely perceptible, but as the funnel narrows the sand suddenly runs down and is gone. By this he intended to convey both his denial of the imminence of his leaving and the intensity and variety of emotional experience that came in a rush towards the end.

Endings arouse strong feelings and anxieties not only in the person who is leaving, but also in other members of the group or community, and in the staff who work there.

The psychological work of leaving begins well before the point of departure arrives. In the early phase of therapy the work that has contributed to the person's developing sense of identity has been geared towards an increasing sense of membership, acceptance and belonging. But continuing development, as much as it involves the experience of being a part of a common root of human hopefulness and unhappiness, also entails a growing recognition of separateness and difference. As the narrowing of the funnel approaches, a pulling away from the bedrock of the secure attachment begins in earnest. Psychologically, leaving involves internalising the therapeutic experience: taking it into oneself and using it thereafter as a resource.

Leaving a peer group, especially one that has incorporated a psycho-social living experience, involves the severing of real affectional bonds. Every new loss evokes memories of earlier losses. As much as the process of leaving is inspired by hope, it is a deeply significant loss. The group can become a plethora of painful recollections of loss, as experiences of feared and actual abandonment and rejection take centre stage. Leaving is therefore a potent therapeutic opportunity, affording further working through of some aspect of the original problem.

In addition to this invaluable revisiting, there is one common problem that it is worth being prepared for. The original complaint can reappear, to take possession of the person. This can too readily be interpreted as therapeutic failure. Frequently, its presentation touches the latent uncertainty we hold about the person's readiness to leave, or our vestiges of concern about work that might have been better done. But while every case bears careful thought, and any thoughtless application of a general principle will have an untoward effect, the task of the staff is, on the whole, to remain steady. One way to think about this is that the demanding and needful infant in the person does not want to accept the requirements of reality. Temporarily, we need to speak for the adult in the person and maintain our firm belief in the work that has been done. One group member was eventually able to interpret her own behaviour as a form of protest:

'The child doesn't want to become an adult. I don't know whether she ever will. She was trying to convince you she wasn't ready'.

A slow, open group, characterised by a steady input and output of members and a culture that remains fairly constant, provides a daily living reminder that the therapeutic situation is a process rather than a way of life. Beginnings and endings are part of the fabric of the organisation. They form a paradigm that staff must hold in mind. As therapists and health care workers, the focus of our relationship to the person is aimed continually at their growth and development and their own responsibility for change. This is worth emphasising because the longing for an idealised parent is never entirely laid to rest. The therapeutic situation powerfully awakens these desires, and the tempta-tion to be a surrogate parent rather than a facilitating therapist can be powerful. It can also be destructive because a failure to point the person in the direction of independent living can engender a regressive longing and cause him or her to encounter leaving with panic and despair.

Although leaving marks an end to membership of the group or organisation, it also marks the beginning of something else that will continue. Many written cards and messages exchanged at Francis Dixon Lodge express the sentiment that leaving is a new or another beginning. The group, which the person will continue to carry internally, will remain important. What is most keenly remembered is the experience of belonging. This supports a continuing mental dialogue with the internalised group. Against the backdrop of ongoing life experience, events will be reinterpreted, and observations or interpretations made in the course of therapy will be seen in a new light or even understood for the first time.

The decision on when to leave is partly determined by the structure of the organisation, but is expressed too by a movement within the person; often by an outgrowing of the organisation, a looking forward to not having to sit through any more meetings. Ideally, the progress of time and the maturing readiness of the individual meet creatively. But usually the decision is made in the face of a conflict between readiness and reluctance. As with the maturing adolescent, who needs to be both allowed to leave and helped to leave home, there is a good deal of all round ambivalence. Reluctance resides not only with the leaving member, but also with the group who must let him or her go, and sometimes particularly with staff, if attachment to the person has remained an unexamined part of the therapeutic relationship. Although a successful leaving usually follows on from a successful therapy, quite what form it will take is not so predictable. Ultimately, it must be meaningful for the individual. An unexemplary, chaotic departure might be a meaningful liberation for the rigid conformist.

At Francis Dixon Lodge, leaving is marked by a party. It takes place on the evening before the day of departure. The leaver has an afternoon off while the community makes preparation. The party is a mixture of food, games, dancing, songs and communality – of being there and being with. The dining room has a large blackboard. For the occasion it is wiped clean of its common purpose of supporting a graffito of community life, and replaced with an artwork epitomising a valued quality of the departing member. A host of well-wishing messages clusters round it. It is an outward and visible sign of graduation. The following morning, at the end of a community meeting that has taken place amidst the remains of

---

Box 6.4 Leaving

- The psychological work involved in leaving needs to start as early as possible: it frequently takes all involved by surprise
- Leaving involves being disappointed
- Leaving is likely to evoke earlier losses and tap into deep-seated grief
- Leaving is likely to trigger maladaptive coping mechanisms that were thought to have been left behind. This needs to be understood as part of the process of leaving, rather than a sign that therapy has failed
- Leaving can be a problem for staff, who need to watch out for the potential unhelpfully to keep certain patients
- Rituals can be helpful in both expressing feelings and assisting the process of leaving

the party, a cake is presented, gifts exchanged and photographs taken. When it is finally time to go, the community crowds into the courtyard and waves the departing member on their way.

All this celebration does more than complement the psychological work. It makes a vital contribution to it. The party is a means by which the community embraces the leaving member with an expression of its riches, providing a backcloth against which the leaver will define and clarify their feelings. In the deepest sense it is a celebration of a self that is finally strong enough to display and support itself. The celebration is not a set formula, individuals alter it to suit their own needs; it is the element of ritual that is the vital part of it. The ritual supports what is, in effect, a rite of passage. The ritual is therefore an external situation that marks an inner process and at the same time assists it. For the community it is the means by which it further releases its bonds (Box 6.4). In anticipation of the event many group members struggle with the thought of a party. Anxiety about exposure is the most commonly expressed fear. More difficult to articulate is a thought that runs something like this: if my going is not marked, I will not really be gone. Premature departures are often rooted in this fear of separation. In an attempt to avoid the psychological task of leaving, going, rather than leaving properly, is less painful. A further common defence against the fear of separation is sabotage. The member who elicits the group's rejection can say to his- or herself 'I knew you didn't love me!' and temporarily ease the pain. Pain, as well as hope, is bound up with the fact that leaving is for real, that there will not be a return and that the present moment will never be lived again.

As leaving deals in issues of separation, loss, death, insecurity and uncertainty, it is often the one area where staff and community members find themselves on a common path. Most of us who work in therapeutic environments have been more fortunate in the circumstances of our early life than our patients. We do not so readily share the identifications they share with each other. But the contingencies of existence affect us all equally. Therefore, it is helpful to be prepared for our own emotional struggles in saying goodbye. Our patients will miss us, but we will miss them too. Among other things, they have supported our sense of value as therapists, and we are indebted to them for what they have taught us about the work we do.

The transition from therapeutic environment to the wider community

One of the reasons we were invited to set this chapter in the context of a therapeutic community is that our client group – who often attract the label of borderline personality disorder – are known to find transitions particularly difficult. Indeed, the concept of 'disordered attachment' is perhaps more helpful and less stigmatising than 'borderline personality disorder', as it gives legitimacy to problem behaviour often regarded as manipulative. If we reframe attention-seeking as attachment-seeking, we can start to learn what has gone wrong in the patient's previous attachment history by studying the demands placed on us instead of repulsing them.

In securely attached children, attachment-seeking behaviour when an internal or external threat is encountered is a normal and healthy attempt to restore proximity to a comforting, protective parent. If successful, and the parent is sufficiently attuned to the child's anxiety to contain most of it successfully, the child will learn to manage what remains. Over a period of time, after many such repetitions, the child will gradually internalise the experience of being reassured, enabling it to tolerate increasing periods of separation from the parent. Threats managed without the parent increase the child's sense of confidence and competence until a healthy level of autonomy is achieved. Failure of this developmental task in early childhood can mould a template that interferes with all subsequent relationships. Most therapeutic community residents who stay for a year will have overcome significant difficulties in forming an attachment to the community, but perhaps not have undergone sufficient separation to feel confident of survival on their own. Leaving can therefore represent unbearable disruption to what is, for many, a first experience of secure attachment, evoking earlier terrors of abandonment and perhaps neglect or abuse, that often result in dramatic regression. This needs to be managed thoughtfully, as safely as possible and very much with an appreciation that the experience will be different for each individual, even though some aspects of loss are common to all. Perhaps the hardest task for the therapist is to engage emotionally, time after time, with the terror, anguish and rage that accompany the feeling of being abandoned.

Successful transition from the therapeutic community to the wider community requires residents to relinquish intense relationships based on emotional support and common problems. Great importance is placed on residents developing work, occupational and leisure interests when they leave, because these offer a wealth of opportunities for making new friends in more conventional settings. However, it is also helpful to try to identify what can potentially go wrong in the separation experience. From a psychoanalytical perspective, successful reintegration into wider society depends on the achievement of internal reintegration of conflicting parts of the self.

While in the residential programme, the healthy and creative aspects of the self are recruited in the service of a thinking, supportive and nourishing culture that permits growth and healing to take place. Such a culture is also strong, tolerant and resilient enough to contain and modify the more primitive, destructive parts when the individual can no longer contain them internally. The greatest risk involved in leaving is that, following the loss of this strong, supportive psychological container, the internal world is threatened with fragmentation and the individual is overwhelmed by unbearable anxiety, which can be experienced as a kind of nameless dread.

How, then, can these conflicting parts of the self be held together, while the experience of loss and grief is worked through? What kind of attachment is required to withstand the intense turmoil until an individual's inner resources are stable enough to permit independence? An outreach team, by definition, cannot hope to contain disturbance to the degree that a residential community does, so what elements does it need if it is to have some hope of providing good-enough psychological containment? In our experience, it is helpful to think of the therapeutic alliance during this difficult transition stage as representing an 'elastic attachment', a good relationship between outreach staff and residents that is both tough and flexible. A good alliance built on trust is able to both stretch and support as necessary in response to individual needs, without undue constraint on the one hand, or giving way on the other.

Several elements therefore combine to make up our continuing care programme at Francis Dixon Lodge, including a strong emphasis on building a network with other agencies. First, as outreach staff, we make sure that we meet with residents before they leave the residential programme. Hopefully, this helps to reduce their anxiety about joining our out-patient group; it also gives us the opportunity to identify important issues that leaving might raise for them. Francis Dixon Lodge is a Monday-to-Friday unit, so all residents are used to leaving on a Friday and returning on a Monday, an experience that can be seen as a kind of repeated rehearsal for the leaving at the end of their stay. Most of them will also have spent their last few weeks or months attending the programme as day patients, not as residents – again, a good preparation for leaving proper. A member of the outreach team will also attend a care programme approach review meeting with the residential team as the time for leaving approaches. This meeting is particularly concerned with minimising risks during the transition period, pre-empting incidents and drawing up contingency plans.

Box 6.5 Transition to the wider community

- Patients are particularly vulnerable in the weeks and months after they have left an intensive residential programme
- Staff should aim to establish an elastic attachment, which is both sufficiently tough and sufficiently flexible to respond to individual needs
- Crises during this period are common and need to be understood in the context of the leaving process

Most residents whose discharge is planned are expected to come to Next-Step, our twice-weekly leavers' group, for about a year. A post-therapy 'dip' soon after leaving is very common, so the group provides a structured opportunity twice a week for 75 minutes to receive and offer support. The scope is fairly wide, ranging from practical matters such as housing or returning to an occupational activity to concluding the emotional work described earlier. Working through grief and anger can be especially testing, as the immature longings that can be detrimental to adult relationships are given up in exchange for greater autonomy and self-respect. Peer relationships at this stage in therapy become more complex to manage. Support and encouragement in a crisis from someone a bit further on who has already 'been there' and survived can be a lifeline, but residents also describe the anxiety of being 'pulled down' by others who are reluctant to give up old coping habits such as self-harm or substance misuse.

Although Next-Step is the main platform supporting separation from the community, there is an understanding that residents can telephone staff at Francis Dixon Lodge for support to try to avert a crisis. This does not indicate that the resident or the therapy has failed. Rather, we expect that most people will find the early months difficult, but with flexible and appropriate support when needed they will eventually consolidate the benefits of their stay. Liaising with general practitioners and other agencies or even arranging a short admission to an acute ward may be necessary. A lot of effort is made to encourage former residents to continue attending the Next-Step group and to frame the crisis as part of the process of transition (Box 6.5).

An important aspect of our continuing care programme is the work that we do with those who leave prematurely. It is not uncommon for residents to leave suddenly. When this happens, an appointment with a nurse from the outreach team is offered within a couple of weeks. It is important to regard the departure as a learning experience rather than a failure, and we have been surprised how many attend these appointments. During follow-up appointments it is often possible to identify how an earlier experience in the person's life has been re-enacted in some way. Such insights can be empowering and leave open the option of further therapy at some point.

Further reading

Meinrath, M. & Roberts, G. (1982) On being a good enough staff member. *International Journal of Therapeutic Communities*, **3**, 7–14.

Vaillant, G. (1992) The beginning of wisdom is never calling a patient a borderline. *Journal of Psychotherapy Practice and Research*, **1**, 117–134.

Wilson, J. (1985) Leaving home as a theme in a therapeutic community. *International Journal of Therapeutic Communities*, **6**, 71–77.

Part II

Towards a better future

CHAPTER 7

The physical environment and use of space

Teresa von Sommaruga Howard

Editors' introduction Teresa von Sommaruga Howard works in many different countries as an architect, organisational consultant in the public sector, group analytic psychotherapist specialising in medium and large group work and lecturer. She has had a long preoccupation with how the physical context facilitates or prevents good-enough emotional relationships. In this chapter she combines her diverse professional interests to help us think about the physical components of a therapeutic environment and encourage us to think more creatively about our use of space. She uses the concept of 'container' in the psychoanalytic sense, referring to psychological rather than physical security.

What makes the physical environment therapeutic?

The quality of our physical environment can be health giving or health destroying. Delightful buildings evoke delightful responses, whereas damp, dark and uncomfortable buildings feel cold and inhospitable. In mental health settings, the quality of the built environment significantly influences everybody's experience of the service (Royal College of Psychiatrists, 1998; RIBA Client Forum, 1999: p. 26). Unfortunately, many of these settings look battered and makeshift, with inadequate signage, lighting and finishes that do little to lift the spirit. The first point to make, therefore, is that even the oldest or most carelessly thought out buildings can be very much enhanced by carefully rethinking decorations, providing appropriate floor coverings and, most important of all, installing imaginative lighting.

In researching material for this chapter it soon became evident that 'buildings for mental health' is an almost non-existent category in the architectural literature. Like mental illness it hides in a shadow world. The Royal College of Psychiatrists (1998) Council Report *Not Just Bricks and Mortar* spells out many of the basic considerations (Box 7.1). And, although its focus is the acute in-patient psychiatric setting, much can be extrapolated from it in consideration of other specialist settings. An appropriately designed and furnished building will be 'soothing' for those who live and work there. It will enable discrete supervision and will not increase the likelihood of behavioural outbursts by intruding on privacy or excessively 'forcing' people together.

Box 7.1 Specific considerations in building design for acute in-patient units (Royal College of Psychiatrists, 1998)

- Preferred size: 10–15 beds
- Scale to be carefully considered
- All bedrooms to be en suite
- Space for dining, storage, meeting areas and administration to be carefully considered
- Wet areas to be carefully designed to prevent water penetration and with sensitivity to patient group
- Privacy should be hierarchical, according to the function of the space
- Access and usability for people with disabilities should be provided
- Building security and integrity should be maintained, internally and externally, with minimum necessary compromise for residents
- Good, unobtrusive lines of sight

A major challenge in residential therapeutic working is finding ways of containing anxiety to support the capacity for linking, thinking and informed action. An appropriate physical space does much to enhance the provision of emotional space, which is central to making sense of experience.

A facilitating environment in therapeutic work is analogous to the 'good-enough' facilitating environment that is necessary in infancy. We start literally 'at home' in our mother's arms where, all being well, we see ourselves in the reflection of her eyes. Here we learn to recognise not only our reflected image, but also the emotional feelings imparted by her gaze (Winnicott, 1986). It is from this beginning that we develop our experience of both the emotional and the physical environment. Searles describes the 'total environment' in which we live, and emphasises the importance of stability in the non-human environment in helping this first, most important, relationship (Searles, 1960: p. 3). Using Searles' understanding, the hospital building has a crucial, but often forgotten, containing function. It is the ultimate container. The atmosphere imparted by its design and construction can encourgae or discourage the therapeutic work.

In this chapter, I am concerned more to emphasise a process than to provide a set of patterns for new buildings (see Howard (2003) for a more detailed description of this process). To reflect the sensitivity required of therapeutic work, a step-by-step process of reflection is suggested so that a physical environment congruent with the therapeutic modality is more likely to be created. In this way, it becomes possible to play with dreams and ideas. As links between the internal reality of dreams and the external possibilities of ideas emerge, the new physical environment is discovered and develops meaning for those involved. The process of creating new environments can be seen as 'space therapy' for all those involved (Franck & Lepori, 2000: pp. 80–102).

Rose (1990: p. 99) describes a 'good place' as one that is in all aspects carefully constructed. He emphasises the importance of creating a physical environment that conveys, through its own symbolic language, a consistent message that the individual can be made safe enough to risk experiencing the psychic activity evoked by relationships and daily events. Spaces are given meaning and made into places by those who use them, and it is this process of meaning-making that those contemplating new settings for mental health should attend to. Every detail is important. Although places and materials may have universal qualities, these cannot be assumed. When experiences appear that seem to have universal appeal, they may need to be translated to enable the patient group to use them. Rose used the space around campfires or by rivers. He noticed that when the day shifted into silence and darkness, the young people seemed to respond to the atmosphere and to talk almost as in psychotherapy. He felt that they 'had simply made contact with an experience so familiar to humankind that we tend to forget its immense potential', although this might have been made accessible by his containing presence.

The importance of involving stakeholders

The frame provided for making design decisions profoundly influences the outcome, and it is imperative that the widest possible representation of stakeholders be involved throughout the process – service users, managers, clinicians, neighbours, all have important contributions to make to the future success of the service under consideration (Box 7.2).

The stigma and social exclusion of people with mental illnesses are deeply embedded. At a distance, most of us understand that these are 'people like us', but at close proximity there is often a tendency to experience them as bad. Mental illness is extremely disturbing for those suffering from it and for their families and carers. If stakeholders are not involved in the process, there is a danger that building

---

Box 7.2 The building you work in

- Is your building health-giving or health-destroying? Can you say why?
- Are spaces also places that feel right?
- Are the spaces appropriate for their intended use? If not, why not?
- Does the design help you to contain anxiety?
- Do you know what processes were employed in the design of your building? Who was involved? How long did it take? Was it successful? If not why not?

programmes become an attempt to deal superficially with the dilemmas posed by mental ill health that lie deep in society.

In an effort to reverse the low priority accorded to the design of therapeutic environments for mental health, the Royal Institute of British Architects hosted a 1-day symposium to improve mental health service clients' understanding about the briefing process, which they believe is crucial for creating a good-enough physical environment for mental health settings. Spending enough quality time developing the brief is essential. Architects are often asked to provide buildings that are domestic, friendly in appearance and highly adaptable, with no real explanation of what is intended (RIBA Client Forum, 1999: p. 27). Perhaps these requests are a way of keeping all options open when what is really needed is not known. The problem with such an approach is that the resulting spaces are often good for nothing. Multi-use rooms inevitably have furniture stacked around them ready for other uses, so that every room feels temporary.

The brief evolves through engaging in a collaborative step-by-step process that takes account of how settings will really be used. Those who commission buildings are rarely those who will use them or work in them. In contrast, patients and staff will be there every day. They need to have influence in the design process. By genuinely involving the various stakeholders of the building in this way, a new good-enough environment is more likely to emerge. If everyone, including patients, staff and visitors as well as funders and builders, is involved, a building 'fit' for the dynamic purpose of therapeutic work is more likely. Every new space will develop a meaning and become a place. It will 'make sense' to all involved, enabling the creative use of space and promoting integration.

Involvement in developing a brief is arduous and long-winded, so participants in the dialogue will need encouragement. Staff will need help to make their wishes explicit and to resolve inevitable conflicts between their requirements and those of patients and visitors. They are often the longest-standing residents, with a high degree of investment in the premises, but they often find it difficult to admit their desire for

---

Box 7.3 Some important principles

- The physical environment should support the treatment model
- The process of developing the building brief should also support the treatment model
- The process of developing the building brief should give time and careful thought to enable reflection by those who will be in day-to-day occupation of the building
- Every detail of the building needs careful consideration if it is to feel affirming and soothing, and support therapeutic intention

Case study

(a)

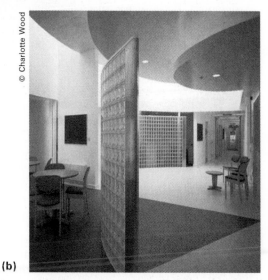

(b)

Figure 7.1 Images from a recently opened in-patient unit in Worthing. The unit is part of West Sussex Health and Social Care NHS Trust. The modern art deco design is spacious, safe and comfortable, and makes maximum use of natural light. It includes three 16-bed wards, all en suite, a café, shop, gym, therapy suite and ample meeting rooms. The values driving the whole project were identitified as hope, humanity, expectation and collaboration. Thanks to Mark Hadcastle, nurse consultant, and Nightingale Associates, Architects, for permission to include this example of good practice.

'time away from their client group during the working day so their need for refuges cannot be made explicit' (RIBA Client Forum, 1999: p. 25).

The briefing process begins with a series of questions (see Hosking & Haggard, 1999). The first of these might be 'Will the total physical environment envisaged support the treatment model?' From this simple beginning, the questions that need to be addressed can emerge (Box 7.3).

The building as a projection

The way we use space, feel about it or relate to it is the consequence of our own personality. As Bettelheim explained, 'The room itself turned out to be a good projective test' (Bettelheim, 1974: p. 133). What is calming to one person may not be to another. Many people have agoraphobic or claustrophobic reactions to open stairs, double-height rooms, narrow corridors or dark spaces. Such 'architectural' features should be used with caution.

Similarly, observing various therapeutic environments in mental health settings has led me to the conclusion that reconstructing the physical environment is not always a rational process, and for most of us it can be a form of acting out our more neurotic feelings and defences. Because we all create our external physical world out of our inner emotional world, buildings are likely to be organised around the task in ways that reflect our own defensive difficulties. When anxiety is high there is a tendency to compartmentalise thoughts, leading to buildings being inappropriately compartmentalised. Even when appropriate physical spaces are provided, they may or may not be made use of.

Despite the best of intentions, workers in psychiatric settings often bring their own unmanaged fears into this work and seek to control them through control of the patient group. One issue that emerges very quickly in mental health settings is security. It is important that a distinction is made between being held safe, being restrained or being imprisoned. A locked door does not necessarily provide security, but it does restrict physical access and provide a powerfully restrictive emotional symbol:

'Mental patients know that locked doors prove the staff's fear of them, whatever the explanation offered. The danger exists only if they are left alone or are put in a setting, both physical and human, that is lacking empathy with their needs' (Bettelheim, 1974: p. 121).

Perhaps this sentiment is rather optimistic, but it does remind us that the best form of security is that rooted in mutually satisfying human relationships.

Despite the fact that human beings do not like to be observed, many hospitals have viewing windows, just like those in prison cells, in the doors to patients' rooms. Although staff may want/need to know what is going on, poorly designed surveillance windows create an atmosphere that is unlikely to be therapeutic.

Rose describes how, in one unit, constant break-ins to the kitchen at night initially led to the reflex response of ever-increasing door strengthening and locks. It was significant that eventually this escalating reaction could be questioned, leading to an understanding that this behaviour was a desperate cry for nurture. Instead of preventing access to food and moving into a cycle of punishment, a table was set up in the dining room with an electric kettle, mugs, bread, butter, jam, tea, milk and sugar that was available day and night in exchange for an agreement that the food store would stay locked at night. For several years it was not broken into again (Rose, 1990: p. 102). At a later stage, the whole process of providing food was carefully rethought and the cooking and dining facilities redesigned so that the cooking of food could be openly observed and participated in. This significantly reduced paranoid anxiety about what might be in the food.

The building as a container

The Royal Institute of British Architects has described the Department of Health's modular design for psychiatric units in general hospitals as 'hopelessly inadequate and fails to take account of the needs of mentally ill patients' (RIBA Client Forum, 1999: p. 10). Unlike the grounds of the old psychiatric hospitals, where patients had lots of space to walk off their agitation, the modern modular hospital allows no such possibility. Also, the meaning of the bed place is misunderstood. In medicine and surgery, the bed is the centre of therapy. In psychiatry, the bed is a place to sleep and, even though few of us want to sleep with people we do not know, most admission units are organised into dormitories rather than single bedrooms (RIBA, 1999: p. 10). Modern recommendations from Royal College of Psychiatrists (1998) for individual en suite bedrooms clearly address this, but it is going to take many years to see this transformation.

Despite the fact that 'there is no such thing as a maintenance free envelope' (RIBA, 1999: p. 40), too often materials appear to be chosen for their ability to weather any storm instead of for their acoustic, tactile or visual qualities. All materials have their own language with which to engage the senses, and they should be chosen for their symbolic as well as their appropriate constructional value. The symbolic always speaks loudly and should not be ignored. The Steiner movement have developed building forms that they believe create a spiritual and healing dimension by fostering an organic quality that responds to the human form instead of simply enclosing it. Their buildings avoid right-angles, and use natural materials and vibrant colour.

In mental health settings, the external appearance of the buildings rarely encourages a good entrance. The Dutch architect Aldo van Eyke often said 'Make a countenance of every window and a welcome of every door'. Strauven (1998) writes that van Eyke was very preoccupied with what he described as 'brief homecoming' (p. 466) by making 'places that always establish a "somewhere"' (p. 471). The architect developed this idea with an inventive use of colour and form in the municipal orphanage near Amsterdam, and later in the Hubertus House for deprived children and parents in need of help.

When a building is entered for the first time it evokes an immediate response. The smallest clues are important, even its smell. 'Unfortunately most psychiatric institutions smell bad to the patient and everybody that enters them', wrote Bettelheim. 'It cannot be covered up . . . getting the right smell has to come from within' (Bettelheim, 1974: pp. 116–117). Any institution is confusing at first, but with care even large buildings can be designed legibly, making it possible to find the way by 'reading' the 'signs'. Orientation is also enabled by getting a sense of the passing day, the weather and when dusk falls. In large buildings it can be difficult to provide good-quality natural light, but the Supreme Court Building in Jerusalem, designed by Ada Karmi-Melamede and Ram Karmi is an illustration of the magic possible where there is the will to be imaginative (http://urban.csuohio.edu/~sanda/pic/travel/israel/jerusalem/court.htm).

Mental health settings can make good use of exterior spaces when they are contained as walled gardens or enclosed courtyards. These can be essential extensions to the building for therapeutic activities and as places for smoking, walking and contemplation, providing shade from the sun and shelter from cold wind and rain.

Many hospital buildings have beautiful public areas at the expense of the more private spaces used for everyday living. These small spaces – the residents' kitchens, bathroom and toilets – which often escape the visitor's notice, also need to be carefully designed. Without skilled attention these 'wet' rooms can trigger hygiene and water-penetration problems. Also, bathrooms and toilets should maintain the dignity of patients by ensuring privacy while allowing the possibility of discrete staff supervision if necessary. More than that, a bathroom is where individuals will most experience their own body as they stand naked. If they have suffered severe abuse or trauma, they frequently feel disgust towards and loathing of their body, so how this is experienced is enormously important. Privacy, in a warm bathroom with fluffy, generous towels can significantly alter the experience of the body and help individuals to 'take back' their own bodies from those who, in effect, 'stole' them.

Sometimes, caringly designed resources are perversely unappreciated by their users, but this is not surprising given the traumatising and depriving past experiences that most patients have had. It is important that the physical surroundings contain something of the patients themselves rather than being 'caring' in an impersonal way (Chapter 21.) New experiences that imply the possibility of a change in their view of themselves can be challenging. The physical situation, therefore, is the very essence of therapeutic confrontation and a patient's attacks on it should be understood in this light.

Perhaps every building has a limited lifespan in a particular form before it needs rethinking. The Mulberry Bush School, a therapeutic school in Standlake, Oxfordshire, was originally built in the 1960s. By the early 1990s, it exuded pain left by the children who had been there. Despite it being spotlessly clean, everywhere was battered and the dank smell of urine emanated from the crevices of the building. When social workers visited to make placements their experience of the building blinded them to what the school could offer. Its worn out, slightly seedy environment lost the school many placements. Following a change in director, a rethink about the treatment model and a change in legislation, funds were raised to rebuild it and, since completion, the school has been more or less full.

Building successfully to meet the needs of deprived and socially excluded client groups can evoke envious attacks. Referring to Peper Harow, a therapetuic community for adolescent boys in the UK which is now closed, Rose describes one local authority case conference where someone sneeringly dismissed it as 'wall-to-wall money!' (Rose, 1990: p. 106). Such envious attacks reveal a frequent inability to comprehend why so much effort needs to be put into making buildings for therapeutic care so beautiful. Every surface and space should be designed to nurture, indicating that the 'mother' community holds the patient in high esteem. No detail is unimportant. A message of security and well-being imparted by the texture, colour and quality of the walls, floors and ceilings, windows, doors, furniture and textiles, lighting and heating should be part of a total environment that imply the same consistent message that the patient is worth it (Rose, 1990: p. 106). At Peper Harow, the young people quickly understood the confirmatory, symbolic messages of the materials and design. They also discovered that their destructive impulses could be endured and that, with safe expression, they could begin the painful journey towards understanding what their behaviour revealed and then change it to something more appropriate.

Conclusion

When considering the reconstruction of any physical environment, particularly for therapeutic work, it is important to remember that the process is not always rational. Much of it is symbolic, reflecting the processes for which the building will be used. As the physical environment is both the envelope for and the essence of the therapeutic encounter, it is important to recognise that the context provided for designing any new building profoundly influences how it will be.

To reflect the sensitivity required for therapeutic work, the design of the new building should be evolved by using not a set of patterns but a step-by-step process of reflection with the widest possible representation of stakeholders. By involving all those who will use the building, appropriate physical spaces that are more likely to be able to contain the emotional space necesary to facilitate return to mental health will be provided. The process of talking together will ensure that every new space will develop a meaning that will make sense to all involved. Symbolically, good experiences in the physical world will imply the possibility of good expereinces in the emotional world.

References

Bettelheim, B. (1974) *A Home for the Heart: A New Approach to the Treatment of the Mentally Ill.* London: Thames and Hudson.

Franck, K. A. & Lepori, B (2000) *Architecture Inside Out.* London: Wiley/Academy.

Hosking, S. & Haggard, L. (1999) *Healing the Hospital Environment: Design, Management and Maintenance of Healthcare Premises.* London: E & FN Spon.

Howard, T. (2003) Finding a place for our soul: working in participatory design. *Therapeutic Communities,* **24**, 193–203.

RIBA Client Forum (1999) *Therapeutic Environments for Mental Health.* London: Royal Institute of British Architects.

Rose, M. (1990) *Healing Hurt Minds: The Peper Harow Experience.* London: Tavistock/Routledge.

Royal College of Psychiatrists (1998) *Not Just Bricks and Mortar* (Council Report CR62). London: Royal College of Psychiatrists.

Searles, H. F. (1960) *The Non-Human Environment in Normal Development and in Schizophrenia.* Madison, CT: International Universities Press.

Strauven, F. (1998) *Aldo van Eyke: The Shape of Relativity.* Amsterdam: Architectura and Natura.

Winnicott, D. W. (1986) *Home is Where We Start From.* Middlesex: Penguin Books.

CHAPTER 8

Connecting with the natural environment

Sarah Paget and Terry White

Editors' introduction The potential for our relationship with nature to be healing and nurturing is encapsulated in phrases such as 'Mother Earth'. Far from being outdated, survey after survey shows that young people in particular put saving the planet and the natural environment at the top of their list of concerns. In this chapter, Sarah Paget and Terry White, who both work for Community Housing and Therapy, describe how they build this potential for connection into the therapeutic programmes in which they are involved.

This chapter describes an important aspect of therapeutic work, namely encouraging relationships with the natural environment. Community Housing and Therapy runs small therapeutic households for severely mentally ill and homeless people in London and the south-east of England. As a charitable company, it has developed a therapeutic community style that enables and empowers clients within the larger context of community care. Our clients are referred by community mental health teams and are funded by the responsible local authority. To date, length of stay has ranged from 6 months to 10 years. Each household runs a full therapeutic programme, the emphasis of which is to maximise the client's potential for independent living. The daily programme is structured and it includes specific group and individual work, although the therapeutic potential exists through-out the client's stay, in all aspects of living together with others. For further information regarding Community Housing and Therapy's approach see Tucker (2000).

Disconnection from the environment

People tend to think of themselves as in control of the natural environment, as if the natural environment belongs to them, rather than that they are part of it. There are those who deplete the resources of the planet and those who have never left the city. Often, people with mental health problems are disconnected from the environment. A dysfunctional family might be one disrupting factor in the client's experience, but a decreasing connection with nature is frequently another. Individuals in touch with their roots, their family, their natural environment, are more likely to be healthy individuals. People in primitive cultures demonstrate a high level of interconnectedness, which would be a template for human experience. They know the name of every animal and tree, they might even have a word in their vocabulary for every different size or shape of leaf, like the Inuit people, who have names for each of the many different types of snow.

Many basic instincts are tied in with nature in an intimate way: birth, death, the nurturing of growing things, experiencing space, enjoying fresh air, feeling one's own breath going in and out and the sound of one's heart beating. These are some of the most frightening experiences, as well as the most rewarding, and they involve powerful emotions. Powerful emotions are often hard for our clients: some have withdrawn from the intense experience of primitive feelings and deep relationships; some have personality disorders that cause them to polarise and split off powerful emotions and work them through ineffectively.

Community Housing and Therapy works with clients to reconnect their experience and their emotional world, assisting them to become aware of the complete ecosystem in which they live. We believe that nature has an overarching effect on all aspects of our lives, and the therapeutic environment within the community reflects this. We try to join the clients with their own *Umwelt*, the world about them, their wider experience (Heidegger, 2001). Engagement in this process is sometimes difficult for clients; they can feel threatened by the strength of their own internal experience and by the responses of other clients and overwhelmed by the wider community. It might seem strange, then, that the most frightening therapy space would be a gardening group, but this seems to be the case.

Gardening as therapy

When made aware of the gardens belonging to our houses, our clients tend to prefer them wild and uncultivated; this might reflect the wilderness in their own minds, or it might simply be easier for them to tolerate a chaotic external environment than to try to remedy its untidiness.

In Community Housing and Therapy, we offer clients opportunities to expand and manage first of all the space in which they live, then their garden. The belief is that reconnection with their environment leads to a shift within their internal psychic world. To the threatened client who perceives the garden as a terrifying space, an impenetrable jungle full of tangled horrors, simple persuasion alone may not enable them to enter that place.

The first stage

The first thing is not to despair of the apparent apathy. We need to make interventions to bridge the gap between the chaotic inner world of the client and the untamed outer garden. We have to construct this bridge. Statements such as 'Come and join us', or 'You have to do some gardening' might not be enough to achieve the goal. There needs to be safety in the invitation. This can be achieved by creating a recognised or familiar structure such as a group, with a clear start and finish time and agreed rules; it might even be made a compulsory part of therapy (Box 8.1). These boundaries allow the client to feel that, in our being able to contain their anxieties, any dangers that might be present could also be contained. As has already been noted, the process of engaging with the natural environment can be as frightening, if not more so, than engaging in personal therapy, and the process of engaging clients mirrors the process of building a therapeutic alliance in more intimate settings. Many clients require a secure hand to get them out onto the path, supporting them all the way. This entails trust. It might be that they will only then be able to give themselves permission to take the risk. It might be that they want to be involved, but that they have not yet received the right stimulus.

When you take the time to get to know a client, you get to know the logic that guides them. If you can place the garden within that logic it becomes easier and the client needs less convincing. For example, a young man refused to be in the garden during periods of activity. He said that it was full of gravestones and therefore a depressing and frightening place. Through weeks and months of attention to this, both in one-to-one sessions and in groups, he began to express his fears of not being listened to in the group. Group members would be engaged in a task and not attentive to him, he found it difficult to distract them and felt unheard and alone. This 'graveyard silence' accentuated his internal dialogue of voices and anxieties and turned the garden into a cacophony of noise, unheard by others. Once this became known, staff and other group members were able to listen to his needs and the gardening became an important weekly event.

Box 8.1 Structuring a gardening session

- Structure a session with clear boundaries
- Develop interest by 'bringing on' plants inside for transplanting outside
- Use other settings to explore fear or resistance, aiming towards inclusion of clients
- Use the clients' understanding of the task as opposed to your own
- Create interest by doing some indoor gardening

Gardening does not have to begin in the external environment. House plants or herb pots on the windowsills can stimulate interest in growing and nurturing living things. Often, the use of propagating trays to bring on seedlings to transplant in the garden later can create a bridge from the internal to the external environment.

Maintaining interest

Once in the garden and in order to maintain the growth of interest, it is important for the clients to see evidence of their efforts and feel that they can achieve something. If there are no results from the smallest actions, it is difficult to believe that they have any personal power to alter their circumstances. Starting with tasks that have immediate noticeable effects provides evidence that there is value in their actions: the grass being tidier when mown, overhanging trees being manicured by pruning, freshly planted seeds sprouting and seedlings growing in days. The more immediate the result, the better the chances of maintaining the clients' interest (Box 8.2).

But this evidence can diminish with time and this decrease can quickly undermine the therapeutic value: clipped trees grow wild again, the grass grows back more unkempt than before, planted seedlings die. These forces can have a more powerful anti-therapeutic effect and need to be understood. Life and death run riot in a garden. However, set against these natural forces is the nurturing effort of the staff, the client's own nurturing power and a growing awareness that these energies can swing the balance. At times, it might be necessary for staff to take extra responsibilities for ensuring that seeds are watered and seedlings nurtured. Working with the client to bring to awareness the consequence of absenting themselves from their work once started is a necessary part of the gardening group.

Sometimes, the task can seem too great for clients even to begin, and reducing the area of garden to be cared for can help them to make a start. Sectioning an area into smaller plots and allotting a single plot to each client to dig and plant has a dual function. First, it can

---

Box 8.2 Generating and maintaining an interest

- Start with tasks in which there are immediately noticeable effects
- Staff should take initial responsibility for sustaining the change, e.g. by watering plants
- Gradually hand over responsibility to the client
- Use small plots or containers to reduce the size of the task
- Try using alternative tasks to attract interest (bonfires, barbeques, etc.)

seem less daunting, and second, it allows for ownership of their individual efforts.

Bonfires are always popular. Some clients will come out for a bonfire when they would not for any other aspect of the gardening group. Perhaps it reminds them of cosier family experiences of autumn, bonfire night, camping, winter log fires and other, perhaps happier, memories. They attract clients who can release aggression symbolically, creating value out of acceptable destruction (Winnicott, 1999). Through this process clients engage with being in the external environment and can be encouraged to continue with other small tasks.

Therapeutic aims

At Community Housing and Therapy, we consider that to 'dwell' is the critical experience that helps our clients to locate themselves and their peers within the spaces provided by a community and thus within their broader environment. We hope to provide a dwelling space in which they can find sanctuary, because nowhere previously has felt safe to them. By placing firm boundaries, we can allow clients to stay and learn to play and dwell in their natural place in the environment. Through the natural world, an opportunity exists to feel and sense and touch and respond to other living things. Growth and activity, the creation of living things, which might otherwise be unknown, can be found by sensation. The process of coming to life, increasing and flourishing is a formative experience that opens the pleasures and the terrors of the clients' own lives. A garden is also a physical representation of death: insect attack, decay, winter, with life being drawn out of the trees as the leaves fall, and bombardment by the elements. In the visible changes of life unfolding, there is a threat of having to nurture something and being responsible for whether it lives or dies. This can mirror the clients' own fears, hopes, loves and hates in life. Small wonder, then, that the garden presents a therapeutic challenge for both clients and staff.

Dialogue with us while engaging with a touching therapy, a therapy of the senses in a garden, is about finding a place in which the client can express their deepest anguishes in relation to birth, life and death, and attain catharsis, a sense of having faced their fears and survived. Rather than viewing a garden as a place in which we do chores, or as an act of constant manicure, we touch on the deeper levels of the individual and offer them an opportunity to get through the story to a cleaner, more nurtured ending. This can be achieved by being alongside the client and sharing with them in a process of sensation, discovery and understanding.

One example of communication through gardening is the case of a young client with a diagnosis of schizophrenia, who engaged little with others. The group had bought propagating trays and planted sunflower seeds in them. One of the trays was left over after the seeds had been sown and I (T.W.) filled it with compost and planted some suaharo cacti seeds, which I had been given a year or two before by a Canadian relative. I left the tray in the games room to watch and water intermittently, with a view to interesting the clients in growing houseplants. This client, although knowing that I had put the tray there, took it away to his bedroom to look after it. However, he soon grew tired of waiting for the first sign of a growing seedling and replanted it with tomato seeds. Although this was a change from my original design, I could recognise in his chain of actions a personalising of the task where something understandable to him had arisen out of someone else's idea.

The therapeutic camp

Traditionally, the wilderness is used to bridge the gap between the mundane and the spiritual. Rites of passage in primitive cultures use the wilderness to achieve contact with more intuitive and esoteric levels of experience. For instance, there is a rite among an Aborigine tribe in Australia called the *karadjeri*, in which at the age of about 12, a boy is carried away from his family and clan in the dead of night into the forest. Here, he is said to hear the sacred songs for the first time and receive the first of many mystical experiences. This process marks the child's entry into adulthood by informing him about the mysteries that make his tribe unique as well as breaking down the barriers of his ego so that he becomes part of something greater (Eliade, 1977).

Community Housing and Therapy has developed a therapeutic camp at which clients can make contact with a more intense and raw form of nature. In concept, it is based on the work of a Polish team, which has been running camps for people with schizophrenia for about 20 years (Cechnicki *et al*, 1999). The experience in our camp is designed to involve clients and staff in mutual work to achieve personal and group goals. Physical activities are planned and include rock-climbing, caving, horse-riding, canoeing and cycling. The event takes clients (and staff) into an unfamiliar environment where their accustomed modes of escape are unavailable. The group is set the task of living, playing and experiencing new things together in this environment and exploring the feelings that arise out of the experience. The preparation for a therapeutic camp is rigorous, as is the client selection process. It is vital that the clients are well prepared for the experience and are able to be contained by the boundaries of the camp. As with all therapy groups, there is a clear beginning and end, and the group remain together in the natural environment for the duration of the camp. Staff and clients have to think and act together as a body, supporting each other, sharing in the difficulties, without the normal distinctions that operate between them within our communities.

During the camp, clients and staff face the border between night and day, the boundaries between air and earth, cliff and sky, shoreline and water. We encourage the use of naturally available food by picking fruits such as blackberries and blueberries and using them in cooking. The process enables clients to reconnect with an environment that is normally frightening and strange and allows them to develop a new set of relationships with others and with the external world.

Alternative methods of reconnection

Diet

Every week in Community Housing and Therapy projects, clients meet to discuss food. One of the major tasks is to produce a rota of meals for the week. Clients share out the tasks, which include shopping and cooking for the community.

Often, their first choice of meals is not healthy: burgers in buns, with chips and onion rings and ice-cream for dessert is a regular choice. This has no connection to the natural world on any immediate level. There are no fresh vegetables in this diet and clients' awareness of the seasons is not reflected in their selection of menu. The staff's role is both to encourage a healthy diet and also to develop sensitivity to the changing seasons and availability of natural produce (Box 8.3). The use of fruit and vegetables from the garden leads to a relationship with the environment, promotes healthier living and is a reward for clients' efforts. Even the relatively small challenge of using herbs grown on a windowsill develops a connection with the natural world from which one can become divorced by the use of dried, frozen or processed foods.

When fruit and vegetables need to be bought, the use of fresh, seasonal produce creates an awareness that can lead to dialogue about the rotation of the earth and the play of the seasons, and increase connectedness with nature.

Box 8.3   Practical connections

- Encourage the use of available produce such as blackberries from hedgerows and herbs from the garden
- Encourage the use of fresh fruit and vegetables
- Encourage the use of seasonal produce
- Use creative groups to explore the meaning of the seasons

Creative expression

Even without access to a garden, staff can help clients to meet nature face to face, to describe their feelings and memories, to hone their senses and to learn new sensations such as identifying the odours of different seasons of the year. In art groups, for example, we collect fallen autmun leaves and add their colours to our work. Using natural materials clients can express what summer holidays mean for them, or a family Christmas.

Reconnection with the environment

It is important not to make assumptions about who will connect with the garden and the seasons, or how. There is something very personal about each individual's relation to the world. Nothing comes about by imposing a rigid plan. The choices and the development stem best from a democracy, hoping to find common ground and working with others to make personal achievements.

If you approach the issue of confronting the garden in the care plan of each client too rigidly or too uniformly, things will go wrong. However, armed with an awareness of a client's fears about nurturing and being nurtured, a spade and a pair of shears, you can make the entry into the garden and begin therapy.

Given time, every one of our clients connects with the natural world. The seasons speak to them. They realign with what they see and hear. It is a slow process, and an outsider who visits infrequently may measure the visible changes more than we do, as our clients begin to internalise the boundaries that we set and value them as a means of security.

Achieving change in a garden enables them to confront a bigger challenge, that of change within themselves.

Conclusion

Community Housing and Therapy aims to create a bridge between the clients' internal and external worlds. In this aim, we use the environment, which is both the object from which they are disconnected and the method of reconnection (Box 8.4). The process of working alongside clients to nurture, camp, dwell and reconnect with the world allows staff members to engage with them and use the experience of the task as a way into their internal representations of disconnection, distress and history. This 'doing together' is a significant factor in building relationships; it is a non-verbal interchange that can be less threatening and intrusive than having to describe in words those experiences that are beyond language. The process can lead clients out of physical and

> **Box 8.4** Basic principles
>
> - 'Doing together' is a more effective way of building relationships with clients who find it difficult to verbalise their needs
> - Building relationships with the environment can lead to relationships being built with the self and others
> - Connection with the environment leads to awareness of the skills of maintaining relationships
> - Connection with the environment is connection with a sense of belonging

social isolation and into a relationship with the environment, others and themselves. Engagement is the first stage, and maintaining involvement carries risks as well as great benefits. Connection with the world is a demonstration of the meaning and responsibilities of relationships: basically, nurture them or they will die. The meaning of care is demonstrated by involvement with the natural world, and the rules that apply there have value for staff as well as clients. In building physical and social relationships we have a responsibility to tend and nurture these connections.

Reconnection with the natural environment is a reconnection with the self. Humans are part of the world and the world is part of them; disconnection from one leads to inevitable disconnection from the other. A client's rejection of their external environment provides some clue to the isolated place in which they often exist, lacking meaningful relationships with the environment, other people or themselves and feeling little or no sense of belonging in the world. By taking clients into the garden or camping we introduce them to the ecosystem, an ecosystem in which they themselves belong and a place from which they may begin to rejoin in relatedness with others and themselves.

References

Cechnicki, A., Bielanska, A. & Walczewski, K. (1999) Therapeutic camp as a part of an integrated community programme for schizophrenic patients. *Therapeutic Communities*, **20**, 103–117.

Eliade, M. (1977) *Myths, Dreams, and Mysteries* (trans. P. Mairet), pp. 195–198. Glasgow: Collins.

Heidegger, M. (2001) *Being and Time* (trans. J. Macquarrie & E. Robinson), p. 93. Oxford: Basil Blackwell.

Tucker, S. (ed.) (2000) *A Therapeutic Community Approach to Care in the Community: Dialogue and Dwelling*. London: Jessica Kingsley.

Winnicott, D. W. (1999) *Playing and Reality*, p. 90. London: Tavistock/Routledge.

CHAPTER 9

A gender-sensitive therapeutic environment for women

Sarah Davenport

Editors' introduction   Sarah Davenport was a rehabilitation consultant in Salford before taking on the role of Clinical Director in the Women's Service at Ashworth High Security Hospital, Merseyside. In this chapter she explores how inequalities within society can be reflected within mental health services, often to the detriment of women patients. She also makes the case for women-only services and outlines ways in which we could all improve our practice. As a woman psychiatrist and feminist, she is particularly concerned about improving services for women; but it should be remembered that our rapidly changing society includes subgroups of men for whom need is unmet by mental health services – most obviously evidenced by the high prevalence of psychiatric morbidity within the prison population. Sebastian Kraemer has highlighted the difficulty boys have in getting their emotional needs met and has sensitively argued and described the ways in which boys can be disadvantaged from conception onwards (Kraemer, 2000). As editors, we wondered whether to balance this chapter with a chapter on men, but felt that the thinking about what constitutes a gender-sensitive environment is more developed for women and the argument for women-only services is more obvious. More generally, this chapter reminds us that psychiatric patients are particularly vulnerable and easily exploited. Perhaps the most worrying inequalities and potential for abusing power are situations that reflect our own experience within society and can therefore be taken for granted and go unseen. This is what is meant here by 'gender blindness'.

'There are differences in the family and social context of women's and men's lives, the experience and impact of life events, the presentation and character of their mental ill health and consequently their care and treatment needs. These differences must be understood by policy makers and those planning and delivering services. Mental health care must be responsive to these differences' (Jacqui Smith, Minister for Mental Health; Department of Health, 2002: p. 5).

The practice of psychiatry has been predominantly influenced by the medical model, with social context being relatively neglected, in terms of both our understanding of aetiology and our intervention with therapeutic strategies. Although there have always been areas of good practice where a more empathetic and eclectic perspective has informed the work, there has in general been reluctance to think about differences such as gender and race, which can profoundly effect our experience. In the case of gender, this is somewhat surprising when whole fields of academic study have been devoted to analysing the differences between men and women, in terms of emotional development, early socialisation and roles in society. This has led to critical feminist analysis:

'There have always been those who argue that women's high rate of mental disorder is a product of their social situation, both their confining roles as daughters, wives and mothers and their mistreatment by a male dominated (and possibly misogynistic) psychiatric profession' (Showalter, 1987: p. 3).

In this chapter, I describe these inequalities from a feminist perspective and make suggestions about improving practice. As Showalter indicated, gender inequalities in society create dependence and powerlessness in women. These inequalities can be played out within mental health services, making it more likely that women feel subjugated as patients, rather than being involved as partners in their own care. The fact that mental health services have traditionally been provided for a male majority by a gender-blind workforce managed mainly by men has exacerbated the situation, and although some things are changing, there are areas such as secure settings where this is still the reality (Box 9.1).

Little attention has been paid to the differences with which women and men present to mental health services and the way in which women's needs differ from those of men. These needs include an understanding of the psychosocial context of women patients. However, there has been more attention recently in medicine generally to understanding the biological differences between men and women and the need for more sensitive drug prescribing.

Encouragingly, there does seem to be support at government level for moving things forward, and a number of helpful documents have been published in the past few years: *Women's Mental Health: Into the Mainstream* (Department of Health, 2002), *Safety, Privacy and Dignity in Mental Health Units* (Department of Health, 2000a), *The NHS Plan* (Department of Health, 2000b) and *The Government's Strategy for Women Offenders* (Home Office, 2000).

Box 9.1 Problems faced by women in mental health

- Women have different needs than men and may present differently to mental health services
- Gender inequalities within society may be replayed in services, recreating dependence and powerlessness
- Because relationships between staff and patients reflect those in society, the workforce might be blind to inequalities and show a lack of understanding of difference

---

Mental ill health in women

Although the overall prevalence of mental illness does not differ significantly between the genders, there are clear gender differences for specific disorders. Depression is the most prevalent mental health problem worldwide and most studies suggest that depression and anxiety are up to twice as common in women than in men. In addition to anxiety and depression, eating disorders, deliberate self-harm (but not suicide) and borderline personality disorder are more common in women. Substance misuse and antisocial personality disorder are more common in men. A significant number of women (2 per 1000 deliveries) suffer from puerperal psychosis and a much higher proportion from perinatal depression. Men and women have a similar disposition to bipolar affective disorder and schizophrenia, but there is some evidence that schizophrenia may have an earlier onset and a more disabling course in men.

There are significant differences in the way in which men and women express their mental health problems, with men arousing more anxiety and fear in others and more often in need of physical containment. At the risk of generalising, this can be understood as women having a tendency to turn their feelings inwards onto themselves, whereas men have a tendency to turn their feelings outwards onto others. In a ward environment, therefore, it is often men that seem most overtly disturbed, chaotic, noisy and dangerous, and this can have an overwhelming effect on the culture and the problem of creating a therapeutic environment for women.

Increased prevalence of social risk factors for mental ill health

Women face an increased prevalence of the social risk factors for mental ill health. In particular, they are much more likely than men to be victims of violence and abuse (Box 9.2). Between 18% and 30% of adult women experience domestic violence during their lifetime (Dobash, 1992) and it is known that domestic violence is a powerful risk factor for mental ill health. Childhood sexual abuse is also known to be a

---

Box 9.2 Violence and abuse towards women

- Increased risk of physical and sexual abuse as children
- Increased risk of domestic violence as teenagers (particularly if pregnant)
- High risk of domestic violence as adults (18–30%)

powerful predictor of adult mental ill health (Mullen *et al*, 1993), particularly where it is part of a complex matrix of social disadvantage.

There are disproportionately higher levels of poverty and unemployment among women, which can contribute to mental ill health. More generally, the social disadvantages for many women in society still include powerlessness, discrimination and stigma, all of which are risk factors, particularly if they are combined with other categories of discrimination such as racism.

Many women are also carers for older or disabled family members, a role that carries an increased risk of psychological morbidity. Moreover, because women have multiple and complex roles in society, particularly as mothers and carers, their mental ill health can have far-reaching consequences.

Case vignette

Mrs A had been received into care at the age of 14, after she began drinking excessively and running away from home. She also began to cut and injure herself. She left care 2 years later, already pregnant. She subsequently married the father and had two more children in the next 4 years. Social services became involved during the months after the delivery of her third child, when her general practitioner (GP) thought that she was depressed and having difficulty coping. He did not notice her bruises, although he made a note of her self-lacerations. The social workers noted bruising on the children, who were then put on the at-risk register. After numerous case conferences, the family was referred for review to a child and family department of psychiatry. The children disclosed physical abuse by their father and sexual abuse by their maternal grandfather. The family was split up, the grandfather was prosecuted and the couple were divorced. No one thought to ask Mrs A if she had herself been sexually abused by her father.

Mrs A began to hear voices telling her that men were perverts and that she was useless. She continued to injure herself, usually by cutting deeply with a razor blade. She told her female social worker, who made an appointment for her to see her GP. She could not tell him about the voices, but she did appear to be irritable, depressed and drunk. The GP referred her to the community alcohol team, who said they had little to offer as she was not ready to stop drinking. In an intoxicated rage that evening, she set fire to the rubbish bins outside of the team's office and attacked a man with one of her own razor blades.

The dynamics of the institution

The manner in which the primitive dynamics of an institution amplify many women's sensitivity to unequal power relationships needs both recognition and reflection. Women with a history of abuse might find it difficult to confide in a male mental health professional. Absence of

---

Box 9.3   Gender-sensitive issues within the therapeutic relationship

- Choice of gender of professional might be important
- There might be difficulty confiding in a male mental health practitioner
- A sense of oppression and powerlessness might be recreated, particularly in women who have suffered abuse
- Institutionalised gender bias may amplify abuse dynamics

---

choice in the gender of a doctor, keyworker or therapist might therefore detrimentally affect communication and trust, and make the diagnosis and formulation unreliable and the establishment of a therapeutic alliance less likely. The characteristic dynamics of abuse include difficulties with trust and boundaries, revictimisation and transference problems; these can be amplified within any institutional setting (Davenport, 1997). Particular skills and an appropriate structure are needed to redress these institutional dynamics, to optimise engagement and sustain therapeutic relationships (Box 9.3).

The Bowness Unit in Salford, for example, is a low secure rehabilitation unit where the staff have developed an integrated model. There is a framework for case formulations that attempts to focus on the potential dynamics of the institution, the dynamics of abuse and the dynamics of psychosis and on the way these three sets of dynamics can feed off each other and amplify each other in the process. Because the emphasis is on safety and avoiding abusive interactions, the ward has separate sitting and smoking rooms for each gender, in addition to separate sleeping, toilet and bathroom facilities. Social mixing between men and women can occur in the dining areas and activity and rehabilitation facilities, but there is considerable staff support and supervision within these areas in order to reduce the development of exploitative relationships (Davenport, 2002).

The physical and social environment

Generally speaking, there is surprisingly little attention paid to the physical safety of women in mental health units. Women experience sexual harassment and bullying, lack of privacy and infringement of their personal boundaries, with a resultant loss of personal dignity. Bedrooms might not be lockable. There might not be separate day, dining or smoking areas, offering no choice to women who are vulnerable and who find coping with male patients difficult. Forced socialisation can create the opportunity for sexual harassment and coercion. In addition, some units have difficulty scrutinising visitors or public access, making the continuation of domestic violence or opportunistic exploitation a real threat. Some of the central difficulties experienced by women during periods of in-patient care have been highlighted by the Department of Health (2000a) and confirmed by user surveys and listening panels across the country.

Women patients should have the choice to attend women-only social activities and women-only therapy groups, particularly where the focus of therapy is domestic violence or sexual abuse. This is particularly important for some religious and cultural groups. The need for women-only activities has been recognised in the NHS Plan, which specifies the development of women-only day services in every health authority by 2004.

Lack of privacy and appropriate facilities (crèches and family visiting rooms) to maintain relationships with children frequently hinder recovery and promote social isolation. There should be formal acknowledgement of the importance of women's role as carers (of children and older relatives) through the provision of appropriate facilities and flexible visiting (Box 9.4). If these are not provided, there is increased danger that women will leave hospital prematurely because of their worries about their responsibilities. An example of good practice in this area is Drayton Park in Islington, London, which provides an alternative to in-patient admission for 12 women, (and up to 4 children). It offers 24-hour support for up to 1 month, with a variety of different forms of care, provided in close liaison with local services, previous users and other agencies. Formal evaluation has confirmed positive user views and improved outcome (Department of Health, 2002: p. 62).

In many areas there is a relative absence of respect for cultural and religious differences in relation to gender. There are particular constraints expected within a domestic environment, for example for Muslim and Jewish women, which are often not provided for in in-patient units. An example of good practice is Linfield Mount Hospital in Bradford, which has reconfigured its acute in-patient care services to provide four self-contained single-gender units together with single-gender external areas. There is also a visitors' recreation centre within the service, allowing service users to mix, receive visitors and to spend time with their children (Department of Health, 2002: p. 61).

Box 9.4 The physical and social environment

- Ensure privacy, dignity and safety through safe single-gender accommodation and therapeutic space
- Appropriate gender staffing
- Culture-specific requirements for women
- Family and child visiting facilities

Staffing

Many female service users wish to have the choice to avoid having to mix with male patients during a period of illness and wish to access services where the focus of care recognises their specific needs in relation to their gender (Women and Equality Unit, 2000). This is particularly true for women from certain ethnic minority groups.

The Department of Health supports the idea that women might need access to a female member of staff and to a female doctor for physical and reproductive health care (Department of Health, 2002). All physical examinations should be undertaken by a female member of staff and with a female chaperone present; and at least one female member of staff should be present if restraint of a woman patient is needed (Box 9.5). The fact that there is often little choice as to the gender of staff contributes to women's feelings of being unheeded and unheard.

In the worst situations, a male-dominated hospital culture can fail to see the danger to women from other patients and fail to protect them properly. Although some women find contact with non-abusive male role models useful in their recovery, others experience as repressive the presence of any man when they are vulnerable. For this reason, it has been suggested that a ratio of 70% women staff to 30% men would be ideal, although this has understandably caused controversy and would be difficult to implement.

More generally, there needs to be a focus on training and supervision to develop a more gender-sensitive workforce. Training in therapeutic skills usually avoids thinking about gender; there is often a lack of focus on the negotiation of partnership relationships and, at the worst, a re-enforcement of the inequitable power relationship present in earlier abusive relationships. This occurs in both one-to-one relationships and communal settings, between the team and the individual. The amplification of regression, dependence and powerlessness in institutions make sustaining a more collaborative and equal partnership a real challenge for the practitioner. Sensitive therapeutic skills are essential to empower the woman as an equal partner in her own care, with individual and team clinical supervision crucial to avoid scapegoating and splitting. Specific advocacy services are also important.

Case vignette, continued

Mrs A (the same one) was seen on remand for psychiatric reports, where the male visiting psychiatrist regarded her as suffering from a personality disorder and alcohol dependence. However, a female community psychiatric nurse attached to the prison talked with Mrs A and heard her report not only mood instability, but instructive auditory hallucinations to rid the world of male perverts and cleanse herself by cutting and suicide. This led to a revised formulation and an hospital order.

Team supervision allowed the care staff to examine what was known of Mrs A's history and identify the gaps, review her behaviour on the ward and agree a consistent therapeutic response. They were then able to agree a trial of medication and package of psychological support, within which Mrs A went on to disclose to her female care coordinator her own childhood sexual abuse. No one had asked her before why she kept running away from home (despite the fact that her father was prosecuted for the abuse of her own children). Mrs A eventually asked for a change of care coordinator; she asked for the opportunity to work safely with a man, as this had not been an option for most of her life. He helped her to plan her discharge, her relapse prevention and her coping strategies. Mrs A went on to recover and regain her life, within a service that had begun to be aware of gender issues affecting women.

Gender-sensitive prescribing

One specific area in which gender blindness and lack of attunement to and awareness of women's needs is visible is that of prescribing medication. Many psychotropic medications have effects on the pituitary ovarian axis (female hormones), affecting menstruation and fertility, or producing galactorrhoea (oozing milk), osteoporosis (weakening bones) and weight gain. Some interfere with the effectiveness of oral contraceptives; some are contraindicated in pregnancy or are excreted in breast milk. Conventional antipsychotic medication is associated with an increased risk of tardive dyskinesia in older women. Sensitive prescribing practice is vital to avoid the worst side-effects (and toxic effects during pregnancy and breastfeeding) of psychotropic medication. The effects on fertility and weight gain are major concerns for most women and often lead to poor adherence to medication. Low-dose, gender-informed prescribing is central to good clinical care, although as yet there are few guidelines to underpin this approach.

Secure/forensic services

The problems facing women patients are particularly extreme in secure settings, where the service tends to be organised around the male majority. Women make up only 14% of the high secure population and 16% of the medium secure, and they are more likely than men to have been transferred from other NHS facilities (often after severe self-harm or assaulting staff or patients), rather than through the criminal justice system. Because of the lack of appropriate provision, women's problems are often compounded by their placement in levels of physical security greater than their security needs. One of the key objectives identified in *The Government's Strategy for Women Offenders* (Home Office,

> **Box 9.5** Women have a right to:
>
> - Good-quality physical and reproductive health care
> - Gender-sensitive prescribing
> - Physical examinations by a female doctor and with a female chaperone
> - At least one female member of staff present during any restraint procedure

2000) is therefore to make women in high secure hospitals a priority for moving out into more appropriate local secure services by 2004. Two of the other key objectives are to improve mental health services for women in prison and to tackle drug misuse.

The grim situation facing women in secure services has led to a number of initiatives to improve working practice and training of staff. For example, a comprehensive set of Standards for Women in Secure Services has been produced in the North West Regional Health Authority, to cover policy and practice development (Department of Health, 2002: p. 32). Another example of innovation is the 'Gender Training Initiative', funded by the Department of Health. This is a joint venture between the University of Liverpool and an organisation called Women In Secure Hospitals (WISH). It was developed to raise gender awareness among multidisciplinary staff working with women patients in secure settings, and is now administered by the Tizard Centre at the University of Kent in Canterbury. (Department of Health, 2002: p. 38).

Vision for the future

- Every woman patient should have the choice to have her treatment provided within a gender-sensitive setting if this will more appropriately meet her care needs. Accommodation should be safe, separate from male patients, spacious, supervised and designed to include family and child visiting areas.
  Care should be provided within a whole-systems approach, so that women can move seamlessly through services according to need, without being 'ghetto-ised' or 'bolted on to' male services. A full range of community-based services for women is needed to avoid bottlenecks within the system because of the lack of alternatives. The importance of women's role as carers needs to be acknowledged, with family support seen as a crucial part of recovery.
- All professional staff should have gender-sensitive training, both as undergraduates and as part of their professional development.
- There should be a strong emphasis on the provision of gender-sensitive psychological therapies to deal with the longer-term impact of trauma, as well as a full range of biopsychosocial treatments.

> **Box 9.6** Requirements of a gender-sensitive model of care
>
> Gender-senstive care should:
>
> - Recognise the impact of trauma on the genesis of mental disorder
> - Recognise that the power relationship between a service user and practitioner might be particularly difficult for a survivor of abuse/violence
> - Take into account how social inequalities particularly affect women in relatively powerless positions
> - Address how the dynamics of institutions can influence the therapeutic relationship

- Women's views must be heard if they are to become partners in their own care, and supervision should address the power structures of the organisation within which care is provided.
- Gender-sensitive service development should be led within each health care trust by a nominated senior professional, preferably a woman.
- Patients should have the option of choosing the gender of their primary nurse or therapist and, ideally, their doctor. A gender-ensitive advocacy service is also important.

Conclusion

Within the general struggle for gender equality, women have continued to be oppressed and exploited within the mixed-gender settings of some mental health institutions. In some secure units, women are segregated in subunits, but their needs are invisible in the shadow of the male-oriented majority provision; others are simply unheard and unheeded in mixed wards, where male noise and violence is the focus of attention.

However, there is reason to be optimistic owing to the 2002 policy directive demanding a sharpening of focus on the components of gender-sensitive treatment and care (Box 9.6), and on the attitudes and composition of the workforce providing it (Department of Health, 2002). One outcome of this should be more open reflection by professionals on the power structures of the institutions within which care is provided, and this should lead to a more sensitive service for both women and men.

References

Davenport, S. (1997) Pathological interactions between psychosis and childhood sexual abuse in in-patient settings: their dynamics, consequences and management. In *Psychotherapy of Psychosis* (eds C. Mace & F. Margison), pp. 199–219. London: Gaskell.

Davenport, S. A. (2002) The rehabilitation approach to in-patient care. *Psychiatric Bulletin*, **26**, 385–388.

Department of Health (2000a) *Safety, Privacy and Dignity in Mental Health Units.* London: Department of Health.

Department of Health (2000b) *The NHS Plan: A Plan for Investment. A Plan for Reform.* London: Department of Health.

Department of Health (2002) *Women's Mental Health: Into the Mainstream.* London: Department of Health.

Dobash, R. (1992) *Women. Violence and Social Change.* London: Routledge

Home Office (2000) *The Government's Strategy for Women Offenders.* London: Home Office.

Kraemer, S. (2000) The fragile role. *BMJ*, **321**, 1609–1612.

Mullen, P., Martin, J., Anderson, J., *et al* (1993) Childhood sexual abuse and mental health in adult life. *BMJ*, **163**, 721–732.

Showalter, E. (1987) *The Female Malady.* London: Virago.

Women and Equality Unit (2000) *Voices: Turning Listening into Action.* London: Stationery Office.

CHAPTER 10

In-patient care and ethnic minority patients

Leela Thampy and Dinesh Bhugra

Editors' introduction In this chapter the authors describe some of the research relating to ethnic minority patients and advise how we can be more culturally aware in our practice. They particularly emphasise the importance of working closely with communities and of listening attentively and without prejudice to the experience of individual patients. Leela Thampy and Dinesh Bhugra both work in London, where they share an interest in cultural diversity and its role in the development of psychiatric distress and service provision. Professor Bhugra has written extensively on various aspects of cultural psychiatry.

Britain's past history as a colonial power, the interim years as a facilitator accepting foreign labour and its more recent attempts at encouraging, to a small extent, assimilation of immigrants have resulted in a multicultural, ethnically diverse population. This has produced myriad demands on the existing resources of psychiatric service units throughout the country. In a general context, the establishment of a nurturing and therapeutic environment to reinstate mental and physical well-being has become increasingly difficult in recent times. The provision of psychiatric services for ethnic minorities has special problems. The challenge is to maximise therapeutic benefit for the ethnically diverse users of the health services.

Ethnic minorities have lived in Britain since the 17th century, with a greater influx since the 1950s. Foreigners, whether temporarily or permanently resident in the UK, all to a certain extent adopt the ways of their host country through the processes of acculturation. However, at times of crisis, particularly when suffering ill health, we all tend to revert to the comfort zones of our own cultures to a greater or lesser degree. Assimilation has to be seen as a two-way process: those of the indigenous population exposed to other cultures, through foreign travel or favourable contact with other ethnic groups, adopt some of the dress modes, food habits and treatment options of those cultures; and the individuals who migrate and settle down in a 'foreign' country go through the same process (Box 10.1).

A therapeutically beneficial environment can be created only if it provides the essentials of a nurturing experience within the context of

---

Box 10.1 The process of acculturation

Changes may occur in:
- Language
- Attitude
- Behaviours, e.g. food, entertainment and dress
- Religious practice
- Assimilation
- 'Deculturation' – loss of the original culture

---

currently available knowledge in health care and disease management. Resources, be they financial or human (i.e. appropriately trained staff), invariably affect the ability of services to deliver health care that is both culturally appropriate and acceptable. This chapter refers only to general adult in-patients and not to specialties such as learning disability, although many of the principles are the same.

Patients' and carers' experiences of services

Bhui (1997) has summarised the issues surrounding the needs of ethnic minorities regarding in-patient psychiatric services in London. However, these are no different in other parts of the country. He argues that ethnic minorities often suffer from the 'double jeopardy' of living in inner cities and having increased levels of mental distress. It has been suggested that African–Caribbeans have 3–13 times the rates of admission for schizophrenia than White patients. Admission rates under compulsion are also much higher for African–Caribbeans (Bhugra & Cochrane, 2001) and fewer Black in-patients are diagnosed as having depression or neurotic illness. Misdiagnosis of odd and challenging behaviour has been suggested as one cause for this finding. However, several studies have shown that South Asians have lower admission rates for schizophrenia and fewer readmissions than their White counterparts. Black patients are also said to receive more depot injections and other physical treatments such as electroconvulsive therapy than their White counterparts (Bhui & Bhugra, 2002). Additional issues that affect ethnic minority patients' care, especially at an individual level, include pluralistic approaches to health care and help-seeking, i.e. using more than one treatment method simultaneously (Table 10.1).

The background from which the patient comes (e.g. whether they are first-generation immigrants or British-born children of immigrants, their socio-economic status, whether they are economic refugees or political asylum-seekers) will dictate the stresses felt and how these are expressed. Another problem is posed by the often stereotypical and

Table 10.1 General issues for Black and ethnic minority patients on wards

Factor	Associated problems
Language	Interpreters required
Gender	Sensitivity regarding mixed-gender wards
Food	Poor quality, quantity, lack of respect for religious and cultural beliefs
Privacy	Cultural taboos, e.g. regarding bathrooms
Pluralistic help-seeking	Drug interactions
Psychological treatments	Ethnic matching, culturally insensitive treatments
Stigma	Fear of acknowledging problems and seeking help

simplistic views held by clinicians, for example that non-White races are not 'psychologically minded', that members of the African–Caribbean races are 'druggies' and 'psychotics', that other European races are overemotional in their interactions, and that Asians somatise their medical distress. These will naturally lead to difficulties in correct diagnosis and also in structuring effective management plans, tailored to individual needs. Cultural stereotyping leads mental health professionals to construct cultural differences in terms of fixed and immutable categories, and these operate to make some communities seem inferior (Bhugra & Cochrane, 2001). Professionals' knowledge of other communities may itself be based on their stereotypes of Western culture revealed as superior in their constructions of other cultures, for example a White female clinician might see an Asian culture as repressive and patriarchal, especially towards younger women (Burr, 2002).

General issues for ethnic minority in-patients

Research in the area of race, culture and ethnicity and in-patient care is limited. The few studies that have considered it do not have representative samples or have not used appropriate satisfaction questionnaires. Koffman *et al* (1997) reported from their 1994 point prevalence survey of 3710 adult acute and 268 low-level secure psychiatric patients that Black patients were more likely to be admitted and to be admitted compulsorily, that they had a higher than expected diagnosis of schizophrenia and were less likely to be registered with a general practitioner. This suggests that attention needs to be paid to identifying other sources of care in the community that these patients may be using. The authors recommend that the complement of services to all minority ethnic groups needs to be examined and that racism awareness and staff training are essential. Interestingly, in a similar study from the USA it was shown that African Americans obtained comparatively higher therapeutic benefits from hospitalisation (Fabrega *et al*, 1994). In one of the few studies from the UK, D. B. and colleagues used a satisfaction survey schedule on 53 in-patients (Bhugra *et al*, 2000). This found that, although patients were generally satisfied with the services provided, they felt very strongly that they had not been sufficiently involved in their own treatment planning. In this small sample, African–Caribbean patients were more worried about recontacting the services in the future. This anxiety might reflect their past experiences. Secker & Harding (2002) reported from a small sample of patients that loss of control and lack of assistance in understanding the problems they were experiencing were important issues. Furthermore, the patients felt that their views about their care and treatment were disregarded and that there was no redress for treatment they thought had been inappropriate.

There is an ongoing discussion on issues of privacy within the hospital in-patient setting. The fashion of mixed-gender wards has fallen into disrepute. For most ethnic minorities, the lack of privacy in such wards is a major problem. Not only are they grappling with gender issues (see Chapter 9, in relation to women), some are also dealing with cultural taboos, the contravening of which can generate guilt and resentment.

On in-patient units, provision of food is also a key factor in the dissatisfaction experienced by Black and ethnic minority patients. Mainly for budgetary reasons, most UK hospitals are unable to satisfy all ethnic groups, and food – its quality and quantity – is an important issue. For in-patients, the food provided in hospitals takes on great significance. Most cultures have accepted norms of what is good to speed up recovery during a specific illness. Some foods are even seen as detrimental to recovery. It is important to work with these beliefs, even if the food item required cannot be provided by the hospital. The notions of hot food, cold food, gas-producing food, as well as interactions between food drugs might be important (see Bhugra & Bhui, 2001).

Some in-patients complain if they feel that they are not getting enough food, but others are extremely reluctant to ask for more for fear of refusal or ridicule. Furthermore, in some cultures etiquette dictates that one should not ask for more. Different ethnic food habits and preferences have evolved over generations to suit the climate and food production patterns in the parent country. To condemn another culture's diet as being nutritionally deficient and inadequate (as was the fashion in some parts of Britain in the 1980s regarding the Asian diet) is stigmatising and ill-informed.

Another issue observed on the wards with Black and ethnic minority patients is pluralistic help-seeking, where patients may be using more than one method of treatment. Drug interactions are a known hazard in all fields of medicine. The problem is compounded here by the fact that patients might not divulge the use of alternative medicine, either because of fear of ridicule or because of ignorance of the significance of possible drug interactions. There is also the possibility of drug intolerance, perhaps owing to lack of the enzymes required to break down the drugs (e.g. anti-malarials), and certain races require lower doses (e.g. of anti-depressants) because of the quicker appearance of side-effects (Bhugra & Bhui, 2001). It is therefore wise to be cautious in starting medication and in determining the initial dose.

In most in-patient units, talking treatments are provided at a limited level, and formal psychotherapies might not be available at all. For both, the underlying requisite is good communication skills. The mediums of communication, both verbal and non-verbal, have specific meanings. The accessibility of psychotherapies to patients of ethnic minorities might be restricted because no service is available at all, or because of the prejudice that people of non-White origin are not psychologically minded. More generally, the understanding and validation of each other's cultural mores are essential to the establishment of rapport between practitioner and client.

Treatment models and problems associated with ethnic matching

Mathews *et al* (2002) studied 10 645 admissions (for 5983 patients) between 1989 and 1996. At the time of admission, the patients were placed in either ethnically matched or standard units. They found that matched patients (i.e. those admitted to ethnically focused units) were more likely than unmatched patients to accept referral to post-discharge treatment. Ethnic matching was not related to length of admission or time to rehospitalisation, but they concluded that, for severely mentally ill patients, ethnically focused units might be important for enhancing communication and trust, leading to improved participation in ongoing treatment programmes. In another report from the same data, the group observed that Black patients had high levels of diagnosis of psychotic disorders and fewer diagnoses of affective disorders. Matching patients to ethnically focused units did not affect patterns of diagnoses among Black patients. African Americans, however, had better coping strategies (outside the treatment centres) than their White counterparts. This is another factor that clinicians and researchers need to remember when planning in-patient treatments.

To achieve exact ethnic matching in the diverse multicultural settings found in some parts of Britain is an impossible task. The number of available professionals skilled in handling the various aspects of treating mental illness is already short of the current requirements. Within each broad ethnic group (e.g. Africans, African–Caribbeans, Arabs, Asians, East Europeans) there are significant differences. In addition, hostility towards the health care system can preclude meaningful dialogue between patients and clinicans. In countries in which political forces are not well disposed towards the well-being of minorities, managing political refugees by using keyworkers of the refugees' ethnic region might prove counterproductive.

Cultural mistrust has often been used as an explanation for Black patients' dissatisfaction with services. However, cultural differences can contribute either to a mismatch of expectations or to a creative accommodation of them on the part of both patients and therapists. In India, for example, families maintain considerable control over many aspects of the psychiatric process such as defining disorder, out-patient consultation and record-keeping. These resources are often under-utilised in in-patient settings and service providers should start to think about strategies that acknowledge and make use of this human capital.

As noted above, there is considerable evidence to suggest that some ethnic groups have differential rates of admission – this obviously depends on diagnosis, ethnicity, pathways into care (Bhui & Bhugra, 2002), explanatory models of distress, and so on. Secker & Harding (2002) found that experience of racism both within and outside mental health services was widespread. A lack of trust in staff also meant that patients could not talk to the staff about this. Relationships were influenced by staff attitudes, which were often perceived to be brutal and discourteous. Although there are problems with that study and its data collection, it is an important step forward in that it looks at qualitative experiences. As mental health workers, we have to work with and understand the stigma attached to mental illness, even though, on another level, we might be involved in education program-mes designed to challenge it. Within the social set up of most communities, the words 'mad' and 'insane' have pejorative connotations and implications for social and employment advancements. It is small wonder that patients and their relatives shy away from seeking help, for fear of repercussions.

The way forward

Belief in the efficacy of various traditional forms of treatment differs from culture to culture. It is essential that a planned intervention be discussed with the patient and with relevant family members. It might also be critical to the success of an intervention to include an elder of the family in the dialogue, if the patient so wishes, owing to the heightened significance of the extended family network. At the same time, we must keep in mind that the changing infrastructure of many ethnic minority families in Britain might deprive them of the network of support that is assumed to be available to them (Table 10.2).

Table 10.2 Good clinical practice

Factor	Associated best practice
Language	Employ trained, bilingual staff
Explanatory models	Understand pluralistic and non-medical approaches
Drug actions and interactions	Be aware of the possibilty that patients are also being treated elsewhere
	Be aware of the sensitivity of different ethnic groups and of gender to side-effects
	Start with low doses
Psychotherapies	A common world view is more important than ethnic matching of patient and therapist
Physical environment	Try to ensure appropriate levels of privacy
	Allow for gender differences
	Provide culturally appropriate food
Stigma	Communicating with communities
	Appoint individuals to liaise with communities, e.g. culture brokers

An increase in the knowledge base and better dissemination of information about various cultures through dialogue would help in creating a more effective approach to addressing mental health care needs. The recent report *Inside Outside: Improving Mental Health Services for Black and Ethnic Minority Communities in England* (National Institute for Mental Health in England, 2003) is to be welcomed as part of this process. We have much to gain from understanding the traditional health care approaches of other cultures. In exploring these cultural settings, we become more open to interactive learning. Acknowledging the particular significance of a psychological pain or loss relevant to an illness presentation is an expected approach in any psychotherapeutic discussion. If the same attentive listening model were used when dealing with ethnic issues of mental health care, it might improve understanding of patients' problems without the need for an ethno-specific approach to the issue. But it is important that health professionals do not automatically lay the blame for an illness on the cultural background of the patient.

Community and voluntary organisations have an important part to play in providing ethnic minority groups with a focus for their cultural identity and also a voice in dialogue with both governmental and non-governmental organisations. They also act as a forum in which to express concerns, initiate changes and organise services to meet the needs of the group. For example, the Confederation of Indian Organisations, Newham Women's Project, the Afro-Caribbean Mental Health Association and MIND all offer support and examples of advocacy and preventive strategies. Self-help and self-sufficiency create awareness and justified pride in the achievements of the members of a community.

To offset the shortage of mental health professionals from ethnic minority backgrounds and with skills and interests in cross-cultural approaches, other sources of support for patients from ethnic minorities are required. These include recruitment targeted at individuals within minority communities who have an interest in mental health and cross-cultural approaches. Another possible source of recruitment and joint working is the voluntary organisations. In either case, it is important to clarify with those concerned issues of confidentiality and recompense for time. Resources should be set aside for workshops and lectures to increase awareness and dispersal of knowledge. Ideally, the cross-cultural dialogue needs to be a two-way process, although this may take time to develop with groups who have a strong sense of feeling threatened and a long history of not being heard.

Conclusion

It is often said that psychiatric wards are dangerous places for psychiatric patients, but in-patient psychiatric treatment is still necessary for some. It is therefore imperative that avenues for improved service provision be explored. Multi-professional forums and the inclusion of community groups in discussions are important in ascertaining the needs and changing patterns of requirements of the spectrum of psychiatric service users. Effectiveness depends more on the quality and sensitivity of treatment offered than on the ethnicity of the professionals involved. Good links with other parts of the service (such as primary care and rehabilitation facilities), as well as with the patients' community, are also important. The core of the mental health needs of ethnic minorities is, in a sense, the same as that of the White majority ethnic group, and increasing knowledge of and sensitivity to difference will improve the services for all involved. As in any service provision, the type and intensity of the service offered must be tailored to the needs of the service users. A concerted effort needs to be made to research and collate information regarding illness patterns, response to medication and other treatments, availability of resources and response to present service provision.

References

Bhugra, D. & Bhui, K. (2001) *Cross-Cultural Psychiatry*. London: Arnold

Bhugra, D. & Cochrane, R. (2001) *Psychiatry in Multi-Cultural Britain*. London: Gaskell.

Bhugra, D., La Grenade, J. & Dazzan, P. (2000) Psychiatric in-patients' satisfaction with services: a pilot study. *International Journal of Psychiatry in Clinical Practice*, **4**, 327–332.

Bhui, K. (1997) London's ethnic minorities and the provision of mental health services. In *London's Mental Health* (eds S. Johnson, R. Ramsay, G. Thornicroft, *et al*), pp. 143–166. London: King's Fund.

Bhui, K. & Bhugra, D. (2002) Mental illness in Black and Asian ethnic minorities: pathways to care and outcomes. *Advances in Psychiatric Treatment*, **8**, 26–33.

Burr, J. (2002) Cultural stereotypes of women from South Asian communities. *Social Science and Medicine*, **55**, 835–845.

Fabrega, H., Mulsant, B., Rifai, A., *et al* (1994) Ethnicity and psychopathology in an ageing hospital based population. *Journal of Nervous and Mental Disease*, **182**, 136–144.

Koffman, J., Fulop, N. J., Pashley, D., *et al* (1997) Ethnicity and use of acute psychiatric beds. *British Journal of Psychicatry*, **171**, 238–241.

Mathews, C. A., Glidden, D., Murray, S., *et al* (2002) The effect on treatment outcomes of assigning patients to ethnically focussed in-patient psychiatric units. *Psychiatric Services*, **53**, 830–835.

National Institute for Mental Health in England (2003) *Inside Outside: Improving Mental Health Services for Black and Ethnic Minority Communities in England*. Leeds: NIMHE.

Secker, J. & Harding, C. (2002) African and African Caribbean users' perceptions of in-patient services. *Journal of Psychiatric Mental Health Nursing*, **9**, 161–167.

For a more extensive reference list please contact D.B. at spjudib@iop.kcl.ac.uk

CHAPTER 11

Leadership and management in therapeutic institutions

Graeme Farquharson

Editors' introduction Graeme Farquharson uses his experience of working in residential settings, running a therapeutic community and, more recently, acting as a consultant for organisations, to discuss and describe the role of leadership and management. He also describes the particular tasks and difficulties associated with starting up and closing a residential unit.

'The story is told of a new chief executive who comes into an institution, and the departing leader gives him three envelopes labeled "1", "2" and "3". He tells him to open one at each crisis. The first crisis comes and he opens the first envelope and it says, "Blame your predecessor." The second crisis comes and he opens the second envelope and it says, "Blame the environment." The third crisis comes and he opens the third envelope and it says, "Make three envelopes" ' (Shapiro, 2001: pp. 195).

Shapiro gives an instructive story. It tells that leaders will have crises to deal with, that they may or may not take some responsibility and that they are vulnerable. It is also despondent about the ability to contend with powerful group and organisational forces. It should, however, be taken as a warning rather than a statement of the inevitable.

Every therapeutic institution will have a central person whose task is to take overall responsibility for, and be accountable for, the workings of that service. The exact nature and extent of that responsibility will vary according to the context and the setting, but the local specifics need to be understood by that person and by the staff team.

Some might think that groups and work teams ought to be able to organise themselves, without resort to formal leadership. The fact is, however, that therapeutic establishments and organisations are of such complexity that there is invariably a need for a single person (chief executive, principal, manager, clinical director or whatever) to provide overall direction and to ensure that each member of staff knows what the collective purpose is – that they each know what their role is within the larger endeavor and how these roles fit together. It should be noted that in groups where no leader is formally appointed, one invariably emerges through the group process. This can lead to considerable problems, the most obvious of which are: first, that there has been no appraisal of suitability for the role, and second, that there are no constraints on this leadership role because it has not been discussed.

Setting the scene

The elements that have to be managed are many and varied. Some of these are obvious, some are not.

Staff bring to their jobs their formal role prescriptions, as well as their personal histories, personal and professional experiences (these cannot always be assumed to have been benign), and their own hopes, fears, ambitions and anxieties. In turn, the service users (usually referred to as 'patients', 'clients' or 'residents') bring the 'disturbance' that led them to seek and receive help. They also bring their wish to change and their various resistances to that. Many will have endured adverse (often early) life experiences, which will probably have had a significant negative impact on their self-confidence, their general social competence and their ability to make and sustain enduring, and mutually satisfying, personal relationships.

The simple act of stating some of the ingredients of this particular therapeutic situation renders its complexity clear. Add to this something of the understanding that we have of the ebbs and flows and regressive pulls of group life, and the potential for disturbance and disruption to dominate can be seen to be enormous.

The final point to be made, by way of introduction, is to remind ourselves that we usually admit people to therapeutic institutions to help them as individuals. At the same time, for the duration of their stay, they become members of a living group. Some perspective on the relationship between the individual and the group is therefore essential. To attend to all aspects of daily therapeutic institutional life, it is important to have a 'bifocal' approach – sometimes on the individual, sometimes on the group. For this purpose, a group-analytical approach (Foulkes, 1964) is particularly well suited. In particular, its foreground–background emphasis is especially useful for attending to specific individual concerns, while helping to locate these in their social context. By this kind of linkage, Foulkes elaborates a model that emphasises that everything and everyone in the therapeutic situation is connected, and casts light on the vexed question of the relationship between the individual and the group.

Tasks of leadership and management

In the literature, a distinction is conventionally made between 'leadership' and 'management'. Typically, the former is characterised as being concerned with future development, the pursuit of an ideal or of 'what might be possible', whereas the latter is typically portrayed as the over-seeing of day-to-day operations. In practice, in a therapeutic institution, these concerns are usually interwoven in the role of the central person, who is mindful of the need to give due attention to both realms of activity.

One of the ever-present traps for the unwary leader is to become so preoccupied by the internal world of the establishment as to forget about the external world, which in the meantime will not have forgotten about the establishment. This can jeopardise the very existence of the service.

'Case study': The Northfield experiment (Harrison, 1999)

At the beginning of the 1940s, at Northfield Hospital, a large military psychiatric hospital in Birmingham, UK, the Military Training and Rehabili-tation Wing was placed under the charge of Wilfred Bion. Bion (who went on to make a major contribution to our understanding of group behaviour), with another colleague John Rickman, embarked on a radical innovation. They were engaged in the creation of a therapeutic community, a 'culture of enquiry', which would promote exploration of the common group problem of neurotic disability, and how this affected individuals and social relations.

What they were doing was profoundly disturbing to the rest of the hospital, which was following rather conservative and traditional methods, and inevit-ably the new development attracted criticism and opposition. A small incident occurred, which was potentially embarrassing to the new discipline of army psychiatry; and, once this was conveyed to the senior psychiatrist at the War Office, he summarily removed Bion and Rickman. The first Northfield experiment was over. (A second experiment was more successful because it put more effort into persuading the external authorities of the benefits of what the new clinicians were trying to do (Foulkes, 1948).)

Lessons of Northfield

The Northfield example vividly demonstrates how dangerous it is for any institution to become out of step with its environment. When an institution causes anxiety in others and is experienced by others as troublesome, it is at high risk. Staff's excessive preoccupation with the institution's internal world means that this risk is barely seen and therefore cannot be addressed or responded to. These are conditions for closure.

An external check can be a very positive factor where there is, indeed, cause for concern about the conduct of a leader or any other aspect of the functioning of a service. Something will have gone seriously wrong, however, when the wider organisation assumes operational control and it marks a breakdown in the relationship between the senior representa-tives of the internal and external worlds of the institution. In a healthy

---

Box 11.1   Tasks of leadership: internal

To ensure that:
- the central purpose of the unit is appropriate
- the central purpose is understood and held in mind by all staff
- all members of staff are clear about what their own role requires of them
- all members of staff understand how the different staff roles combine and support each other
- the nature of authority is understood and its differential distribution within the staff team
- adequate resources are available to permit that the central purpose is achievable

---

exchange, there is room for creative innovation and for the respecting of wider social mores, without one becoming dramatically out of step with the other.

The various dimensions of leadership and management in a therapeutic institution can be divided into those that focus on the internal world of the unit and those that focus on the external system. These are outlined in Boxes 11.1 and 11.2.

There is a third dimension that needs to be considered, and that is the personal survival and development of the leader. The story at the beginning of this chapter underlines the vulnerability inherent in the role, and it is likely that you can think of examples of leaders who have not 'survived'. The rate of burnout in this role is unusually high and the cost can be seen in physical or emotional ill-health and in damaged personal or family relationships as much as in the job itself. Box 11.3 shows some of the steps that leaders can and should take to protect themselves in role. Within all this, there is a clear need to establish a robust social fabric, the hallmarks of which are:

Box 11.2   Tasks of leadership: external

- To ensure that the work of the service conforms sufficiently to the aims of its own wider organisation that its continuing support is maintained
- To maintain an adequate dialogue with referrers to ensure the best possible match between the individual's need and the therapeutic approach
- To engage appropriately with family members and/or others who will be important in the individual's continuing well-being
- To engage appropriately with relevant step-down services, where immediate return to self-care or family care is not viable
- To audit the various treatment outcomes
- To comply with the appropriate regulatory framework and the relevant inspectorial agencies
- To be responsive to (and, where possible, to influence) developments in health care and/or social care policy

---

> **Box 11.3** Personal survival and development of the leader
>
> Leaders can protect their position and well-being by:
> - developing a competent senior management team to oversee day-to-day operations
> - elaborating the principle of 'maximum feasible devolution' within the staff team, so that each member of staff is expected and enabled to work to the limits of competence
> - working hard, but not unsustainably so
> - attending to the key relationship between leader and chairman of the board or other senior figure to whom accountability is owed
> - giving due attention to family and social relationships
> - maintaining and developing personal interests outside of work
> - taking the proper holiday entitlement
> - arranging appropriate external professional support (leaders do not need supervision in the same sense that junior colleagues do, but they are likely to need and to benefit from regular, intermittent role consultation)
> - being in touch with professional peers to exchange experiences

- safety for all
- consistency of approach, regime and personnel
- reliability of social structure and expectations
- predictability that what was 'true' today will be true tomorrow.

These features must be constructed in the context of a clear ethical framework, which is mindful of the need to respect individual boundaries (including that of confidentiality) and which demonstrably treats everyone justly. With these qualities designed into the therapeutic environment, a structure is created that will emotionally nourish the patient/resident group and will underscore the therapeutic efficacy of staff endeavors.

It is also worth remembering that leadership does not mean that leaders have to do everything themselves. I hope that I have made it obvious that the leadership task is principally to create, within a given framework, an open culture in which everyone can make a creative contribution and perform appropriate leadership acts. Being a leader certainly does not mean having constantly to be to the fore. Indeed, an approach in which all decisions, big and not so big, have to go through the leader is damaging both to the leader (the burden becomes untenable) and to the team (who are likely to feel that their input is not valued).

Location

The 'location' of the leader is important. When life is progressing fairly straightforwardly, the leader will usually 'base' him- or herself at the boundary of the internal and the external, in order to monitor and regulate exchanges across this boundary. When life within the institution becomes turbulent, the leader will usually 'move' (and be pulled) towards a much more central position. Once the turbulence has been stabilised, the leader is free to move again towards the boundary position. In reality, therefore, the leader treads an invisible path between the centre and the boundary, with the exact location being largely determined by the degree of internal flux.

Another aspect of location is the subgroup to which the leader belongs. Typically, people think of there being two subgroups – staff and patients – with the leader being part of the staff group. In fact, dynamically, the leader has to constitute a 'group of one', situated between staff and patients, available to both, so the usual dyadic relationship may be better thought of as a triad.

Leadership styles

Leadership style derives from the combination of personal characteristics and beliefs about group functioning. Important information on group functioning is available from a classic leadership experiment (Lewin *et al*, 1939) that investigated leadership styles. Three styles were established: the laissez-faire leader, the democratic leader and the autocratic leader. Within these roles, leaders were given legitimate power in pursuit of similar projects. Significantly different group atmospheres emerged and the findings were stark. Not only did the experiment demonstrate something of the efficacy of different leadership styles, it also cast light on relationships between the group members and between the members and the leaders under the various regimes, and on the ability of both sides to cope with stress. The findings clearly demonstrated that the best leader was the democratic leader.

The three styles studied fall on a continuum, from letting the group get on with it, with no guidance or comment (laissez-faire), to all direction coming from the central person, with the sole requirement on the group being to follow instruction (autocratic). Perhaps unsurprisingly, the intermediate model (democratic), wherein there is guidance and direction, with opportunity for group members to contribute to and to influence the process, was more successful in terms of both project accomplishment and member satisfaction.

So influential have these findings been that the studies have been replicated many times, with the early hypotheses continuing to be valid. Of course, this gives rise to other questions such as what it means to create a democratic group. The answer to this lies essentially in open communication, in evaluating ideas and opinions and in negotiating how to proceed. Critically, the group needs to retain some self-observing capacity; all too often groups are in fact 'pseudo-democratic', they have some of the trappings of democratic groups, but

113

decision-making is in the hands of one or two individuals or a particular subgroup. Democratic teams do not just happen. They are the result of a great deal of commitment to a particular way of working and a willingness to struggle daily with competing viewpoints and differing beliefs (see Chapter 12). The work is hard and demanding, but the results are usually clear to see. Of course, for teams to function in this way, they need to meet sufficiently often to allow for the necessary exchange, which in turn has implications for the team's meeting structure, particularly its regularity, frequency and purpose.

Authority

A common error is to mistake democratic teams for collectives in which consensus has to be achieved before any action is taken. Although the democratic team and the collective share the feature of all having a voice, the two are not the same. Clearly, it is desirable to have common agreement within a team, but it is unrealistic to make that an invariable requirement as it is usually a recipe for inaction and resentment between members. In a democratic team, after everyone has had the chance to contribute, there are likely still to be competing viewpoints. It is then for the leadership to draw the various strands of the discussion together, to weigh things in the balance and to spell out what the direction will be. From this point forward, all are bound by this commitment and it is not open to individuals to pursue their own path if it is divergent from the agreed general line. This is an example of authority at work.

The exercise of authority is central to the role of leader. Authority may be described as the legitimate use of power within an organisational context. In practice, there are various dimensions to this authority. The one most commonly thought of (and sometimes only thought of) is 'top-down' authority, which is mandated by the appointing body in the form of statements of what it expects to be achieved and, importantly, of what the limits to that authority are. Alongside this, however, goes what might be termed 'bottom-up' authority, in which individually and collectively the staff team ascribe formal power to the leader and, in effect, 'agree' to work for him or her. A third important dimension is the internal relationship that the leader has with his or her own personal authority. This will have been influenced by many factors, most importantly, past experience of benign authority. Where all of these exist, the conditions are set for all to work for the common good within a framework in which each has a voice, but it is clear whose voice will hold sway in the absence of unanimity. It all sounds terribly easy and, of course, it is not. All of this has to be worked at every day. The creation of such a climate takes a long time: it can be lost in what feels like the blink of an eye.

Another important aspect of authority in institutional life is to do with how decisions get made. There are frequent arguments (not to say fights) in teams about decisions: 'We didn't decide that!' 'Half the team was missing!' 'I thought we were just discussing it!' and so on. This will always be fertile ground for dispute and it underlines the need for clarity within the decision-making structure. It is desirable that people are broadly clear on who has what authority to decide what in respect of whom, and which meetings are decision-making and which are not.

Transference

One of the consequences of being a powerful central figure is that you attract strong reactions, some positive, some not so. A leader is attributed with all sorts of qualities, both benign and malign, by the staff team as well as by the patient group.

One day, when I was director of a residential treatment centre, a young man came into my office to see me. He spoke (about nothing very much) for a short while and then fell silent. I asked him whether there was something more specific he needed to talk with me about. He said 'No – I just want to be in here.' 'Why?' I asked. 'This is where all the power is', was his reply.

The point about all the attributions (and projections) is that they derive from other people. They may or may not be accurate; they may or may not correspond to how the leader sees him- or herself; but they come from others. Thus, leaders frequently find themselves being related to by individuals who see them differently from how the leaders see themselves. This is not good or bad, or right or wrong, it simply is. It cannot be wished away. It must be borne in mind and worked with.

Transitions and change

Managing change is fundamental to any leadership role in our present turbulent society and it should be an ongoing focus of thought. More rarely, leadership involves starting-up or closing a unit and these deserve special consideration. Apart from some notable exceptions, therapeutic institutions come and go. They have a life pursuing a particular purpose, and they come to an end. There are many reasons for closure, but the fact is that things usually come to an end, even if it is after several decades. By the same token, new establishments are opening all the time, which, it is hoped, will be responsive to current need and current thinking about what constitutes best practice. They will have new staff teams (and, if they are lucky, they will have appropriate new premises) and these will savour the excitement of creating something new and embrace the opportunity to put their stamp on the new service by establishing the ethos and developing a regime unhampered by history and objections to change.

Beginnings

The opening of a new service always has a particular excitement to it. A target population will have been identified, as will the optimal staffing complement, usually multidisciplinary. A few key personnel will be in place – usually the clinical leader, perhaps a project manager and another senior clinician. They will have the task of recruiting a staff team, identifying a therapeutic programme (locating this within the current knowledge and evidence base for best practice), establishing working protocols, managing the progress of the built environment, liaising with local (and perhaps central) governmental agencies and so on.

Once the staff team is appointed, there is the business of preparing them for the task. They will be inducted in the new operational policies and procedures. They will receive training in other procedures such as first aid, health and safety, food hygiene, and perhaps restraint techniques. Alongside this, there are likely to be specific team-building events, development of supervision arrangements and other forms of staff support. Depending on the sector and the resources of the agency, this process will involve days, weeks or even months.

It is in this early stage of development that a new staff team commonly succumbs to, or at least struggles with, a particularly powerful fantasy: 'If we just spend a bit more time on design – design of the building, design of the treatment programme, design of whatever – we can design out some of the disturbance, the difficult behaviour, that we might otherwise expect.' This is particularly seductive if there is some reliance on new technology – especially locks – that seems to offer the promise of control. The problem here, of course, is that the 'disturbance' cannot be designed out. The 'disturbance' business is the business they are in and, although it is undoubtedly true that the various aspects of design as described can support or detract from the therapeutic task, ultimately the disturbance will be addressed and engaged with only through the various human relationships.

In a new secure unit for young adults, built at a cost of £7 million, the planners were very proud of the sophistication of the new electronic locking system. Within a month a young man with lots of time on his hands, a keen native intelligence and a strong anti-authority disposition had brought it to a (temporary) standstill. He had worked out that, by wetting a toothbrush and rubbing this for long periods around electrical sockets, the plaster would collapse and the sockets would fall out of the wall!

Where the purpose is to utilise technology to exercise control, it is almost always doomed to fail. Never underestimate the ingenuity of those who are intended to be restricted by it. One of the most useful pieces of guidance that older staff can offer newcomers is that they need to realise that mental health facilities 'live' in their own psychological (and sometimes physical) 'mess'. The daily task is to try to make some sense of the mess and to work towards its reduction. Depending on a variety of factors, sometimes the mess will be less, sometimes it will be more and these will exist in dynamic equilibrium.

At the start-up of an institution, ideas and idealism flourish. These will be tempered only by the impact of reality and there is no greater reality than the arrival of the first new residents.

Endings

The closure of established residential services is always difficult, even when they are planned well in advance. And, of course, many closures are not given much advance notice. This usually depends on the circumstances precipitating the crisis, the sector in which the closure is occurring and resources available. Policy shifts, changes in perceived need, financial considerations and scandal are the most common causes of enforced closure. Powerful feelings of loss and grief often predominate in patients and staff alike and, except where closure has been to bring bad practice to an end, these are usually accompanied by anger.

Closure has many practical considerations. The first obligation is to the well-being of the resident or patient group. If they can no longer be here, where are they to be? On the basis of their identified need, alternative provision needs to be made. The liaison with referrers and the planning and execution of transfers is difficult for staff. It is desirable to be open and honest in sharing information with the patients concerned, but it is important to avoid the unhelpful communication to them of uncertainty. This is a counsel of perfection, of course, and a difficult balance to strike. The point is to not stoke anxiety unnecessarily in an already anxious situation. This task is rendered all the harder if staff are being made redundant (unlikely to happen in public services, but very common in the voluntary sector).

In any event, it is crucial to attend to the needs of staff. What are the terms of their redundancy or relocation? What are the implications financially, for their career, their place of work, their family? In parallel with the need for staff to contain the residents' heightened anxiety, there must be a very active structure put in place to contain massive staff anxiety. This must address their emotional turmoil and their very practical need for clear information and support in finding the right kind of new work. Ideally, it will involve bringing in 'outsiders' to assist in the task – psychotherapists to help the team to process its own emotional reactions, and specialists and out-placement personnel to ensure that all relevant practicalities are identified and options understood. This is an obligation to the departing staff on the part of the wider organisation.

At any stage in the life cycle of an institution, many of the same dynamics will be at play. But at each individual stage, particularly the beginning and the end, there are specific factors that require urgent attention (and can be easily missed). At the start, such is the excitement and anticipation that some of the complexity and day-to-day difficulty can be minimised or overlooked. Equally, at the end, when all may feel burdened by sadness, it is likely to be difficult for staff to retain a sense of hope, some sense of optimism that they still have a valuable contribution to make to a new service elsewhere. None the less, it is true.

Conclusion

The need for strong and clear leadership in institutions is frequently asserted. However, the nature of the strength and the clarity is less frequently defined. Clarity must reside in structural factors such as defined purpose and role expectations, with known limits to authority, all in the context of ethical practice. Strength derives from commitment to taking clinical and organisational responsibility for working with the complex individual and group dynamics that can be relied on to present themselves.

Leaders are necessarily involved in complex relationships and dynamics and for purposes of discussion, the various phenomena can be isolated and described. Unfortunately, in practice, they are met in combination, often generating high emotion and set against tight time constraints. Leadership is demanding and difficult, needing good analytical skills, space for reflection, humility and generosity. (And never forget the restorative effects of humour!)

References

Foulkes, S. H. (1948) *Introduction to Group Analytic Psychotherapy: Studies in the Social Integration of Individuals and Groups*. London: George Allen & Unwin. Reprinted (1983) by Karnac Books, New York/London.

Foulkes, S. H. (1964) *Therapeutic Group Analysis*. London: George Allen & Unwin. Reprinted (1984) by Karnac Books, New York/London.

Harrison, T. (1999) A momentous experiment: strange meetings at Northfield. In *Therapeutic Communities: Past Present and Future* (eds P. Campling & R. Haigh), pp. 19–31. London: Jessica Kingsley.

Lewin, K., Lippitt, R. & White, R. K. (1939) Patterns of aggressive behaviour in experimentally created social climates. *Journal of Social Psychology*, **10**, 271–299.

Shapiro, E. (2001) Institutional learning as chief executive. In *The Systems Psychodynamics of Organisations. Integrating the Group Relations Approach, Psychoanalytic and Open Systems Perspectives* (eds L. Gould, L. F. Stapley & M. Stein), pp. 175–195. New York/London: Karnac Books.

CHAPTER 12

The quintessence of an effective team: some developmental dynamics for staff groups

Rex Haigh

Editors' introduction   Rex Haigh is Chair of the Association of Therapeutic Communities; he has a particular interest in how this long tradition of compassionate care can be adapted to our current environment and respond to topical concerns. His paper about the essential ingredients of a therapeutic environment (Haigh, 1999) has already become a classic in the field; in this chapter he develops the theme, focusing on staff teams.

There are some irreducible human needs that we all have, whether we are children, patients, juniors, seniors or royalty. These are the experiences that we all require to grow into well-enough adjusted people in the first place and then to cope with, and hopefully grow from, whatever emotional demands we meet later in our lives. The sequence starts with attachment, the experience of which makes us feel that we belong; this requires psychological containment, so we feel safe; it then encourages and expects open communication between us and demands involvement, so we can start to understand our place among others; and finally it empowers us, so we feel a sense of our own personal agency and are thus responsible for our own feelings, thoughts and behaviour.

These processes have been called 'primary emotional development' when they are first negotiated – in infancy and childhood – and 'secondary emotional development' when they occur during personal growth in adulthood. The developmental sequence has been described in more detail as a theoretical framework for therapeutic communities (Haigh, 1999) and is outlined briefly in Box 12.1. In this chapter, I look at how the needs of staff in health care settings parallel the needs of patients, which is turn parallel the needs of us all in our primary emotional development. I try to show what happens when it goes right, understand what can go wrong and give some ideas for helping to achieve the former and avoid the latter.

Attachment: being part of it

Attachment should, perhaps, be seen as a universal human right, because without the emotional and nurturant bond that every infant

---

Box 12.1 Five qualities of a therapeutic environment presented as a developmental sequence

Attachment	A culture of belonging, in which attention is given to joining and leaving, and staff are encouraged to feel part of things
Containment	A culture of safety, in which there is a secure organisational structure and staff feel supported, looked after and cared about within the team
Communication	A culture of openness, in which difficulties and conflict can be voiced, and staff have a reflective questioning attitude to the work
Involvement	A 'living–learning' culture, in which team members appreciate each other's contributions and have a sense that their work and perspective are valued
Agency	A culture of empowerment, in which all members of the team have a say in the running of the place and play a part in decision-making

---

needs to grow, people cannot become proper human beings. In terms of the parallel process for staff working in developmental environments, it is a fundamental requirement for establishing the relationship needed to one's work on which safe and effective practice must be based. The following example shows the benefits of fostering a sense of belonging in a working environment.

Example 12.1 The importance of induction

On an adolescent mental health unit, student nurses spent 6 weeks learning what they could by being in therapy groups and spending informal time with patients. Although some seemed to thrive on the experience, a number dropped out and asked to be placed on general ward work, with which they were more familiar. The ones who dropped out were sometimes heard to complain that they never felt that they belonged, because they did not understand why things were done as they were and what their role was in the process. They felt afraid to ask, as the permanent staff were always busy. Also, the students did not want to be seen as inadequate, for all the other staff seemed to be acting quite normally, not mentioning that anything was unusual or difficult and generally not making a fuss.

A new nurse tutor introduced an induction procedure, with written material, a day visit well before the placement and a first week during which the students had twice-daily meetings with two 'hosts': a qualified staff member and a patient. Fewer students subsequently dropped out before the end of the 6-week placement, and they reported being less worried about 'saying the wrong thing' and being much less frightened of appearing inexperienced.

It is a widely held management belief that staff who are 'happy' are also more productive, but it is important to pick apart what this 'happiness' is – particularly in a mental health setting, where the experiences being discussed as part of the day-to-day work are often extremely unhappy ones. The earliest emotional experiences for all of us – which nobody can consciously remember, but we can all observe in infants – are about attachment. They include being distressed (for any reason), then having that distress melt away through being in physical and mental contact with somebody we know, with whom we have a special bond and in whose company we know we are not alone.

To translate this into the adult experience of being a staff member on the adolescent ward mentioned in the above example, a staff member feels emotionally exhausted and upset after a difficult meeting with an angry teenager and his dismissive parents. She will cope much better with this if she feels part of a team to which she can go to talk about the session or just to feel in comfortable (and comforting) social contact with others. This contact need not now be physical, as it is for infants, but verbal and non-verbal, practical and emotional. It is through this sense of belonging to a team that one is valued, not for doing very clever things, but just for being there together and being human together.

This attachment to the team is the emotional bedrock on which a therapeutic environment is built. Several modern ways of working hamper this. They are bureaucratic, efficiency-driven solutions to practical problems that fail to recognise the unconscious attributes of a workplace. These matters are ignored at considerable cost, as team cohesion – which is the demonstrable result of successful attachment – is replaced by fragmentation, alienation and lack of commitment. Examples of policies that hamper this attachment are dispersing staff from a shared base, moving them to cover shortages elsewhere, rapid training rotations, preoccupation with targets and performance management, and generally treating staff members as commodities to be dealt with impersonally and mechanically. To promote a stronger network of relationships between staff, each member must be individually valued and must feel valued.

A great deal of this can be done by paying careful attention to the way in which staff join and leave. Before anybody new joins, some thought should be given to their arrival and how their first day will be organised, to avoid making the place appear alienating or forbidding. To give written information about who everybody is and about practical matters of how the place works and also references to papers about the underlying philosophy will all be worthwhile; so will any social rituals of joining such as a meal out together, or a party, or just a few minutes of friendly introduction scheduled into a regular staff meeting. Teams who are good at helping staff to attach securely are not so good at letting them go, but attention to leaving is just as much a part of attachment. The principles are similar to those in therapy: give it plenty of time, allow feelings about it to emerge and be properly discussed and digested, and acknowledge it with whatever mixture of sadness and hope it requires – being aware that a student on a 3-week placement will have a level of attachment very different from that of a consultant who has been there for 25 years.

Containment: feeling secure

Safety at work is about much more than panic alarms, locked doors and security officers. To feel safe at work of course requires physical safety, but it also demands something much deeper than official notices warning the public that they will be prosecuted if they are rude to staff. Where the work has any emotional component, it must also pay heed to the experience of psychological safety. This requires us to think about the primitive and preverbal phenomenon, and experience, of containment.

Example 12.2   The sinking of a happy ship

A unit for specialised cardiac catheterisation had a team of 12 nurses, doctors and radiographers. They had weekly business meetings, and a monthly research and audit seminar. The service was often one of the first units to implement new techniques after they were published in the research litera-ture, and its managers met with staff regularly, supported their bids for new equipment and helped to coordinate their service with others in the hospital. It was a popular unit for trainees and had a very low staff turnover. It had an enviable reputation for being a 'happy ship' when other hospital departments were demoralised and could not attract enough good staff.

The senior radiographer retired at 60 and one of the others radiographers stood in for 6 months while a successor was appointed. At much the same time, the senior consultant, who had been taking on new responsibilities in the medical school, reduced her time in the unit to 2 days per week. She could not make it to most of the business meetings, and the research and audit meetings happened less and less frequently.

In the following months, two members of staff went on long-term sick leave and three others found work elsewhere. Although the remaining staff were fully competent to continue clinical work as before, the unit lost its reputation for being safely able to undertake high-risk procedures. Within 2 years, the unit was closed down in a hospital reorganisation and the staff were redeployed elsewhere.

Many things can conspire to make an environment feel unsafe, for example practical issues such as low staffing levels and the direct consequences of them. But these are less important than the culture of a unit. It is the culture of a unit that determines whether staff feel sufficiently contained to be able to work well, and this culture is determined by the staff's relationship with each other. At its most basic, staff will feel safe if they feel sufficiently looked after by those above them. This 'being looked after' means having a relationship that they can trust. If junior staff know there is somebody they can turn to for advice, support and guidance – who respects them for themselves as well as for their professionalism and clearly enjoys a playful interchange of ideas – it is very likely that they will feel themselves to be trusted and secure in their work, however busy or stressful it may be. A trusting relationship like this depends on many ordinary human qualities as well as on an authentic willingness to put oneself out for somebody else. In more psychoanalytic language, it is an ability to tolerate projections, to hold on to uncertainty and discomfort without striving to seek immediate relief, and to engage in reverie – or thoughtful and creative reflection. There is often a chain of command involved in hospital hierarchies, and this relationship of trust must hold true for each of its links: so more senior staff members need somebody who can contain their anxiety and with whom they feel secure. Then the most senior staff in a unit need to feel the same safety with those outside with whom they relate. The problem with this system is that anxiety is passed up the hierarchy, and although it should not be the case, it is often those in charge who have less access to support and supervision.

Even better than a single relationship within which a staff member feels safe is a network of them. When this network of relationships works well, all will experience support from each other: senior staff will realise that thinking things of an emotional nature through with a group of student nurses or junior doctors can sometimes be as valuable as seeking expert advice.

Another important aspect of containment concerns limits, discipline and rules. It is the safety of knowing what is and is not possible. It means working in a culture that is clear about the task and has realistic expectations of staff. In mental health settings particularly, boundaries need to be firm but with enough elasticity to allow individuals to be humanly responsive and to prevent a military rigidity. This means that boundaries need to be a constant focus of thought and attention. In caring institutions, there is always a tendency for staff to overstretch themselves and become ill and exhausted. This risk needs to be acknowledged and careful thought should be given to developing a structure that can sustain a culture in which staff feel sufficiently looked after and cared for.

Communication: putting it into words

The lack of 'communication skills' has become a clichéd explanation for all sorts of problems, misdemeanours and clinical disasters. But this is to miss much of the point: to be able to communicate well and thoroughly, many other elements of a complex system must be in place.

Communication needs time, channels and relationships – it often requires more than simple conveyance of information. And it will never work well unless staff want to make contact and communicate.

Example 12.3   Dangers of isolation in a team

Jonathan was an experienced community psychiatric nurse when he joined a new 'early-intervention in psychosis' service. He was used to working independently, and did not want to attend the staff sensitivity group which had been running since the service had started. The other staff, including the part-time consultant and the service manager, all attended fortnightly.

Jonathan's colleagues were concerned that he was visiting one particular family out of his working hours and, somewhat unusually, that there had never been any need for other members of the team to see this family. At his case-load supervision, Jonathan told his line manager that the situation was fine and that no other intervention was needed. He spoke with other members of the team progressively less, and came to be regarded with some uncertainty by his colleagues.

The following year, the trust's medical director received a complaint from a patient's general practitioner. The patient, who was a member of the family that Jonathan had been visiting out of hours, claimed that Jonathan had been having an affair with her mother. He was suspended pending the outcome of an investigation chaired by one of the hospital's non-executive directors.

In an age of e-mailing, text messaging, faxing and wholesale photocopying, a great deal of our communication at work is becoming more immediate, insistent and impersonal. Many of us have become so busy and pressurised that we follow the 'don't just think about it – DO something!' approach; how much better we might feel if we could follow the opposite one – 'don't just do something – THINK about it!' The result is that, however much we might belong and feel safe, we do not have much opportunity to talk to each other; we make little meaningful contact and are more likely to make errors through not sharing decisions.

But in heavily stressful emotional environments such as psychiatric units, it is essential that members of a team can openly and honestly talk to one another, for the power of the mental mechanisms that patients use – particularly when encouraged to confront issues at the core of their psychopathology – is formidable. Projective processes can leave staff feeling abusive, abused or simply useless; splitting can set therapist against therapist (a particularly subversive process when it is unconscious); vigorous denial can leave staff lost in a miasma of fragmented or disconnected experience (see Chapter 4).

By way of amelioration, the staff team's group task should be to follow the general principle of rendering the unconscious conscious. This involves talking at some depth of their own and each other's experience with the patients. In this way, much of the disturbance will be dispersed, as rational thought is applied to the clinical material and

---

Box 12.2 Benefits of having a staff sensitivity group

- Improved morale, less burnout
- Sense of safety and containment at work
- Greater understanding of others' roles and responsibilities
- Enhanced, open communication
- Prevention of destructive subgrouping
- Power, leadership and hierarchy issues can be addressed
- Better relationships between staff
- Playfulness and creativity in a team are encouraged

---

their reactions to it. But without this space to think, the staff are at risk of engaging in defensive behaviour themselves and of acting out feelings that are not questioned or communicated (as in Example 12.3).

Real communication goes hand in hand with a questioning, reflective attitude and needs to be integrated into the work on an everyday basis and at many different levels. A facilitated staff group, which focuses specifically on this task during a regular, protected slot in the programme, can be very important in promoting such a culture. The main advantages of such a group are listed in Box 12.2 (for a more detailed discussion see Haigh, 2000).

Inclusion: finding one's place among others

Feeling included – and having conscious awareness of one's relationships with others in a team – is in some ways the conscious counterpart of the predominantly wordless and unconscious experience of attachment. It is about the network of relationships in terms of which we define our own identity, and without which any of us would be at risk of becoming dangerous outsiders. It can make all the difference to individuals working a difficult night shift, for example, to have a sense of being part of a network of staff, some of whom will have them in mind and will pay careful attention to their account of the shift the following day.

Example 12.4 Building an esprit de corps
A new manager of a rehabilitation service instituted an annual 'away-day'. This was for all the professionals who worked in the service, and it was planned well in advance, so that the clinical work was covered and all the permanent staff could attend. The day was to have three parts: a morning of discussing new clinical developments that the team needed to know about (presented by different disciplines), an afternoon of relaxation (3 hours at a health spa was paid for) and an optional evening's entertainment with spouses and partners (visiting a local comedy club was the first activity chosen, by a staff vote).

125

The first away-day started fairly formally, in the familiar format of a continuing professional development meeting. However, it was arranged so that, for example, a senior staff nurse presented the points from a recent *BMJ* editorial on new neuroleptic drugs. In similar style, one of the consultants spoke for 10 minutes on the advantages and disadvantages of a proposed trust merger, and the psychologist on a cognitive–behavioural approach to hallucinations.

Because the senior staff, including doctors and managers, were willing to participate, a strong espirit de corps soon developed during the day. Hierarchical relationships, although clearly necessary and present, did not predominate: staff knew each other for their human qualities and interests as well as for their clinical role and technical expertise. When they returned to work, all felt more valued – not only for their tasks in the team, but also for a more intangible sense of being part of something that was more enduring and powerful than they could be by themselves, something that relied on more than operational policies. They also became more socially involved with each other outside work and, although their performance indicators did not register any immediate change, most of the team claimed to feel more relaxed and fulfilled at work.

Sometimes diversity can be seen as a problem in a staff team, as those who deviate from the norm might destabilise whatever effort is in progress. However, it is a cornerstone of group analytic theory that 'the group constitutes the norm from which the individuals may deviate' (Foulkes, 1964) and, as such, a well-functioning group can be a self-regulating, creative and homoeostatic process. If they are handled well, this means that differences in a staff team are to be cherished and enjoyed for the richness and variety they bring, rather than resented or feared for the sense of otherness they carry.

In most mental health settings, the value of multidisciplinary input is recognised. Having nurses, psychiatrists, psychologists, occupational therapists and social workers using their different professional skills and bringing different perspectives to a common issue is evidently sound practice, not only to cover different areas of problems likely to be encountered but also because of the potential for creativity. A way of gaining an even wider perspective would be to take account of non-professional opinions as well, such as those of families, carers, ex-patients, managers and commissioners. For example, the Open Psychotherapeutic Centre in Athens responds to crisis calls by sending out a 'flying squad' that includes two current patients, a doctor and a non-medical member of staff. They visit the prospective patient's home, have discussions with all members of the family present and decide together which parts of the therapy programme will help.

These working practices and the psychological processes behind them can be held together only if the groups in which they happen are dynamic, trusting and free-thinking enough to allow all members to find their place in a way that is more sophisticated and complex than in a simple hierarchy or line-management system. This requires a high level of trust – so that a junior nurse, for example, can openly disagree with the consultant, and the group as a whole can then negotiate an outcome that has shared agreement. It is probable that such groups will often function at a more defensive or defended level, where such frankness cannot happen. However, the task of working together increasingly effectively is not static but developmental, where fleeting moments of such contact are acknowledged and valued – so that, over time and with increasing intimacy, they become more frequent. Various comings and goings, and practical issues, will perturb this intimacy from time to time; but once staff members grow in confidence, it is likely to be sufficiently valued to generate enough positive outcome, as well as enthusiasm, to continue.

Although this could be positive and optimistic, we should not forget how much it is against the general tide of individualism. With individuals' rights to confidentiality and anonymity so highly prized, we are approaching a situation where 'you can only care about me if you have permission'. This leads to a world in which there is no normal compassionate contact between people, where, for example, patients in a psychiatric ward could live in their own rooms as if they were in a hotel and could automatically veto others (except the professionals) knowing anything about them. This would prevent the normal compassionate and therapeutic processes of making ordinary but caring relationships, and would effectively make any group therapy impossible. The same tightly held defensiveness over their own privacy could also have the same effect in staff teams: it could become impossible to be mindful of each other, for fear of being intrusive. Although there is no easy answer to these problems, the human value of establishing meaningful contact with each other must be allowed to speak for itself. This means treating the process very gently, leading people into it step by step, without force, and allowing them to judge for themselves once they get a taste of what they are letting themselves in for.

Agency: making change possible

Institutional routines often stifle creativity, through their insistence that efficiency, or performance management or any of the new governances is organised with a level of bureaucracy that seems to extinguish mutual trust, and with it any passion one feels for the work.

Example 12.5 The value of compromise
A hospital's risk manager became increasingly worried about one of four psychiatric admission wards. The senior nurse on the ward would not send staff to important meetings about ligature points, new building regulations and observation policies. The manager's annual review noted that this nurse's

specific targets relating to such matters were frequently not met. This was puzzling, as there were almost never any formal complaints made about the ward by patients or relatives.

The manager made an appointment to visit the ward to talk to the senior nurse, and found himself in one of the twice-daily group meetings involving all the patients and staff. He explained his role and the problems that could arise from the way the ward was organised. The patients and staff explained to him how they valued his and the senior management's concern – but that they prioritised therapeutic relationships above administrative meetings.

They came to the agreement that any forthcoming meetings would be discussed in one of the daily ward groups, and it would be decided there and then whether any patients or staff could attend the meetings. Furthermore, the risk manager would come once every 3 months to explain current issues to them. This system was so successful that it was introduced, with variations, on the other three wards. Patients are now involved in looking for ligature points and making sure that the environment is physically safe, and work in partnership with staff to supervise patients needing high levels of observation.

The unthinking imposition of policies creates a closed culture in which staff respond to queries with 'because that's how we work here' or with silent or spoken reluctance to engage in questioning. This can be comfortable: the staff 'know their place' and can carry out the work without much anxiety. Repetition and familiarity mean that problems are dealt with in a routine way using a routine solution and little intervening thought. This approach is similar to what is sometimes called 'micromanagement' – every problem, however small, has a managerial solution – and it is often delivered in a caring and sensitive way. But this is to give a fundamentally authoritarian and undemocratic process the veneer of reasonableness: what has been lost is the ability to scrutinise and to think and decide together. Only the micromanager has authority; the rest of the team is reduced to the precision of following detailed instructions. Professional judgement is undermined, flexibility is lost and responsibility is projected upwards and outwards. Intelligent clinicians are left disempowered, and quite possibly resentful and at risk of acting out that resentment in destructive ways.

The idea of allowing patients and staff to exercise their personal agency is indeed a challenging one. When Wilfred Bion tried it with battle-shocked soldiers of the Second World War at Northfield Military Hospital in the UK (the first formal attempt to organise a therapeutic community), the experiment was stopped within a few weeks (Harrison, 1999). Tom Main was the leading clinician in a subsequent experiment, which lasted longer and seemed more successful, perhaps because it was working with rather than against the grain of military authority (Kennard, 1998). Main commented that

'both the Commanding Officer and his staff were condemning and rancorous of Bion's refusal to own total responsibility for the disorder of others'.

The very idea of giving to patients (or staff) the power and responsibility that had always been in the hands of professionals was a radical and subversive one (see also Chapter 11). Yet in the current age of high individualism, in some ways this is just what is being demanded and achieved by advocacy services, pressure groups and even government policy (although there are criticisms of the often tokenistic and insincere way that this is done). The next challenge is to recognise the shared nature of the responsibility involved – so that something more than an adversarial and consumeristic clamour can emerge. At a clinical level, a meaningful partnership means a new type of relationship between the provider and the recipient of services, where the former is a collaborative guide and the latter shares the decisions, but with awareness of the facts and the uncertainties behind them. For staff and their managers, the same process means that the manager and clinician together agree what should be done, with a mutual understanding of the context, thinking together and shared responsibility for decisions.

If this is done in a group, or collection of groups, involving all the 'stakeholders' in authentic and sensitive ways, it gives a new power to the process and anchors it in socially negotiated and shared responsibility. For example, managers with ideas for change will need to earn the support and respect of the stakeholders, rather than relying on enforcement. Although this can be more cumbersome for individuals with drive and energy, it is where the concept of developing personal agency within a group has so much value: group members will be valued and cherished for what they bring (as well as being brought into line for antisocial tendencies), but only through a process of giving as well as receiving – or of caring as well as demanding. Within the remit of a staff team, nobody needs to make a decision without talking to others, although an appointed person will carry formal responsibility. For example, medical responsibility normally rests with a consultant, although how she delegates and shares that responsibility within the team – and uses the skills and insights of others (including patients) – is up to her.

However, sharing repsonsibility effectively demands a considerable degree of intimacy and trust and is hard work, both institutionally and personally. In a truly open culture, staff are exposed to continual scrutiny from all directions and this opens a door to uncertainty and anxiety. Institutionally, senior staff need to have a high level of trust in their staff and to convey that to them. This is frequently unachievable in the prevailing ethos of bureaucratised accountability, which itself does not sit well with the moves for increased patient power and responsibility mentioned above. But it need not be unachievable – for team members who feel responsible for their own actions and have pride in their work are likely to perform better than those treated like robots; the opportunity to experience the trust in them that the bureaucratic processes deny is a powerful generator of effective personal agency. Mechanisms of accountability should run quietly and smoothly in the background, and not dominate the task. Witness how preoccupation with hospital waiting lists has skewed and distorted the very concept of care – and helped to make 'health care' barely recognisable as the human and compassionate endeavour we all know it must be. A team that functions well dynamically (by providing members with enough of the five developmental experiences listed in Box 12.1) will easily be able to account for itself to anyone.

For clinicians themselves, to eschew superego functioning can be tiring and demanding, it might be derailed by high emotions and it has an uncertain outcome – but it is the only way of remaining true to the spirit of enquiry. It is an attitude that we all need to grow into – and continue to monitor; it is not possible to impose it as a managerial 'quick fix' or policy directive from above. But it is only through this process that the prevailing fear of blame and response of defensiveness can be made more thoughtful of others, and so more tolerant, humane and creative.

Conclusion

Perhaps the contemporary answer to the problem of establishing interdependence in the midst of individualism is a postmodern one – no grand narratives but the need for intimate, local dialogues. So we all need to find our own solutions – individually and as clinical teams – to respond in a truthful and authentic way to the demands of the forces impinging upon us. And here, I have tried to argue that thinking about the emotional needs that we all have in establishing our relationships with each other – the five developmental ones – is a good place to start.

References

Foulkes, S. (1964) *Therapeutic Group Analysis*. London: Allen & Unwin.

Haigh, R. (1999) The quintessence of a therapeutic environment. In *Therapeutic Communities: Past, Present and Future* (eds P. Campling & R. Haigh), pp. 246–257. London: Jessica Kingsley.

Haigh, R. (2000) Support systems. 2. Staff sensitivity groups. *Advances in Psychiatric Treatment*, **6**, 312–319.

Harrison, T. (1999) A momentous experiment. In *Therapeutic Communities: Past, Present and Future* (eds P. Campling & R. Haigh), pp. 19–31. London: Jessica Kingsley.

Kennard, D. (1998) *Introduction to Therapeutic Communities*. London: Jessica Kingsley.

CHAPTER 13

Preventing and managing violence and aggression in in-patient settings

Mick Collins and Paul Munroe

Editors' introduction Mick Collins and Paul Munroe work at Rampton Hospital, a high-security hospital in Nottinghamshire. Mick is a senior nurse researcher and honorary research fellow; Paul is the hospital's clinical risk coordinator and instructor in the management of violence and aggression, with over a decade's experience. In this chapter they draw on their long experience of working as nurses in forensic settings to give us a clear and practical account of how to minimise violence and aggression in clinical settings.

By definition, a therapeutic in-patient environment will be one where there is little or no violence and aggression. Where these do exist, they will be kept to a minimum and managed efficiently and in a professional manner. Yet, violence and aggression are a feature of modern societies, and history shows us that this has always been the case. They are not exclusive to in-patient mental health settings. For the purposes of common understanding it is useful to briefly look at a definition of violence and aggression. In discussion of the earlier work of Megargee (1982) and Siann (1985), Hollin & Howells (1989: p. 4) define aggression as 'the intention to hurt or gain advantage over other people, without necessarily involving physical injury', whereas violence 'involves use of strong physical force against another person, sometimes impelled by aggressive motivation'.

Some of the more sensational media presentations of in-patient mental health settings give the impression that violence and aggression are endemic in them. They are present to varying degrees in these settings and there is an established, but complex, relationship between mental disorder and violence (e.g. see Taylor, 2002). Yet the reality is often far less sensational than the foreboding images that the uninitiated may take with them on their first placement in or visit to such a setting.

Within mental health care, violence and aggression are not the sole preserve of high-security or other forensic in-patient settings. The potential can be greater in other in-patient settings, where an inadequate skills mix, unknown patients, an inappropriate mix of diagnostic groups and lack of resources can combine, with serious results.

The problems of violence and aggression in these settings can be exacerbated by resource issues such as pressure on bed occupancy and the focus on crisis management that is a feature of this. Rapid turnover of staff and reliance on inexperienced staff can be equally disadvantageous. The availability of time and space for a person to heal and of strong therapeutic relationships are cornerstones of any therapeutic environment that will minimise acts of violence and aggression.

This chapter is written from our collective experience in in-patient mental health settings. The focus is on the core principles that we believe will be of most use to professionals in these environments. Many of these principles are basic but may be inadvertently missed, have been forgotten or were never taught. We examine the complex interplay of factors at work and how due regard to them can help prevention and management. We also offer some practical principles on dealing with violence and aggression when they occur. Our aim is that professionals who read this chapter have, at a glance, an overview of the subject area and some immediate practical considerations. These can be used to reflect on past incidents, examine the current practice environment and help in the management of future situations.

We do not discuss the evidence base for the relationship between mental disorder and violence, or the long-term prediction of violent behaviour. These concepts are covered very well in other texts (e.g. Blumenthal & Lavender, 2000). Nor do we cover the aspects of the management of chronically assaultive behaviour; for this we refer the reader to Chandley (2001).

To prevent or manage violence and aggression there is a need to understand a series of complex dynamics. Most professionals will give a reasonable account of what they saw at the moment an incident of violence or aggression occurred, but may not break it down into the core elements to look at what really happened before and after. The minimisation and management of violence and aggression require detailed examination of the concept of the in-patient environment.

What do we mean by the environment?

It is rarely a single element that causes violence and aggression. The environment can be thought of as the interplay of four main factors, each of which has varying degrees of influence: the patients; the staff; the 'care context', which includes the care setting (the structural environment of the ward, unit or hospital) and the philosophy of care; and external constraints and influences. These factors interact and make a varying contribution to the environment, depending on their characteristics at any given time. Although some factors may be more constant (the care context, for example), each is affected by the others. Considering the environment in its totality is the first vital step in preventing or managing violence and aggression. An analysis using the four factors listed enables a more focused view of the elements that may surround incidents of violence and aggression and can play a part in identifying short- or long-term antecedents.

The primary characteristics of these four factors are examined below in terms of what each brings to the environment. When any one of these characteristics creates an imbalance or is in conflict with the others then the potential for violence and aggression is increased and an may incident occur.

The patients

Each patient will bring a combination of characteristics:

- physical/mental health problems
- fears, anxieties
- feelings and attitude
- personal life history and personal identity.

The staff

Similarly, each staff member will have a combination of positive characteristics:

- willingness to help others, positive attitudes and enthusiasm
- ability to exert and maintain a professional level of control
- personal and professional skills.

There are, however, negative characteristics, and these also have to be acknowledged:

- negative attitudes and feelings towards patients based on personal dislike of an individual or a group (e.g. patients with a history of paedophilia)
- inappropriate managerial style
- general anxiety about work, feeling vulnerable
- lack of confidence and/or training
- attitude, feelings towards workplace and place in hierarchy
- aspects of private life inappropriately brought into the workplace
- lack of life skills and a general attitude that is inappropriate to the workplace.

The care context

Both the care setting (the structural environment of the ward, unit or hospital) and the general philosophy of care need to be considered:

- the general appearance of the care setting and the quality of upkeep, internal fixtures and fittings

- claustrophobic, noisy or disruptive surroundings
- staffing levels across the whole multidisciplinary team (particularly direct care staff), training facilities, opportunities and general budget resources
- whether there are regular and cohesive staff teams with shared goals and consistency of approach, or heavy reliance on unfamiliar bank staff
- the quality and style of general and local management (is the style one that supports staff in their decision-making or is it autocratic and based on a blame culture?) and general morale
- the effectiveness of systems of communication across the whole multidisciplinary team
- overt and covert power struggles
- whether it is a time of major organisational change.

External constraints and influences

A number of external factors which are beyond the control of staff nevertheless influence their work and their working environment. These include:

- the level of financial support, which affects human and other resources
- local procedures
- government guidelines, service frameworks and legislation, e.g. from the Mental Health Act Commission
- requirements of statutory bodies.

Causes of violence and aggression

It is not our intention to enter into a sociological or philosophical debate regarding causes; we do not have the space. Instead, we are thinking about immediacy and practical elements that professionals working in in-patient mental health settings can focus on and utilise.

Patient violence and aggression may arise from obvious physical, behavioural or psychological causes. These are examined in more detail in Table 13.1. Environmental elements such as those listed in Box 13.1 can exacerbate or diminish the potential violence and aggression.

Picking up early warning signs

Before violence or aggression occur, there are usually warning signs of arousal. When any one of the causes in listed Table 13.1 and Box 13.1 evokes a reaction there is generally (but not always) a pattern of escalation. At first, the individual may express dissatisfaction or seek

Table 13.1 Individual causes of violence and aggression

Physical[1]	Psychological/behavioural
Pain, trauma	Mental illness, personality disorder, mental impairment
Intoxification, misuse of alcohol, drugs, solvents	Greed, jealousy, resentment
Confusional states (e.g. severe constipation, accidental overdose of drugs, problems with prescribed medication	Rigid interpersonal style, extreme views, intolerance
	Lack of insight, poor communicative ability, inadequate social skills
Organic disorders (e.g. dementia)	Sexual frustration, sexual perversion
Sleep deprivation	Anger, fear, frustration, boredom
	Stress, anxiety, bereavement
	Perceived deprivation or inequality
	To gain attention or reward (secondary gain)

1. Physical causes can often be ruled out quickly or remedied, but they are often overlooked.

resolution. It may be that their concern is reasonable, and it is at this point that prevention and management are most effectively practised. Of course, a request or reaction may be entirely inappropriate and driven by one of the factors discussed above (e.g. a patient detained under the Mental Health Act and under close observation might insist on going shopping unaccompanied). Spotting early escalation is much more likely if the relationship between the professional and the patient is a strong one, or the patient is well known to the staff of a particular ward or unit. Even if this is not the case, many of the signs are evident with careful observation and, in many cases, experience. However, early resolution may not always be possible. Common signs of arousal are shown in Box 13.2. Some of these could be regarded as violence or aggression in their own right, but they are also important as warning signs of acts of greater severity.

Box 13.1 Common environmental causes of violence and aggression

- Changes in routine, staff or patients (e.g. low staffing levels, poor skills mix or change inpatient mix)
- Competition or conflict (e.g. prejudice, peer-group pressure or provocation)
- Inconsistency of management and treatment approach
- Ineffective communication within the multidisciplinary team
- Accidental or purposeful restriction of liberties or infringement of rights
- Overcrowding or invasion of personal space; extremes of temperature or noise levels
- Boredom or lack of stimulation

Box 13.2 Warning signs of arousal

- Changes in body language, e.g. gesticulating, change in facial expressions, increase or decrease in normal eye contact
- Changes in physical aspects, e.g. dilation of pupils, clenched teeth, looking flushed, excessive sweating, wringing hands or forming fists, posturing, tremors and hyperventilation, draining of colour
- Deviation from normal patterns of behaviour, e.g. agitation, pacing, banging doors/furniture, attacking other inanimate objects, production of a weapon, self-injurious behaviour
- Changes in verbal delivery, e.g. shouting, screaming, raised tone, slow deliberate or accelerated speech, unwillingness to communicate verbally
- Threats and abuse
- An increase in attention-seeking

The importance of the therapeutic relationship and good knowledge of the patient

Although the items in Box 13.2 are useful predictive signs, no list can replace a solid therapeutic relationship in which the professionals concerned know the patient and all aspects of their care and management.

On occasions, an individual may give little indication of their feelings, and violence and aggression may be entirely spontaneous and occur without warning. Violence and aggression should always be managed and never ignored. Sometimes they may be channelled therapeutically (for example, the patient can be taken away from the situation and allowed to vent feelings without damage to others), but this needs to form part of a plan towards alternative coping strategies. This may be particularly true for patients in an acute phase of illness, when they are responding to stimuli that are a feature of their illness. However, a good care team will quickly build a relationship that allows them to predict such acts with each individual.

Violence and aggression can be usefully categorised under three headings, which can be at any level of severity.

- *Spontaneous ('out of the blue'), with no warning signs* This is usually over with very quickly: it might require management strategies (see below) or be channelled constructively as a means of preventing escalation. However, an act of violence seen by one staff member as spontaneous might have been seen by a more discerning member of the team as an escalation with warning signs.
- *Escalation of conflict* This is usually recognisable and can be prevented or managed. It is most likely to arise as a result of disharmony in the environment and any of the causes listed Table 13.1 and Box 13.1.

- *Planned and manipulative, with a specific goal* This may be more severe and long term. Careful knowledge of the environment and a patient's relationship to it can minimise or prevent violence. This may be more common in individuals with particular diagnostic profiles, for example personality disorder.

It is useful to revisit the definition of violence and aggression that we began with. A physical act of causing harm may be more immediately serious than, for instance, verbal abuse, but the long-term effects of verbal abuse or other methods of intimidation of either other patients or staff can be severe. For example, there are instances of bullying that have led the victim to suicide. Such instances may never have involved any physical contact, but staff need to be aware of certain patients' capacity for manipulation and intimidation.

Prevention and management

Environmental factors are the most important contributors to therapeutic practices that minimise and manage acts of violence and

---

Box 13.3 Components of a therapeutic environment

- Consideration of temperature, noise levels, natural light, fresh air, personal space and privacy (although the design should also ensure ease of observation by direct care staff)
- Access to diversional materials and activities for patients
- Facilities available for patients to air their views and feelings
- A shared philosophy of care appropriate to the patient group that all the multidisciplinary team and patients (where practical) are aware of and agree with
- Supportive management, policies and procedures
- Effective communication within and between disciplines and patients (see Example 13.1)
- Availability of staff training on the causes and management of violence and aggression, including physical management techniques (this should include regular updating)
- Adequate staffing resources to manage and care for the patient group and recourse to additional resources in times of crisis
- Recruitment and skills-mix strategies that employ the most suitable staff for the patient group
- Support for staff after traumatic incidents
- Adherance to relevant safety policies and procedures
- A focus on the therapeutic alliance and a detailed knowledge of individual patients and their needs
- Open and constructive review of practice that avoids a blame culture and scapegoating

---

Box 13.4 Important characteristics of an effective multidisciplinary team

Effective communication There should be systems in place that record all pertinent patient-related information. This information should be easily accessible and formally shared between all members of the multidisciplinary team (where appropriate, this may include the patient to whom the information relates and any relevant carers). All of these individuals should be aware of significant events and particular factors that might trigger or prevent an incident involving aggression or violence.

Consistency There should be an agreed treatment programme, which should include the patient wherever practical and carers or relatives if appropriate (see Example 13.2). Any changes in approach should be well communicated to all involved.

Balance of power Any environment where the balance of power rests predominantly with one group is open to abuse and may provoke conflict or disruption (see Chapter 2, particularly the discussion of Zimbardo's experiment). Wherever possible, patients should be encouraged to contribute and influence their environment. However, staff may need to protect more vulnerable patients and the therapeutic environment itself from patients with a tendency to control, manipulate and subvert.

Compassion It is a hallmark of any therapeutic environment that the care team has compassion and sensitivity for all those under their care. In-patient mental health settings care for many individuals with complex presentations who have been very traumatised. Compassion, empathy and a focus on the therapeutic alliance between practitioners and patients may prevent many untoward events.

Support The team must support patients through the care process and one another in their work and decisions. In turn, the team should be backed by a supportive external management structure that is understanding and does not focus on blame (see Chapter 17). This support should be dynamic in response to changing needs of patients and the care team.

---

aggression (Box 13.3). Good team working is perhaps the most important component of a therapeutic environment. In Box 13.4, we outline the constituents of effective teamwork.

Basic individual skills

A number of individual skills can help in the prevention and management of violence and aggression (Box 13.5). It is good practice to exercise these at all times, and particularly when an incident appears to be imminent or has begun. Impending violence or aggression usually provokes fear or apprehension. Anyone who claims that it does not is probably in the wrong career. It is a sad fact that any profession can attract the wrong people and there are some who relish the thought of violence and aggression and may actively encourage it.

Box 13.5 Individual skills for managing violence and aggression

- Consider your personal safety and think before you act: ill-conceived heroics can worsen a situation either for yourself, the patient or those that have to intervene to manage resultant problems. Know your own limitations and the skills of those around you: someone else may be better placed to handle the situation
- Listen attentively and always adopt a passive, non-confrontational posture. Maintain personal space where possible (i.e. the space between you and the other person)
- Talk clearly, use words that are clearly understood and treat with respect (see Example 13.1)
- Offer possible alternatives to violence/aggression, e.g. the option to withdraw safely. Do not corner the person
- Learn and use verbal de-escalation skills
- Offer the opportunity for the person to work through obvious frustration in a safe situation where it will not harm them or affect others (we consider this to be a short-term technique, preparatory to the person building more effective strategies through the therapeutic alliance)
- Do not enter into a battle of wills
- Attempt to show competence and composure, but not overconfidence
- Do not defend causes of aggression
- Avoid false promises
- Learn effective observation skills and pass on information to the multidisciplinary team

Others may have an inappropriate and provocative interpersonal style and a lack of insight that singles them out for far more incidents than any other staff member. Such individuals should be quickly identified and offered the necessary training or removed from a direct care situation.

Physical management

It is a fact that at times it becomes necessary for professionals to intervene physically – to engage in physical contact to stop patients from harming themselves or others. Any physical intervention should be for the minimum period possible and physical contact should be withdrawn as soon as it is safe to do so. We cannot describe techniques here as they need to be taught through practical experience, but we can point out some of the pertinent issues. Physical intervention techniques should be taught on special courses tailored to the particular care environment. These courses should include theory and management techniques to be tried before resort is taken to physical intervention. Box 13.6 shows an overview of the essential components of a course on the management of violence and aggression.

> **Box 13.6** Essential components of a violence and aggression management course
>
> *Theory*
> - Definitions of violence and aggression
> - Verbal de-escalation techniques
> - The antecedent behaviour consequence model
> - Prevention of postural asphyxia
> - The relationship between training and local policies and procedures
> - Mental health and other legislation covering, for example, self-defence, minimum force and assault
>
> *Physical training*
> A course should be tailored for the particular hospital/unit, and may include:
> - Breakaway techniques
> - Physical restraint and the safety and well-being of all involved
> - Disarming
> - The use of protective equipment
>
> *Who should provide the training?*
> - A qualified instructor, who can show that training has been undertaken, and that it can be traced to a recognised centre willing to vouch for it
> - Support staff should be available to observe and monitor training
> - Instructor/s should hold a current first-aid certificate and be able to produce full lesson plans
>
> *Refresher training*
> - Current guidance suggests that, after initial training, refresher sessions should be given every 12 months
> - Refresher sessions should include an update of the theory session, to jog memories and maintain skill level

Clinical examples

Example 13.1 Poor communication and misunderstanding

John had been transferred to a secure forensic hospital for assessment from prison, where he was nearing the end of a long prison sentence. He reported hearing voices and believing strange things about the people around him. He was prescribed medication, which quickly seemed to alleviate these symptoms. During his stay John became a very conscientious member of the ward. He spent much of his time helping patients who were less able than him, and there was never any evidence that this was done with any ulterior motive. One morning an appointment came through for John to have an electrocardiogram (ECG) as part of a basic physical assessment. A nurse told John that he was to 'have his ECG in the afternoon'. John became very quiet and looked quite anxious, and then strongly refused to have it. The nurse thought this very strange but thought little more of it: John did not have to have the ECG if he did not want it. Throughout the morning John became more anxious, pacing the ward and clenching his fists. He gave curt answers to staff and patients entirely inconsistent with his usual easy-going and affable manner. The nurse returned to John to try to deal with what was clearly an escalating situation. Initially, John was unwilling to talk; as he started to walk away the nurse said that he could not understand why John was upset and asked whether it anything to do with the heart investigation. John immediately returned to the nurse, seeking confirmation that an ECG is a heart investigation. The nurse confirmed this, and John revealed that he had thought that the nurse had meant electroconvulsive therapy (ECT), which he had seen on TV, and of which he was petrified. When he realised his misunderstanding, John returned to his usual self.

Example 13.2 Inconsistency within the staff team

Mr E was a middle-aged man compulsorily admitted to an acute psychiatric admission ward. He had been acting in an increasingly bizarre manner at home, responding to auditory hallucinations and becoming increasingly unkempt. On a number of occasions he had assaulted his parents. On admission, Mr E presented little management problem and took all prescribed medication. His symptoms began to decrease. However, a pattern emerged where Mr E wished to leave the ward unaccompanied although it was clearly not appropriate to do so. Mr E began to resort to threats of violence when his requests were not met. These were handled in a varied fashion: some staff told him that threats were unacceptable, whereas others felt intimidated and backed off without any attempt at de-escalation. Mr E began to push the boundaries, culminating in an incident in which he raised his fist to a young student nurse in order to leave the ward. This went unchallenged and Mr E began to experiment in the use of violence and aggression to get his way with staff and patients. The approach to this violence and aggression was inconsistent: some staff intervened by 'talking Mr E down'; others intervened physically when an assault was imminent or had begun and other methods of de-escalation had failed; other staff ignored the violence and aggression, preferring to let Mr E leave the ward, potentially putting himself and others at risk; others said that it was just Mr E 'expressing his feelings'. The level of violence began to escalate, and Mr E became unmanageable in this environment, each incident becoming more severe. He eventually ended up in a secure hospital, where he stayed for many years. When this situation was subsequently discussed with Mr E, he admitted to becoming very confused in the initial situation: on some occasions the use of violence and aggression gained him what he wanted, yet on others it did not. He assumed that by increasing the level and severity he would always get what he wanted. This situation did not help Mr E at all; in fact, his transfer to a secure hospital might have been unnecessary if a consistent management strategy had been applied.

Conclusion

We have attempted to underpin this chapter with basic principles that minimise the potential for violence and aggression, and manage it effectively when it occurs. Within an in-patient facility the emphasis must be on having the right environmental factors in place for the particular patient group.

Injuries to staff within the health services have been regularly highlighted in the UK over the past 10 years, leading to policies of 'zero tolerance' in some areas. The idea of such policies within in-patient mental health settings is superficially attractive, but the focus should probably be on minimisation, understanding and resolution. The idea that all violence and aggression could be eradicated in all in-patient mental health settings is unrealistic. To practice zero tolerance in the sense of ejecting an individual from an environment (were that legally possible) might mean just passing the problem to someone else and the possibility of a more dangerous outcome. We need to do more to help health care professionals understand the underlying dynamics of violence and aggression, and to offer good-quality training in their prevention and management.

References

Blumenthal, S. & Lavender, T. (2000) *Violence and Mental Disorder: A Critical Aid to the Assessment and Management of Risk.* Hereford: The Zito Trust.

Chandley, M. (2002) Nursing interventions and future directions with severely assaultive patients. In *Therapeutic Interventions for Forensic Mental Health Nurses* (eds A. M. Kettles, P. Woods & M. Collins), pp. 102–119. London: Jessica Kingsley.

Hollin, C. R. & Howells, K. (1989) An introduction to concepts, models and techniques. In *Clinical Approaches to Violence* (eds K. Howells & C. R. Hollin), pp. 3–24. Chichester: John Wiley & Sons.

Megargee, E. I. (1982) Psychological determinants and correlates of criminal violence. In *Criminal Violence* (eds M. E. Wolfgang & N. A. Weiner), pp. 81–170. Beverley Hills, CA: Sage Publications.

Siann, G. (1985) *Accounting for Aggression: Perspectives on Aggression and Violence.* London: Allen & Unwin.

Taylor, P. (2002) *Expert Paper: Mental Illness and Serious Harm to Others.* University of Liverpool, NHS National Programme on Forensic Mental Health Research and Development.

Further reading

Linaker, O. & Busch-Iversen, H. (1995) Predictors of imminent violence in psychiatric in-patients. *Acta Psychiatrica Scandinavica*, **92**, 250–254.

Royal College of Psychiatrists' Research Unit (1998) *Management of Imminent Violence. Clinical Practice Guidelines to Support Mental Health Services* (Occasional Paper OP41). London: Royal College of Psychiatrists.

United Kingdom Central Council for Nursing, Midwifery and Health Visiting (2002) *The Recognition, Prevention and Therapeutic Management of Violence in Mental Health Care.* London: UKCC.

Woods, P. & Almvik, R. (2002) The Brøset Violence Checklist (BVC). *Acta Psychiatrica Scandinavica Supplementum*, **412**, 103–105.

CHAPTER 14

Measuring the therapeutic environment

Christine Timko and Rudolf H. Moos

Editors' introduction The process of measuring something as complex and ephemeral as a therapeutic environment may be unfamiliar to many readers. Rudolf Moos has been involved in such work for over 30 years, initially through the Ward Atmosphere Scale (WAS). In this chapter Christine Timko and Rudolf Moos describe the use of two instruments, the RESPPI and COPES, used extensively in the USA to measure and evaluate psychiatric treatment programmes.

To understand psychiatric treatment programmes and their outcomes, it is important to measure the therapeutic environment. That is, in order to examine the influence of treatment programmes on patients' adaptation, we need systematic ways of measuring key aspects of the treatment process. Although treatment programmes for psychiatric patients are diverse, a common conceptual framework can be used to evaluate them. We have developed and used a conceptual framework that highlights the social environment and its association with patients' mood and behaviour (Moos *et al*, 1997). The social climate is the 'personality' of a programme and gives the environment unity and coherence. For example, some treatment programmes are more involving and supportive than others, more encouraging of independence and self-understanding, and clearer and better organised.

In our conceptual framework, the social climate is shaped by organisational factors, which include programme policies (such as how much choice patients have in their daily life and how much they participate in making decisions about programme practices), services and recreational activities. Other factors are also influential in shaping the social climate in psychiatric treatment programmes, including the institutional context, physical and architectural features, and supra-personal factors (Box 14.1).

In this chapter we describe measures that can be used to identify specific aspects of treatment programmes and to analyse their influence on patients' adaptation within the programme and, post-discharge, in the community. We also describe measures of the social climate and of organisational factors that shape it, and illustrate their application in understanding the process and outcome of psychiatric treatment.

> **Box 14.1** Factors that influence the social climate in psychiatric treatment programmes
>
> - The institutional context: e.g. for-profit or not-for-profit ownership; the programme's size and staffing
> - Physical and architectural features: e.g. physical amenities; social and recreational aids; saftey features; space available
> - Organisational factors: e.g. patients' choice and control; policy clarity; programme services; social and recreational activities
> - Suprapersonal factors or the aggregate characteristics of the patients and staff: e.g. average age; gender composition; cognitive and functional impairment

The Residential Substance Abuse and Psychiatric Programmes Inventory

We have developed a systematic objective method, the Residential Substance Abuse and Psychiatric Programmes Inventory (RESPPI), to assess both substance misuse and psychiatric residential treatment programmes for adults. The RESPPI was adapted from the Multiphasic Environmental Assessment Procedure (MEAP; Moos & Lemke, 1994), which assesses the quality of geriatric care settings. In accordance with our conceptual framework, the RESPPI focuses on four sets of programme characteristics: policies and services; physical and architectural features; aggregate patient and staff characteristics; and treatment climate. Separate instruments cover each of these domains; within each instrument, the items are organised into sub-scales.

One portion of the RESPPI measures the programme's policies and services. Known as the PASCI (pronounced 'pass-key'), the Policy and Service Characteristics Inventory contains 140 individual items, which are organised into nine dimensions (Table 14.1). For each sub-scale, a percentage score is obtained such that 0% represents an absence or lack of the construct assessed by the sub-scale and 100% represents the full presence of that construct in the programme.

The Community-Oriented Programmes Environment Scale

To assess the social climate, the RESPPI relies on the Community-Oriented Programmes Environment Scale (COPES; Moos, 1996a). In the light of the growing importance of residential communities in the continuum of psychiatric care, Moos developed the COPES to assess

Table 14.1 Policy and Service Characteristics Inventory (PASCI) sub-scales, descriptions and item examples

Sub-scale	Sub-scale description and item examples
Requirements for patients' functioning	
1 Expectations for functioning	The minimum levels of psychological and physical functioning necessary for admission to the programme (Are individuals with serious mental confusion or disorientation accepted? Are individuals who are unable to make their own bed accepted? Yes=0, No=1)
2 Acceptance of problem behaviour	The extent to which uncooperative, aggressive or other problem behaviour is tolerated in the programme (Is refusing to participate in programmed activities tolerated? Is refusing to bathe or wash regularly tolerated? No=0, Yes=1)
Individual freedom and institutional structure	
3 Policy choice	The extent to which the programme provides options from which patients can select individual patterns of daily living (Does breakfast time last for at least an hour, thus allowing patients some choice of when to eat? Are patients allowed to hang pictures or decorate their rooms? No=0, Yes=1)
4 Resident control	The extent of formal structures that enable patients to influence programme policies (Is there a patients' council – a group of patients who represent the others at meetings related to the general operation of the programme? Do patients have input on the planning of orientation activities for new patients? No=0, Yes=1)
5 Policy clarity	The extent to which programme policies are communicated clearly through formal mechanisms (Do new patients receive a handbook that outlines procedures, available services, etc? Is there a newsletter for patients? No=0, Yes=1)
6 Provision for privacy	The amount of privacy given to patients (Do no more than two patients share one room? Are there locks on all bathroom doors? No=0, Yes=1)
Provision of services and activities	
7 Availability of health and treatment services	The availability of health and treatment services within the programme (Are regularly scheduled psychiatrists' and/or psychologists' hours available to patients through this programme? Is detoxification used in this programme? No=0, Yes=1)
8 Availability of daily living assistance	The availability of services provided by the programme that assist patients in tasks of daily living (Is assistance with spending money, banking or other financial matters available to patients? Is help with personal care/grooming available? No=0, Yes=1)
9 Availability of social and recreational activities	The availability of organised activities within the programme (How frequently are exercise or other physical fitness activities offered? How frequently are films or movies offered? Very rarely or never=0, Once or twice a month=1, Once a week or more=2)

the treatment environment of residential-community programmes. The COPES is conceptually similar to the Ward Atmosphere Scale (WAS; Moos, 1996*b*), which assesses the social climate of hospital-based psychiatric programmes. The COPES and WAS are based on participants' perceptions, in that patients and staff members are asked to report on the characteristics of the treatment environment.

As shown in Table 14.2, the COPES has 10 sub-scales. The involvement, support and spontaneity sub-scales measure relationship dimensions. The next four sub-scales (autonomy, practical orientation, personal-problem orientation, and anger and aggression) are the personal growth dimensions. The last three sub-scales (order and organisation, programme clarity, and staff control) assess system maintenance dimensions. Higher scores on a sub-scale indicate that the programme puts more emphasis on that aspect of the treatment climate.

Table 14.2 Community-Oriented Programmes Environment Scale (COPES) sub-scales and dimension descriptions

Sub-scale	Sub-scale description
Relationship dimensions	
1 Involvement	How active and energetic patients are in the programme
2 Support	How much patients help and support each other; how supportive the staff are of patients
3 Spontaneity	How much the programme encourages the open expression of feelings by patients and staff
Personal growth dimensions	
4 Autonomy	How self-sufficient and independent patients are in making decisions and how much they are encouraged to take leadership in the programme
5 Practical orientation	The extent to which patients learn social and work skills and are prepared for discharge from the programme
6 Personal-problem orientation	The extent to which patients seek to understand their feelings and personal problems
7 Anger and aggression	How much patients argue with other patients and staff, become openly angry and display other aggressive behaviour
System maintenance dimensions	
8 Order and organisation	How important order and organisation are in the programme
9 Programme clarity	The extent to which patients know what to expect in their day-to-day routine and the explicitness of programme rules and procedures
10 Staff control	The extent to which staff use measures to keep patients under necessary control

Because clinicians and programme evaluators have focused considerable attention on patients' ideas about optimal treatment programmes, one of us (R.H.M.) also developed the COPES Ideal Form (Moos, 1996a: pp. 8–10) to enable patients and staff to describe the type of programme they prefer; that is, to measure their goals and values about treatment programmes. The COPES Ideal Form is useful for identifying areas in which patients and staff members have similar or different goals and to find out how much staff members' goals vary from programme to programme. It is also useful for comparing actual and preferred programmes and for giving patients and staff an opportunity to identify areas they want to change.

Uses of the PASCI

The PASCI provides clinicians, administrators, programme evaluators and researchers with an instrument to describe quantitatively a programme's policies and services, so it has a number of applications.

Describing programmes

The rapid proliferation of new types of psychiatric programme, such as specialised programmes for female patients or patients from ethnic minorities, or those with post-traumatic stress disorder or a dual diagnosis, has increased the need for more accurate and complete descriptions of these programmes. The PASCI provides information on how a programme is functioning at a particular time and can be used to determine how its policies and services compare to a normative sample of programmes. Assessments and comparisons of single programmes using the PASCI can provide useful feedback to staff members, in that they are given a differentiated structure for considering their programme's policies and services. The PASCI may also be useful for indicating potential areas for changes in a programme, for increasing communication among staff about possible changes and for monitoring the effects of programme innovations.

To illustrate how the PASCI can be used by individual treatment programmes, Figure 14.1 presents the policy and service profile for one psychiatric setting. On the profile, scores are expressed as standardised scores ($M=50$, s.d.$=10$) compared with norms developed from a large sample of mental health in-patient and residential programmes (Timko, 1995). The programme profiled is located in a hospital owned by a not-for-profit corporation, and has 16 patients who stay an average of 10 days.

Although this programme seemed to be a fairly typical hospital-based psychiatric programme, its PASCI profile shows that it is quite distinct in several areas. The programme scored below average on expectations

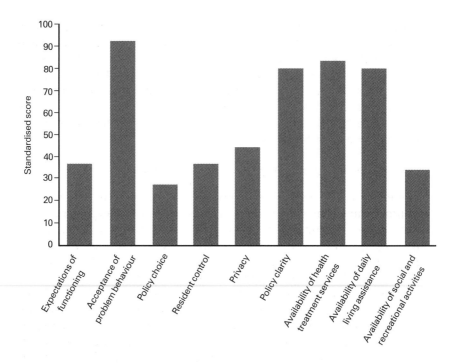

Figure 14.1 Profile of policy and service dimensions assessed by the PASCI for a psychiatric treatment programme. (Data from Timko, 1995.)

for functioning and substantially above average on acceptance of problem behaviour. Consistent with the fact that it admitted relatively impaired patients, the programme was above average on policy clarity, availability of health and treatment services and availability of daily living assistance, and below average on policy choice, resident control and privacy. Unexpectedly, however, the programme scored quite low on availability of social and recreational activities. An important question is whether this distinctive set of programme characteristics, which appears to be highly supportive of impaired patients, sufficiently promotes their independence, self-confidence, and post-programme adjustment.

Comparing types of programme

In addition to describing treatment settings, the PASCI is useful for understanding different types of programme. For example, we and others have compared psychiatric and substance misuse programmes on PASCI dimensions (Timko, 1995; Kasprow *et al*, 1999; Timko *et al*, 2000). Compared with substance misuse programmes, psychiatric programmes had lower expectations for the functioning of patients on admission and were more tolerant of problematic behaviour by patients.

Psychiatric programmes provided fewer formal mechanisms for patients to influence programme policies and communicated policies to patients less clearly. However, they also gave patients more choices about selecting day-to-day living patterns and more privacy. The two types of programme did not offer different amounts of health and treatment services or social and recreational activities. Consistent with their lower expectations for patients' functioning, psychiatric programmes offered more daily living assistance.

Linking policies and services to patients' outcomes

The PASCI is also applicable to surveys designed to examine the impact of programme characteristics on patients' outcomes. Programme evaluators can use information from the PASCI to compare patient outcomes in settings with varying policies and services, and to understand programmes in which patients have superior outcomes. The monitoring of successful treatment programmes is essential in the effort to implement such programmes at different sites. Specifically, the PASCI can be used to examine the connections between policies and services and programme-level outcomes such as patient participation in programme activities and drop-out and discharge rates, as well as longer-term outcomes such as patients' adaptation in the community and rates of readmission for acute in-patient care.

In examining PASCI dimensions and in-programme outcomes, we found that psychiatric programmes with higher expectations of functioning, more policy choice or less daily living assistance had greater proportions of patients who were asked to leave treatment for not following programme rules. In contrast, programmes that were more accepting of patients' problem behaviour had a higher rate for patients successfully completing treatment. Having more health and treatment services and social and recreational services available was associated with higher rates of successful programme completion, whereas more daily living assistance was linked to fewer patients being asked to leave because they had disobeyed programme rules (Timko, 1995).

Moos *et al* (1997) reported that higher expectations of functioning and policy clarity, and having more mental health, medical and social and recreational services available were associated with patients' greater engagement in substance misuse treatment. More engagement in treatment predicted a better outcome at discharge, for example having a stable place of residence and being employed. The extent to which programme policies and services play a role in influencing patients' engagement in treatment, which, in turn, may improve their outcomes at discharge could similarly be examined in psychiatric programmes.

Policy and service dimensions assessed by the PASCI can also be examined for their relationship to other aspects of programmes. Because

149

the PASCI is one portion of a comprehensive assessment tool, it may be useful for examining interactions between programme characteristics as they affect patient outcomes. Interactions between patient characteristics and the policy and service dimensions on the PASCI may suggest strategies for matching treatment to patients, to achieve optimal patient outcomes. In this regard, Moos *et al* (1997) found that higher expectations for functioning enhanced programme participation among better-functioning patients. In contrast, among patients with greater impairment, more acceptance of problem behaviour and having a wider array of services available enhanced treatment engagement. These results suggest that better-functioning patients may benefit more from programmes with greater demands, whereas poorly functioning patients should be matched to programmes with more support and structure in order to promote positive adaptation.

Uses of the COPES

As for the PASCI, the COPES is useful for describing both a single psychiatric treatment programme and the diversity of psychiatric programmes, and for comparing different types of psychiatric programme. It is also useful for providing meaningful feedback to clients and staff about their treatment programme, thus helping them to improve it, and for examining the determinants and outcomes of psychiatric programmes. In addition, the COPES can be used to monitor the process of change in existing programmes and to guide the development of new programmes.

Policies and services, social climate and patients' outcomes

A key reason to assess and understand the policies and services of treatment programmes is that these characteristics can contribute to a positive treatment environment. This idea was supported by Timko & Moos' (1998) examination of associations between policies and services and the social climate in a sample of mental health programmes. More policy clarity, resident control, and availability of health and treatment services were related to more supportive, autonomous, personal-problem-oriented and practically oriented environments. In contrast, more policy choice and daily living assistance were associated with less support, personal-problem orientation and practical orientation. These findings held for both patients' and staff members' judgements of the social climate.

Treatment environments and in-programme outcomes

In reviewing the large body of work in which clinicians and researchers have applied the COPES, Moos (1997) identified some general relationships between aspects of the treatment environment and patients' in-programme outcomes. Most broadly, patients in supportive programmes that emphasised self-direction, the development of social and work skills, and self-understanding tended to be more satisfied with treatment and to report that treatment enhanced their self-confidence. Patients in well-organised and clear programmes that played down staff control also did better on these in-programme outcomes. In general, these findings apply in both hospital and community programmes.

The associations between the treatment environment and patients' coping behaviour were more focused. Specific aspects of the programme were linked to patients' initiatives in consonant areas. Programme involvement promotes patients' affiliation; personal-problem orientation facilitated patients' self-revelation; and a focus on anger enhanced patients' expression of anger. High staff control made it more likely that patients would passively follow staff directives; it was also associated with low patient morale and self-confidence, less affiliation and open discussion of personal problems, and less liking for staff members (Box 14.2).

Supportive and well-organised programmes that emphasised the development of social and work skills also improved patients' positive interpersonal behaviour, especially being friendly to other patients and trying to enhance their self-esteem. Moreover, patients in such programmes were less likely to engage in overt aggressive behaviour. More emphasis on autonomy and self-understanding was also associated with less aggressive behaviour.

These aspects of the treatment environment were also linked to patients' drop-out rates and engagement in treatment. Programmes that lacked focus on the relationship and system-maintenance areas

---

Box 14.2 Associations of staff control with patients' initiatives during treatment and their outcomes

High staff control is associated with the following

Patients' initiatives during treatment
- Less affiliation (e.g. joining in conversations)
- Less self-revelation (e.g. telling staff about feelings)
- Less aggression (e.g. arguing for the fun of it)
- More submission (e.g. obeying a member of staff even when the patient does not like to)

Patients' in-programme outcomes
- Less engagement in treatment
- Less satisfaction with programme
- Less liking for staff
- Weaker belief that programme is helping to increase self-confidence

> **Box 14.3** Association of support, personal growth orientation and organisation with patients' initiatives during treatment and their outcomes
>
> *More support, personal growth orientation and organisation are associated with the following*
>
> Patients' initiatives during treatment
> - More affiliation
> - More self-revelation
> - Less aggression
> - Less submission
>
> Patients' in-programme outcomes
> - More engagement in treatment
> - More satisfaction with programme
> - More liking for staff
> - Stronger belief that programme is helping to increase self-confidence
> - Less anxiety
> - Lower attrition

had high drop-out rates; patients who reported less focus on these areas were more likely to leave treatment prematurely. Engagement in treatment seemed to be more dependent on an emphasis on patients' personal growth, especially autonomy and self-understanding. Overall, as summarised in Box 14.3, these findings show that a supportive, well-organised treatment environment that is somewhat self-directed and sets moderate-to-strong peformance expectations contributes to patients' better in-progamme outcomes.

Treatment environment and adjustment in the community

Moos (1997) found that, in general, characteristics of the treatment environment that were associated with better in-programme outcomes were also linked to better psychosocial functioning and integration in the community. Cohesive programmes that were relatively well-organised and emphasised the personal growth dimensions, especially autonomy and practical and personal-problem orientation, tended to mitigate patients' symptoms and contribute to their psychosocial functioning and self-care and community-living skills. Programmes that focused on the personal growth areas, especially independence, self-understanding and skills development, as well as on maintaining supportive relationships and a moderate level of structure, tended to keep patients out of the hospital. Moreover, patients who reported more emphasis on these areas in their programmes, which may reflect the formation of a therapeutic alliance and integration into treatment, tended to do better on these community adjustment criteria. Moos'

(1997) review also noted that programme structure might be more important for more impaired and more impulsive patients. For example, for patients with schizophrenia, greater staff control was associated with longer times in the community before readmission for treatment.

Improving treatment programmes

Information obtained by the COPES, for example patients' feedback and measurements of a programme's treatment environment, can be used in programme development and planning interventions (Moos, 1997). Before trying to improve the social climate in a treatment programme, it is important to understand the programme, to outline the process of implementing change, and to anticipate potential problems. Managers and programme evaluators or trainers often collaborate in these activities.

There are eight steps involved in the process of changing a treatment programme (Figure 14.2). The first step is to develop an overview of the change process by answering, for example, questions about the programme's objectives, how the changes can be accomplished and who needs to be involved in the planning. The second is to establish an

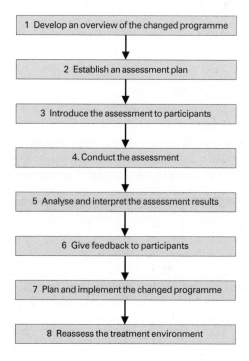

Figure 14.2 Steps in assessing and changing treatment programmes.

assessment plan by figuring out the programme elements that need to be evaluated, the anticipated time frame for the assessment and how communications with patients and staff will be handled. The third step is to introduce the assessment to participants by giving reasons for it and outlining the possible uses of the treatment climate information. The fourth step is to conduct the assessment: the COPES is administered to relevant groups of individuals, and it may be supplemented by interviews and other data collection forms. The fifth step is to analyse and interpret the assessment results by, for example, comparing different groups of patients and staff. In this part of the process, the nature and causes of any problems are identified, and objectives and procedures for any interventions deemed to be necessary are developed. The sixth step of the change process involves giving feedback to participants in a form that is easily understood. Patients and/or staff may be given the opportunity to discuss the results. The seventh step consists in planning and implementing the changed programme. Finally, in the eighth step, the treatment environment is reassessed after adequate time has passed for changes to occur. Again, feedback of results is given to patients and/or staff, and the changed programme can be fine-tuned as needed.

Moos' (1997) eight-step process is especially effective in small, stable settings in which participants interact frequently and can exert control over at least some aspects of the intervention programme. The social climate measures are easy to administer, and the process does not require technically trained evaluators. The scales encourage patients and staff to think about their programme along 10 meaningful dimensions, each of which can be changed. The resulting information can guide patients' and staff members' efforts to improve their programme, focus these efforts on a few well-defined areas, lessen the chance of conflicting goals and make effective change more likely. Moreover, systematic feedback about the treatment environment provides an opportunity for managers and staff to consider their impact on the programme and on patients' satisfaction and self-confidence.

Programme policies, treatment climate and patient outcomes

To tie our findings together in practical terms, we show in Figure 14.3 the treatment climate and in-programme patient outcome profiles for two programmes (Timko & Moos, 1998). On the profiles, scores are expressed as standardised scores ($M=50$, s.d.$=10$) compared with programme norms. Programme A is a non-profit, community-based programme with 14 residents. Programme B is a for-profit, community-based programme with 15 residents.

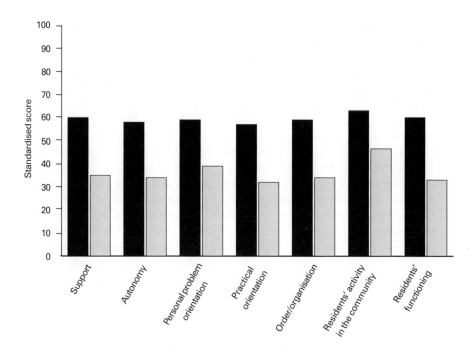

Figure 14.3 Programme policies as determinants of treatment climate and patient outcomes. Programme A (black bars) has high resident control and policy clarity and low policy choice. Programme B (grey bars) has low resident control and policy clarity and average policy choice. (Data from Timko & Moos, 1998.)

Programme A scored above average on resident control (72) and policy clarity (73) and below average on policy choice (27). It also scored above average on support, autonomy, personal-problem orientation, practical orientation and organisation. Furthermore, patients in this programme were above average on two programme outcomes: resident activity in the community (i.e. the rate of patients' participation in activities outside the facility) and resident functioning (i.e. the overall functioning of patients, as rated by trained programme observers).

Programme B, in contrast, scored below average on resident control (28) and policy clarity (9) and average on policy choice (50). It also scored below average on each treatment climate dimension. In addition, patients in this programme were below average in their functioning and in their participation in activities in the community. These results show how programme policies are associated with the treatment climate and, in turn, influence clinical outcomes.

155

Conclusion and future directions

This chapter presented two inventories, the PASCI and the COPES, which can be used to describe and compare psychiatric treatment programmes. The information yielded by these inventories can help clinical managers and staff to describe their programme to patients and family members. In addition, the PASCI's survey of the programme's policies and services, and the COPES' method of viewing the social climate, can be used by staff members to monitor and improve the programme in which they work.

There is a need for continued research that links the PASCI and COPES dimensions to psychiatric patients' in-programme and longer-term community outcomes. In particular, future studies should develop, implement and evaluate strategies based on the PASCI and the COPES to better match patients to treatment programmes. Hopefully, matching-strategies based on key aspects of the therapeutic environment that are measured by the PASCI and COPES will be shown to benefit psychiatric patients' in-programme and community adaptation.

References

Kasprow, W. J., Rosenheck, R., Frisman, L., *et al* (1999) Residential treatment for dually diagnosed homeless veterans: a comparison of programme types. *American Journal on Addiction*, **8**, 34–43.

Moos, R. H. (1996*a*) *Community Oriented Programmes Environment Scale Manual* (3rd edn). Palo Alto, CA: Mind Garden.

Moos, R. H. (1996*b*) *Ward Atmosphere Scale* (3rd edn). Redwood City, CA: Mind Garden.

Moos, R. H. (1997) *Evaluating Treatment Environments: The Quality of Psychiatric and Substance Abuse Programmes*. New Brunswick, NJ: Transaction Publishers.

Moos, R. H. & Lemke, S. (1994) *Group Residences for Older Adults: Physical Features, Policies, and Social Climate*. New York: Oxford University Press.

Moos, R. H., King, M. J., Burnett, E. B., *et al* (1997) Community residential programme policies, services, and treatment orientations influence patients' participation in treatment. *Journal of Substance Abuse*, **9**, 171–187.

Timko, C. (1995) Policies and services in residential substance abuse programmes. Comparisons with psychiatric programmes. *Journal of Substance Abuse*, **7**, 43–59.

Timko, C. & Moos, R. H. (1998) Determinants of the treatment climate in psychiatric and substance abuse programmes. *Journal of Nervous and Mental Disease*, **186**, 96–103.

Timko, C., Yu, K. & Moos, R. H. (2000) Demand characteristics of residential substance abuse treatment programmes. *Journal of Substance Abuse*, **12**, 387–403.

Part III

Acute wards

Part III addresses the particular problems of acute wards from six very different perspectives. The problems are well-known and include staff shortages, bed shortages, rapid turnover of patients, an increasing level of violence and substance misuse, an increasing proportion of detained patients, lack of research and leadership vacuums. These are outlined in recent reports by the Sainsbury Centre for Mental Health (1998), Mind (2000) and, most recently, the Department of Health (National Institute for Mental Health in England, 2002).

References

Mind (2000) *Environ **mentally** Friendly?* London: Mind. http://www.mind.org.uk/News+policy+and+campaigns/Press+archive/New+Survey+Reveals+Un-Therapeutic+and+Depressing+Conditions+on+Psychiatric+Wards.htm

National Institute for Mental Health in England (2002). *Adult Acute Inpatient Care Provision: Mental Health Policy Implementation Guide.* London: Department of Health. http://www.nimhe.org.uk/whatshapp/item_display_publications.asp?id=310

Sainsbury's Centre for Mental Health (1998) *Acute Problems: A Survey of the Quality of Care in Acute Psychiatric Wards.* London: Sainsbury's Centre for Mental Health. An executive summary is available at http://www.scmh.org.uk/8025695100388752/GenerateFrameset1?OpenAgent&doc=wpASTN4SUJQD

CHAPTER 15

What users want

Joel McCann

Editors' introduction Joel McCann starts this section on the particular problems of acute wards with his perspective as a user. He is an active member of the People's Forum (a local user group) and is involved in a group looking at reconfiguring services in the Leicestershire Partnership NHS Trust. He has recently taken up a post as an advocacy worker in an assertive outreach team.

The task of contributing a service user's views and experience to collective writings on the value of therapeutic environments in mental health settings is a daunting one for me, a service user. Unlike general medical treatment, respite and treatment for the mind touches on a primeval fear that most of us have: 'Am I losing the plot?' or 'Am I going round the bend?' These crude terms encapsulate the bewilderment felt by patients when entering the world of the mental health services and leaving behind the world they usually function in. My experience is of adult in-patient provision, from stays in acute psychiatric wards. For almost half a decade, from my first admission in 1994 through to my most recent discharge in 1999, I have required acute care during times of crisis. Both patients and clinicians should acknowledge how highly emotive and stressful the receipt and provision of care in acute psychiatric hospital wards can be. There are good and bad practices and practitioners in all professions, and this chapter is not meant to single out individuals or institutions for criticism.

In setting out to try to answer the question 'What do users want from therapeutic settings?' I made a list of what I think are service priorities (Box 15.1). It is very easy to write out a list of needs, but harder to isolate and expand on each item. My approach will be to relate 'hot spots' in the experience of my own acute care provision and then to set out positive proposals and conclusions that might increase the effective delivery of therapeutic services in acute settings.

There is a balance to most things, and striking that balance is important in mental health. The responsibility for caring for mentally distressed people at present is heavily weighted towards the statutory mental health services. This relegates other stakeholders such as the voluntary sector, including self-help groups, to second in line every time government departments such as the Department of Health and the National Health Service Modernisation Agency order reorganisation

---

Box 15.1 What do users want from in-patient care?

The following list summarises service priorities, from a user's perspective:

- Protection from harm to myself or to others
- Expert, accurate information about my medical condition
- Preservation of dignity, when mine feels lost
- Holistic nursing care incorporating attitudes that validate my efforts
- Advocacy and advice
- Involvement in planning my care
- Access to creative therapies such as writing, music and art therapy
- Opportunities for occupation and recreation that do not make me feel that I am back at playschool
- Help to reintegrate into society

---

or changes in provision. Service users are towards the back of the queue, whereas they should be at the front.

For you to understand what I mean, we need to look at the points I identify as hot spots; these are the most likely areas of contention when a person is admitted into acute care. Disagreements can arise between the providers of care (mental health services) and both the patient and the carers. Mental ill health is a complex compilation, which includes physical illness, loss of social skills, loss of financial opportunities (i.e. occupation) and the unearthing of psychological trauma. Some schools of thought believe the latter to be fundamental. It is important not to forget increased isolation from family and friends.

Easing the admission process

A patient may suffer physical and emotional alienation from peers in their own community because of a range of symptoms, which may include high or low moods and behavioural changes that are out of character. The decision to admit a patient precipitously to an acute psychiatric ward, where possibly for the first time they will be exposed to a large disparate group of severely ill and disturbed people, can have serious and harmful implications for themselves, their family and their friends and be a detrimental start to the process of recovery. However, a high percentage of patients who are assessed and admitted by mental health professionals are deemed to be in crisis. A place of safety is foremost in professionals' minds; likewise, families of patients fear for their loved ones' safety. Often, an acute admission is the first contact with mental health services. Many users and carers complain that it is difficult to get the attention they need at an earlier stage and that if general practitioners (GPs) were better informed about mental illness, many acute crises could be avoided. The policy of early intervention might improve this situation.

I make the following suggestions, which I believe could minimise the trauma of admission to those closely involved. They involve capitalising on the experience of service users themselves, the people who really know what it feels like. The admission process should involve a skilled liaison worker with 'lived experience' of surviving mental ill health and knowledge of the services. This person would be in a good position to help the patient, by allaying some fears, and to advocate on their behalf if asked. Even if this type of advocacy were not available, other patients on the ward could be involved in making a new patient welcome.

Providing care on an acute ward may not be socially detrimental in the short term, but problems can arise during longer stays if the patient loses confidence, skills and identity within their community. A suggestion to address this is to have much smaller units, located in the community, which would go some way to addressing stigma and loss of self-esteem, thus enhancing opportunities to reintegrate. Again, there is a good argument for workers with lived experience of mental ill health to be involved.

Improved liaison and joint working

At present, statutory services control access to most mental health services and provisions. To increase ownership and create partnerships, voluntary sector mental health organisations with strong user representation should have meaningful input into the planning and delivery of care for people with mental illnesses (Box 15.2). Joint ownership would promote better communications and a cooperative spirit, which could enable appropriate, innovative and excellent service provision tailored to the needs of those who will be using the services.

The role that GPs currently play in community mental health provision is often inadequate. Where are the GPs who further their knowledge and skills in mental health? It is vital that more about mental health is included in all doctors' training and that an appropriate number increase awareness and skills through training opportunities, which could be enacted by primary care trusts offering financial

---

Box 15.2 User involvement

- User groups should be at the forefront of planning and improving services
- Users should be involved in setting standards for acute wards and other residential settings
- Users should be involved as liaison workers in acute wards
- Users should be involved in educating and training staff

incentives. Currently patients experience a 'washing of hands syndrome' with the handover from primary care to specialist services. This increases the feeling of alienation that patients experience when being treated differently from patients who are not mentally ill.

New services that are being introduced address some of the hot spots I have identified and go someway towards modernising people's thinking about caring for distressed individuals rather than just physically containing and medicating them. For example, in Leicestershire and other parts of the UK, practice therapists are dealing with common mental health problems in GPs' surgeries, while in hospitals around the country the setting of user standards for acute wards and the monitoring of these services by users is developing.

The importance of relaxation and leisure

When somebody has suffered an extended period of enduring mental illness, some of which is spent being cared for in acute settings, there can be many issues to work through and come to terms with. I pointed out above that stress and tension exist for both staff and patients in such confined settings as acute wards and I feel it is important to repeat this point. To relieve some stresses why do units not have gyms and swimming pools and other normal leisure opportunities? Drug companies, for example, might enter into financial partnerships with NHS trusts if the trusts, the users, the carers and the voluntary sector united their efforts to emphasise the vital part that these provisions could play in a holistic approach towards mental illness, benefiting provider and patient and community.

Occupational and creative therapy to develop each person's potential

I feel strongly that an expanded role for the occupational therapist is particularly important and that their service is poorly resourced. The provision is always delivered to the lowest common denominator, something everyone can access, such as simple pottery, woodwork, table-tennis or pool. These activities can have their place in a comprehensive package of occupational activities, but they can also have a detrimental effect on people who, when well, are capable of much more. This type of provision can reinforce feelings of helplessness and loss. In my experience, occupational therapy was sometimes delivered in a way that made me feel I was back in playschool. I had been hoping to go on to study performing arts after completing a 2-year foundation course in the subject. I suffered a period of illness and a massive loss of confidence that curtailed my plans at that stage. With hindsight, I can now see that, if I had been encouraged through creative therapy to express painful thoughts and feelings, I might have avoided a devastatingly painful journey back to health that included a serious attempt at taking my own life.

Creativity, initiative and group activities

I remember, when I was ill in 1999 and was being cared for in an acute setting, really believing that it would be possible for my friend to bring my disco equipment onto the ward and that I could set up a mini 'rave' for younger patients in the lounge area (looking back, I wasn't quite ready for discharge!). Of course this was never going to happen, but I cannot help thinking that this was because a patient had initiated the idea and that staff always fear things will run out of control. Yet if somebody can be dragged kicking and screaming down a corridor against their will, forcibly put into a seclusion room and all this done in the sight of other patients in the name of 'care' on acute wards, is it so unreasonable for patients to express themselves through dance and music and interaction with each other? 'Do dance and music impede medical treatment?' is the question I now ask myself. Surely it is important for people to remain in touch with their creative side and express themselves in this way, however ill they are – provided, of course, that it does not upset or hurt other patients on the ward.

My reasoning and my connection may be clumsy, but my experience of the regime on acute wards was that it was authoritarian and inflexible and far from therapeutic. What I am saying is that the acute setting is too sterile and clinical, and too far removed from normal living. Patients have too much time to navel-gaze, and feelings of disempowerment and alienation from society permeate the mind.

It seems to me that care is made up of many components. If I were king for a day, I would decree a more holistic approach, delivering a greater variety of services to patients residing in acute settings.

Good relationships with staff

Another factor that needs attention is the importance of positive relationships between staff and patients. My experience is of a culture of 'us' the patients and 'them' the staff. This is difficult to explain to people who have not experienced the workings of the system from a patient's perspective, so I will draw an analogy from everyday life to try to make it understandable to readers. You have gone to a restaurant and are behaving impeccably. Even though you have already found a hair in your starter, you are reluctant to complain because you do not want 'them' to spit on your main course. There are many patients in acute settings who conform out of fear that their liberties will be withdrawn. Some staff caring for acutely ill people make it clear where the balance

> **Box 15.3**   Qualities that a patient wishes to find in staff
>
> - Respect and understanding – so that patients feel that staff know where they are coming from
> - Kindness – this attribute helps staff go that extra mile with patients
> - Interest and attentiveness – patients find difficulty in talking with staff that 'switch off'
> - Pride – in the sense of self-worth and taking pride in working to the best of their abilities
> - Professionalism – reinvent this term: it should not be the bureaucratic accountability staff are currently bound by
> - Involvement – staff getting their hands dirty, so to speak, and not remaining 'on the outside looking in'
> - Humour – this is a must, an attribute that helps staff to connect to each other and patients

of power lies, sometimes with subtlety and sometimes blatantly, depending on their mood. I believe that this causes patients to feel more vulnerable than is necessary and that the service would be better without practices that encourage a culture of distrust between patients and staff.

Modernisation may require staff to think differently about their place in the service, as a shift of power gives patients, former patients and carers more influence in deciding 'what users want' – a departure from ingrained practices of exclusive decision-making and consultation after the event. Users should be involved in the recruitment and selection of staff. The qualities I would look for in them are shown in Box 15.3.

Staff need to learn from patients

More could be done to train mental health staff at all levels to interact with service users who have survived and recovered from a time of crisis. Staff who see patients only during times of crisis are seeing a snapshot in time rather than a wider picture. This could be addressed in training, by ensuring input from patients/service users who have lived through a mental health crisis. Staff usually see patients only when they are at their most needy and vulnerable. This compounds a stereotype that puts patients in a weak subgroup, and it is hard for all of us to break out of this and be taken seriously; and, more worryingly, we can be perceived as being unstable people all the time. Patients who have come through an acute crisis should also be encouraged to return to the ward and talk to the staff about their experience – what aided their recovery and what improvements they would like to see.

Finding a voice and sharing experiences

I hope that patients' suggestions will be gathered and incorporated into future strategies at both the ward level and at government level to improve patients' experience of therapeutic mental health settings. One hope that I have in writing this chapter is that others who, like me, have had the direction and purpose of their lives changed by enduring mental ill health will fight to have the patients' experience acknowledged and documented. This acknowledgement needs to evolve from tokenism into a true influence on policy and it will do so if the wishful thinking of caring professionals joins with the determination of disenfranchised patients who find a voice.

I'm hopeful that this chapter will contribute to a growing movement of user involvement in mental health. As a survivor, I now have meaningful employment in a user-led organisation, many of whose workers are unsalaried. We propose that we are experts by experience (if reluctant ones) and that our experience is what matters most.

CHAPTER 16

A carer's perceptions of the therapeutic value of in-patient settings

Peter Ruane

Editors' introduction Peter Ruane has many years' experience as a 'carer' and long involvement in Rethink (formerly the National Schizophrenia Fellowship). He writes about his own experiences as a carer of a relative who has experienced severe mental illness.

Context

There has been little systematic research undertaken to ascertain carers' perceptions of mental health care, particularly of acute psychiatric wards. Rethink has recently conducted a national survey of service users' and carers' views of mental health care in the UK. It is the biggest such survey ever undertaken and it has been devised in conjunction with a number of organisations, including the Institute of Psychiatry, Depression Alliance, the Manic Depression Fellowship and Carers UK. The results of this survey are now available (Rethink, 2003).

The reason for this survey is that Rethink wants to be able to present the views and experiences of those who use mental health services (and their carers) in order to influence government ministers, the media, mental health services and the National Institute for Clinical Excellence, with the aim of achieving continuing improvements in mental health care over the next several years.

For the time being, I have to rely on my own experiences as a carer and on the views of very many other carers of people with psychotic illness with whom I have interacted during my 12 years as an active member of Rethink. Hence, the ensuing narrative is not research-based, but it does aspire to moderate the intrusion of too much anecdotal influence.

Who are carers?

A 'carer' is a person who provides support for someone with any form of illness – usually an ongoing illness. In the context of this chapter, the individual will have some form of severe mental illness and the carer will be (in order of likelihood) a parent, a sibling, any other relation, a partner, a friend or a workmate. An individual may have several people who act as carers (e.g. a family), but often there is just one person (a parent or partner) or, indeed, no carer at all (as for the very many homeless people who endure mental ill health).

The following statistics (taken from 1995 General Household Survey; Rowlands & Maher, 1997) refer to carers of all types of people, not just those with mental illnesses:

- the national figure for carers is estimated as 5.7 million, the majority of whom are women; 301 000 people a year become carers
- 20% of carers are between 45 and 60 years old
- 33% of carers are sole carers
- 59% have had no contact with statutory or voluntary services.

The number of people caring for individuals with mental illnesses could be estimated from the 5.7 million total figure above, but it is extremely likely that the percentage within the age range 45–60 is more like 40%, with a further 30% aged between 60 and 75. It has been estimated that, at any one time, one person in every hundred is suffering from a severe form of psychotic illness. From the total population of about 60 million in the UK, one could estimate that there are about 600 000 individuals with mental disorders and about one million people caring for them.

Moreover, the Department of Health (2003) cites survey findings to the effect that, among a total prison population of 68 000, as many as 90% of prisoners have a diagnosable mental illness, substance misuse problem or both. This, of course, implies that prison officers find themselves in the position of being mental health carers, with no adequate preparation for the role.

Carers' experience leading up to hospitalisation

For many carers, their experience during the early stages of mental illness is characterised by ignorance, fear, guilt, helplessness and a great amount of stress. The first port of call for assistance is the general practitioner (GP), whose reassurances may amount to a dismissal of the severity of the situation. Thus, it may need many visits to the GP before the situation is recognised as requiring referral to a mental health specialist. It is estimated that, on average, it takes about 18 months from the first onset of mental illness for this initial referral to a psychiatrist to take place, and it may be many additional months before an appropriate diagnosis is provided (Rethink, 2002). This partly explains the long delay between first recognition that 'something is seriously wrong' and the start of treatment, and this delay is the major contributory factor to the very high number of crisis admissions to psychiatric units in the UK.

A common problem is that during the onset of mental illness, individuals may not be able to recognise that they are really ill and carers cannot enlist support until those they care for acknowledge that it is required. Consequently, a carer's first encounter with in-patient psychiatric amenities often arises from a crisis, and too many people with mental illnesses are first taken into temporary police custody before being provided with necessary in-patient mental health care. Then there is the harrowing role of being part of the 'sectioning' process, an all-too-common means by which hospitalisation is achieved. This leads to feelings of guilt and inadequacy, but also of relief that the demands of crisis management have abated.

Perceptions of acute admissions wards

If you're very lucky, the admission will be directly to a psychiatric unit; usually, psychiatric patients end up in general wards, and then only after a long wait because of bed shortages. This, coupled with a lack of compliance common in severe mental distress, leads to delays in treatment and therefore to an exacerbation of the crisis.

Another common impediment to admission is that the ill person is often able to summon up a short burst of seeming rationality at the moment he or she is being assessed by the psychiatrist who has to decide whether or not the illness is severe enough to warrant hospitalisation. This may happen repeatedly, leading to an inordinate delay between the onset of crisis and eventual admission. It can be the cause of enormous stress for the carers and patient and, in far too many cases, has led to incidents of self-harm and even suicide.

Lack of access to medical records may cause further delays in admission, and it certainly leads to delays in the formulation of a suitable programme of treatment. In the NHS as a whole there seems to be a reluctance to catch up with the modern world of instantaneous computerised data transmission.

On admission, carers frequently receive insufficient information about the planned treatment and might not be given any indication of the expected length of stay. In many cases, patients refuse to allow staff to give carers information about their illness, treatment and so on. This usually arises because of the resentment engendered in patients by their carers' part in the sectioning process, and it often causes hospital staff to form an unwelcoming attitude towards carers. In such a situation, staff are too often disinclined to intercede on behalf of carers and this only compounds carers' feelings of exclusion.

The extent to which carers may or may not feel included in the admissions process, and the pattern of treatment, varies depending on the hospital concerned and the staff employed there at the time. It is probably true to say that any information concerning diagnosis, treatment and prognosis is often not provided unless carers push for it.

Finally, there is the possibility that patients will be released with little or no advance warning. The release may be total discharge or it may be several days 'leave' because of a bed shortage, and it can place carers back in the crisis that they had struggled to resolve. In such circumstances, carers who have been excluded by the patient, and therefore by hospital staff, feel outraged that they are deemed to have no say, but are expected to resume a full caring role at the whim of the hospital.

Carers' support groups

Insights into the nature of hospitalisation can be gained through the shared collective experience provided by carers' support groups. In some parts of the UK (such as Oxfordshire), there is a strong network of such groups, usually affiliated to one of the large voluntary mental health bodies (Rethink, Mind, etc.). In other regions (such as Suffolk), there are relatively few.

These groups constitute a framework for mutual support across the range of mental health needs. They provide shared insights into all aspects of mental health care, from the early onset of illness and crisis admissions to the care programme approach (CPA) and beyond. Organisations such as Rethink and Mind provide ongoing structured support for carers in the form of written information on the nature and treatment of severe mental illness. In England alone, Rethink manages several hundred projects for the benefit of mental health service users. These include nursing homes, sheltered housing units, befriending agencies, telephone helplines, drop-in centres and employment preparation programmes.

Unfortunately, the majority of carers do not know about such groups, and those that do may be reluctant to contact them, for a variety of reasons.

Therapeutic or anti-therapeutic?

Hospitals, and therefore psychiatric units, are institutions, tending to institutionalise those for whom they provide medium- to long-term care. As with all institutions, there are beneficial (therapeutic) consequences and negative (anti-therapeutic) influences. Examples from each category are shown in Boxes 16.1 and 16.2.

Box 16.1 Therapeutic features of in-patient care

In-patient care can benefit both patients and carers:

- Carers, and many patients, regard hospital as a place of safety
- A more accurate diagnosis may be made
- There may be, at last, a welcome commencement of suitable treatment
- Patients can receive moral support from others with whom they have been hospitalised
- Patients are provided with a regular routine of daily activities
- Patients have the option of therapeutic activities (art therapy, discussion groups, etc.)
- A body of caring professionals is devoting its energies to the resolution of the immediate difficulties of the patient and the carer

---

Some of the points listed in Box 16.2 deserve additional comment. For a start, the social mix of those on psychiatric wards is quite remarkable; it may not always be inimical, but for many it proves to be quite traumatic. Occasionally, patients cause violent disturbances and the police are called. There is the gender mix, the wide age range and an enormous gulf in educational and social background, and there is marked variation in the sort of illness that has led to hospitalisation.

Regarding nursing staff, the following comment was part of a report that I presented to a mental health trust that had sought feedback from carers on the progress made by a newly built mental health centre attached to a large hospital:

Box 16.2 Anti-therapeutic features of in-patient care

Patients can face:

- The traumatic process of being compulsorily hospitalised
- Being subjected to enforced treatment
- Being in confined proximity to others to whom they might not be able to relate
- A 'medication only' approach to treatment with no choice regarding any form of psychotherapy
- Side-effects of medication
- Insufficient opportunity to relate to professional staff (nurses and psychiatrists) – nurses may be perceived as being there only to administer medication and to sort out disturbances, and psychiatrists may be regarded as powerful figures, able to administer horrific forms of treatment (such as psychosurgery and electroconvulsive therapy)
- Deprivation of autonomy
- Stigma arising from the 'official' confirmation that they have a severe mental illness
- Sexual intimidation from other patients

'Speaking of psychiatric nurses brings to mind one particular observation regarding the function of the Centre. You may recall that there have been many comments to the effect that "the patients sit smoking in one room whilst the nursing staff sit drinking coffee in the office". We appreciate that emotive comments of this sort may distort the reality, but many of us who have visited the Centre will know what is meant by it. However, pilot projects, which have been undertaken elsewhere, have shown that, with the right degree of training, nursing staff can participate in beneficial processes of psycho-therapeutic treatment for those who are ready to benefit from them.'

This is by no means an overstatement, yet it received no comment from the trust when it sent out acknowledgements of the carers' appraisals of the centre.

One carer of our acquaintance wrote to the trust requesting information on the availability of psychotherapeutic treatment in general and psychotherapy for psychotic illnesses in particular. The reply from the senior consultant psychiatrist was sympathetic but pessimistic. He said that, to his knowledge, the only expertise within the entire panoply of psychiatric services offered by the trust resided in a single cognitive therapist, whose experience of applying it was confined to people with severe depression. Another carer, making a request for psychological treatment for schizophrenia, was told by a psychiatrist that 'It's not that sort of illness'!

Lastly, there is the pervasive belief that consultant psychiatrists are all-knowing figures whose judgement may never be impugned.

In-patient care within the chain of mental health provision

Obviously, those with the most wide-ranging experience of the entire spectrum of the mental health care system are service users themselves. From the onset of psychotic illness, service users interact with some or all of the following:

- distraught family members, friends, etc. (i.e. carers)
- GPs
- the police
- psychiatrists
- hospital staff
- CPA panels
- social workers or community psychiatric nurses (CPNs)
- art therapists
- volunteers from befriending services
- staff at monitored housing units
- a variety of professionals at day centres (for art therapy, rehabilitation activities, etc.).

171

Carers, being the other contingent with direct or indirect experience of most of the components within this chain of provision, can also be said to have a good overview of the mental health care framework. Anyway, the above sequence may constitute first steps in the linear path to recovery, to whatever extent that may be possible.

Arising from research findings from many studies in this country (and overseas), there is a prevailing opinion that treatment for many of the major mental illnesses is too heavily reliant on pharmacology, with far too little use of complementary psychotherapy, and that there is insufficient emphasis on psychosocial programmes of rehabilitation. Consequently, there is a greater risk of relapse, which all too often results in further hospitalisation. The collective insights of carers would be consistent with such a viewpoint, since the typical pattern of association with mental health care seems to adhere to the following route:

1 hospitalisation
2 definition of the medicinal needs of the individual
3 discharge with an after-care programme
4 infrequent contact with keyworker/psychiatrist thereafter.

Unfortunately, this tends to be a cyclic path rather than a linear trajectory towards an integrated life in the community. The reasons for this are, of course, due to the shortcomings of stages 3 and 4 above and the over-reliance on pharmaceutically based treatment. There is, as yet, no realisation of the concept of choice of treatment, which is one of the campaigning focal points of many voluntary mental health groups.

Conclusion

There is obviously much scope for the enhancement of the therapeutic effects of in-patient mental health care, requiring marked changes in current practice. The nature of acute wards needs to be rethought. Many are overcrowded and under-resourced. The approach to treatment is medicinally dominated, and far too many mental health professionals regard psychological approaches as inappropriate. A shortage of adequately trained staff is a considerable impediment to progress. Moreover, morale could be improved: a psychiatrist (of national repute) remarked to me that psychiatry seems to be perceived as the Cinderella of the NHS, commanding far less kudos than other specialties of the medical profession.

The beneficial effects of hospitalisation can be undone quite rapidly as a result of inadequate CPA provision. Discharge from an in-patient setting often constitutes a traumatic discontinuity on the road to recovery: what was provided in hospital may bear little relation to what (if anything) comes after discharge. Sometimes the CPA works well and is followed through with vigilance, but whether or not this happens is a seeming lottery.

Improvements in mental health care must take place across the spectrum of components that constitute it. The staff involved in CPA provision for a particular service user may come from several disparate sources, yet they rarely interact and often come together only at CPA reviews, usually arranged at 6-monthly intervals. Such meetings are brief and it is rare for all concerned to be in attendance. The unavailability of the psychiatrist nearly always leads to late cancellation, creating the impression that the CPA team is hierarchically structured from the psychiatrist downwards. Greater cohesiveness in provision could be achieved by the introduction of a more needs-adapted approach to mental health care, focusing more on users and implemented by less hierarchical teams of mental health professionals, which should include carers.

Useful websites

http://www.carers.gov.uk
http://www.doh.gov.uk/prisonhealth/publications.htm
http://www.mind.org
http://www.rethink.org

References

Department of Health (2003) *Prison Health Handbook*. London: Department of Health. http://www.doh.gov.uk/prisonhealth/pdf/handbook.pdf

Rethink (2002) *Reaching People Early*. London: Rethink. http://www.rethink.org/reachingpeopleearly/index.html

Rethink (2003) *Our Point of View Survey: Who Cares?*. London: Rethink. http://www.rethink.org/information/research/pdfs/Points-of-View-Report.pdf

Rowlands, O. & Maher, J. (1997) *Living in Britian: Results from the 1995 General Household Survey*. London: HMSO.

Further reading

National Schizophrenia Fellowship & Department of Health (2001) *A Commitment to Carers: Help for Relatives, Partners and Friends of People with a Mental Health Problem*. London: Department of Health. http://www.rethink.org/publications/carers.html

NSF/Rethink (2001) *The Quality of Hospital Care*. city of publication? NSF/Rethink.

NSF/Rethink (2001) *A Place of Safety*. city of publication? NSF/Rethink.

CHAPTER 17

Acute psychiatric wards: an overview

Wilson Firth

Editors' introduction Wilson Firth gives an overview of acute psychiatric wards, their historical development, their various clinical pressures and complexities, and some ideas about future development. He draws on many years' experience of working as a consultant psychiatrist and a particular interest in the planning of services. He emphasizes the importance of the therapeutic community approach and how this needs to be adapted to include a broader vision of user involvement.

Historical background

During the decades between the 1970s and the 1990s, when the large psychiatric hospitals were being closed down, there was a tendency to regard in-patient psychiatric care as something of a relic from a bygone age, to be avoided wherever possible. Towards the end of the 1990s, there was a renewal of interest in acute in-patient care influenced partly by a series of tragic events involving psychiatric patients who were cared for in the community and partly by concern about the state of the wards described in an influential report by the mental health charity Mind (Mind, 2000). In response to public concern, a Department of Health report at last emphasised the value of in-patient care (Department of Health, 2001, 2002), and a 'collaborative' process was set up, based on a model derived from cancer care, whose purpose was to promote change and good practice in in-patient care settings (Kerr *et al*, 2002). The Royal College of Psychiatrists similarly recommended a number of improvements and changes (Royal College of Psychiatrists, 1998). These reports provide comprehensive recommendations concerning the design and clinical functioning of in-patient units, stressing the importance of such issues as privacy, dignity and safety. There is an emphasis on the importance of integrating in-patient care within an overall care system and on the primacy of the user in planning a care system. Useful guidance is provided on staffing levels, security and provision of therapeutic activities and on the day-to-day needs of patients. Approaches to setting standards and evaluation are also suggested. The reports were based on concepts derived mainly from human rights, managerial and consumerist perspectives. Therapeutic

---

Box 17.1   Current developments in in-patient care

Recent years have seen a revival of interest in in-patient psychiatric care.

The Government and the Royal College of Psychiatrists have published recommendations concerning the architecture and clinical quality of in-patient units.

The principles underlying therapeutic in-patient care, derived from the therapeutic community movement, are in the process of rediscovery.

Patients have a valuable contribution to make in the planning of services and in maintaining a high quality of clinical care.

---

effects, the authors argued, were likely to flow directly from improvements to the general ward milieu, to staff morale and to communications and from user involvement in planning processes. There was widespread acknowledgement that the pressure placed on wards by patient numbers, expectations of rapid turnover and poorly developed community services had meant that the opportunities given to in-patient staff to use their training, skills and experience had become unduly limited. There was a consensus that radical change was necessary if psychiatric in-patient settings were to fulfil their therapeutic potential for patients and provide a rewarding workplace for staff. In-patient settings have, as a consequence, been subject to a continuing quest to rediscover their therapeutic origins (Box 17.1).

From a psychodynamic point of view, many of the concepts that still inform the clinical management of in-patient units were developed after the Second World War by the therapeutic community movement. Maxwell Jones at Dingleton Hospital in the Scottish Borders and David Clark at Fulbourne Hospital in Cambridgeshire both described the transformations that were possible in large mental hospitals after the war – from ossified, oppressive institutions into care settings that were both dynamic and therapeutic (Clark *et al*, 1962). In varying forms, the principles discovered at that time have been accepted as good practice ever since.

At the time when institutional care was the predominant model, there was a growing awareness of the potential for the institution itself to compromise psychological functioning by the formation of 'secondary deficit'. This was the psychological consequence of residence in an institution where all basic needs were provided for. In these settings, social expectations were such that patients had no personal decisions to make for themselves and, in effect, little responsibility for their actions. The result was a loss of autonomy, indeed identity, which was apparent to those who studied long-term patients at that time (Goffman, 1961; Barton, 1976).

Minimising the effects of institutionalisation

In an attempt to counteract the development of such a harmful dependence, a number of principles of therapeutic care were developed that still have a resonance today. Of especial importance to adult psychiatry acute care settings are the following four.

1   The promotion of personal responsibility: the status of being a hospital in-patient by its nature frees a person from normal obligations and responsibilities. Given the long-term nature of many psychiatric admissions, a patient can, with time, become de-skilled in their day-to-day tasks and fearful of confronting everyday life outside the institution. A more therapeutic approach attempts to counteract this problem by promoting personal responsibility, by maintaining contact with family and friends and by encouraging the patient, as much as possible, to make personal decisions and to take responsibility for them.

2   Blurring of staff/patient boundaries: this does not mean that staff should lose their professionalism in their relationship with patients. On the contrary, staff members are encouraged to use their skills to enable the development of personal autonomy. One of the factors that, in the old institutions, impaired clinical progress was the traditional roles assigned to patients and staff. Members of staff are now encouraged to wear normal clothes, as opposed to uniforms, and to engage in interactions with patients that are reasoned and humane, but not arbitrary or dependent on status.

3   A culture of mutual learning rather than of blame: where behaviour is unacceptable, or where mistakes occur, it is often natural to identify a person who can be held responsible and to want, in some sense, to punish them. Very often, when there is no obvious culprit, a convenient scapegoat is created to satisfy the impulse to find someone to blame (see Chapter 4). Nothing is learned and a sense of injustice is created; problems are perpetuated. A culture of learning places on a community, and on the individuals within it, the obligation to reflect on problems in order to learn lessons and, where necessary, to change and develop.

4   A belief that shared experience can help to overcome isolation and despair: many patients, who may suffer a deep sense of personal pain, are reluctant to share their feelings because of the belief or an experience that has suggested that other people will be rejecting of them if they attempt to be open. A psychiatric setting presents an opportunity to talk to people who may have been through similar experiences themselves and can consequently provide a sense of understanding.

The community ethos

As well as developing a change in the expectations of the patient as an individual, the therapeutic community movement therefore promoted an emphasis on group and community processes, not merely as an economic measure, but as an aid to therapy. It was observed that patients were on the whole more open to learning from other patients, who had acquired their knowledge by personal experience, than to learning from staff, who, it was assumed, had acquired theirs by training and by role. Many patients discovered an opportunity, often for the first time, to engage in relationships that were rewarding, productive and enjoyable.

This principle of promoting an inclusive culture echoed, in certain respects, the ethos that was the initial aspiration of the county asylums. When they were founded in the early 19th century, before they acquired their stern forbidding image, the purpose of the asylum was to provide a humane, productive and varied environment designed to protect people with the mental illnesses from abuse and exploitation. The aim of 'moral therapy' was, in theory at least, to provide asylum inmates with an alternative world, one that was more caring, in an environment designed to improve morale. In some ways the therapeutic community movement, which was largely developed in these same settings in their latter days, could be viewed, without too much sentimentality, as a late return of these sadly diminished and regimented institutions to their earlier ideals. The adoption of the therapeutic community approach was most widespread when acute psychiatry was still, predominantly, sited in county asylums. Possibly, many of the old asylums never functioned better than they did when in the process of closure.

The move to district general hospitals

The closure of the mental hospitals that ringed major cities was underpinned by the often-justified belief that asylum care was, taken as a whole, institutionalising, stigmatising and dehumanising. It was also expensive and inefficient. Although different options were suggested, by far the most commonly adopted of these was the replacement of the acute care part of the mental hospital by a psychiatric unit on the site of a district general hospital. Sometimes the psychiatric unit moved into an existing part of the hospital, with old wards converted, but more often a new unit was built, usually on the very periphery of the site, although occasionally in the body of the hospital.

The intention of this development was to normalise mental illness by treating it exactly as though it was a physical illness – with doctors and nurses in wards in general hospitals, just as they were in other hospital wards. In this way, it was hoped to de-stigmatise mental illness by removing its management from the old institutions, with all their gothic associations, to modern, socially acceptable locations. It was hoped that the isolation of the institutions, which had led to various scandals, could thereby be overcome – and that psychiatric in-patients would benefit from greater access to the expertise of the main hospital, psychiatric illness being comorbid with physical illness to a surprising degree. The efficiency of the mental heath services was to be improved by its new positioning in the midst of a general hospital environment whose ethos was one of rapid treatment and high turnover. On the down side, in therapeutic terms, a general hospital environment tends to shift the balance, perhaps unduly, towards a medical rather than a psycho-therapeutic model of care. In many instances this can work well, especially where clear lines of accountability are seen as an important consideration. Unfortunately, such a model rarely gives patients (or most staff) the opportunity to take responsibility for decisions, and it can undermine the creative potential inherent in the staff/patient relationship. An alternative model, intended to address these concerns, is discussed below, along with other means of promoting a therapeutic culture.

So the typical psychiatric ward in a district general hospital has evolved to absorb all the in-patient needs of a particular geographical sector. In doing so it caters for a very wide range of patients indeed – including those with acute psychoses, those with chronic or recurrent psychoses, those with affective disorders such as major depression or mania, and those who are acutely distressed as a result of a crisis in their life. Many patients also have a concomitant problem with substance misuse, complicating the clinical picture. The position of patients with personality disorders remains ambiguous in this setting, for they do not fit well into a medical model, where entitlement to care is conditional on the presence of a discernible illness. All these factors, perhaps inevitable in a general hospital model, limit the therapeutic potential of many acute in-patient wards at present.

Even so, there is increasing evidence of bridge-building between traditional medical and therapeutic models of psychological disorder. Physical medicine is evolving a more cooperative negotiated approach to treatment. The patient, now less a passive recipient of expertise, is more of an active partner than in the past; there is also a growing awareness, based on research evidence, of the effects of psychological states on physical health. General psychiatry has adopted a more formal approach to assessment and management. In particular, assessment of risk has been accepted as an obligation by all clinical teams.

The problem of risk

This is a complicated and important area which remains the subject of much research. A number of 'risk assessment tools' of varying complexity have been proposed, some of them screening instruments, others

> **Box 17.2** Providing support for staff
>
> Risk-averse clinical environments with strict accountability procedures pose special problems in creating and maintaining therapeutic care.
>
> Team cohesion and managerial support are vital if a clinical unit is to operate therapeutically.
>
> Protected time for support and training of clinical staff is necessary to maintain morale and to promote high-quality care.

comprehensive and extensive. Although the topic is too complex to discuss in detail here, a number of characteristics have come to be regarded as especially indicative of risk. These include: previous violence and/or suicidal behaviour; previous non-compliance with aspects of care; evidence of recent severe stress, particularly of loss or threat of loss; comorbid substance misuse and/or personality disorder; presence of suicidal thoughts; presence of delusions which are acted on or of specific threats to identified individuals.

An excessive emphasis on the minimisation of risk, though, can compromise the development of therapeutic programmes. With the current emphasis on detention and staff accountability, it is not yet universally acknowledged that risk can most effectively be reduced in a culture in which angry and painful feelings are discussed rather than suppressed. Nor does an emphasis on risk aversion always promote a culture in which individual expression is welcomed as a contribution to the evolution of a shared therapeutic vision. Similarly, risk-averse systems tend to disempower patients and staff by pushing decision-making upwards – people who are anxious that they will be blamed if things go wrong are reluctant to take initiatives. The support of its managers is now vital if a clinical team is to preserve, as far as possible, decision-making at the level of the patient, the staff member, the community (Box 17.2). It is therefore now important for a mental health organisation to have a credible system that manages risk and handles complaints, and that supports staff and patients when untoward incidents do occur – that promotes a culture of learning rather than of blame in response to such incidents. Regular meetings involving both managers and clinicians are necessary if an organisation is to develop its risk management policy, and to formulate its internal and public responses to adverse events.

Promoting a therapeutic culture

Managerial and political issues create an ever-changing context within which the therapeutic milieu develops. Adult psychiatry, which has to resolve the tensions surrounding medical, psychosocial, and legalistic models as part of its normal working practice has been set the task of allaying the anxieties of the public and its patients that have resulted from closure of the asylums. It remains the task of clinical teams working within this context to promote a culture, whatever the setting, in which staff and patients attempt to work together. Some in-patient settings are generously staffed, with a suitable layout and enough time for therapeutic interactions to develop; others are hard pressed, with a chronic shortage of beds and a high turnover, where both patients and staff feel under pressure. Certainly in the short term, an adverse environment does not always exclude the possibility of promoting therapeutic work – people often understand each other best where problems are shared and the constraints placed on 'the other' can be acknowledged and worked with. At the most basic level, wartime experience shows that shared adversity can, for limited periods, have a profound effect in raising morale and in reducing disturbed behaviour. A less desirable outcome, in cultures where cooperation is not encouraged, is the generation of 'competitive deprivation', where individuals make bids to be acknowledged as the 'most deprived', in the belief that this is the only way that their emotional needs will be addressed. This behaviour may be evident not only in disturbances among patients, but also in staff meetings where participants are unwilling to say anything positive about their work or team lest they are subject to envious attacks from other teams or are even denied additional resources. To prevent such reactions by members of staff, regular supervision should be available to them as individuals and as a group, and staffing levels should be high enough to allow attendance at training events. Much of the work in acute psychiatry is of a 'pre-verbal' nature, where conflict is expressed through actions rather than words, and where patients may be experiencing emotions that are so primitive that they cannot be expressed verbally. Dealing with such raw emotion can take its toll on the mental and physical health of staff if there are no opportunities to debrief or to step aside from the work setting. There is therefore increasing recognition that in-patient staff should attend regular supervisory sessions, preferably once a week, to discuss not only their performance, but also their experience of work as it affects them emotionally.

Promoting a sense of safety

The first therapeutic task of an acute in-patient unit is to provide a sense of 'containment' among its patients and staff. This means that all those within the ward have a sense that disturbed behaviour and emotions can be approached and dealt with in as kindly and effective a manner as possible and that, for example, anger or violence will not become personally threatening and damaging. Patients should be confident that they will not themselves be subject to threats or acts of

---

Box 17.3 Easing the patient's introduction to the ward

Simple consideration by staff of the practical difficulties faced by patients on arrival on the ward can go a long way to relieving unnecessary tensions:

- Ensure ready access to normal items such as money, clean clothes, beverages and cigarettes
- Familiarise new patients with the layout of the ward
- Issue a detailed leaflet containing information about resources such as:
  - weekly activities
  - the ward timetable
  - names and telephone numbers of people who can be approached if there are problems
- Encourage patients to write a diary of their experiences, which can then be discussed with their named nurse if they wish

---

physical or emotional abuse, and that staff will not themselves react as though hurt or damaged. Practical help from the patient's very arrival on the ward can promote a sense of goodwill and confidence (Box 17.3). This knowledge that bad feelings are held and worked with will in itself help to restore a sense of safety to those whose innate sense of security has been undermined by illness, by personal crisis or by both.

Case study 17.1
A woman in her twenties who had been physically abused in her childhood periodically experienced overwhelming feelings of rage. She had no involvement with the psychiatric services until she began to raise a family and her feelings about her own childhood rose to the surface. Following admission to hospital, after a serious overdose, she became aggressive and difficult to control. When she had recovered from this episode, she returned to her family as a 'model' mother but refused to discuss her problems and feelings. Further episodes resulted in repeated admissions, during which she gradually built up a trusting relationship with the nursing staff, who helped her to cope with her overwhelming feelings of anger. As she developed a sense of trust, she also began to discuss her feelings about her past and, after initial exploratory work on the ward, she accepted a referral to a psychotherapeutic setting, where further exploration helped to prevent the need for future admissions.

Very frequently, a patient's sense of insecurity is related to feelings of threat not from external forces, but rather from internal forces of chaos or from overwhelming emotion, often arising during a psychotic illness. Naturally, the function of providing containment confers on staff the difficult task of taking on the very basic functions of acting on their patients' behalf, for their own interests. In a minority of cases, this occurs under statute, explicitly and legally, but very often it comes about as a result of implicit and unconscious negotiations. Patients may be denied, for their own safety, certain rights and responsibilities (for example the right to be unobserved or to walk about freely or to shave with a razor) and they may be given medication against their will. In the past, when services were able to tolerate more risk, it was possible to allow patients a greater sense of autonomy and for staff to err on the side of risk. It is arguable that the network of obligations, possibilities and responsibilities created by the formation of a trusting relationship is, in fact, the best way of reducing risk, even that an exclusive focus on risk may increase rather than diminish the likelihood of aggressive or self-harming behaviour. Where the psychiatric system has a low tolerance of risk, as is presently the case in the UK, staff are obliged to take on a much more parental role and are thereby less able to respect autonomy and, of necessity, are more restrictive.

A parental interaction can, of course provide a sense of stability out of which a patient has the potential to grow, provided there is an opportunity to do so in a culture in which parental forms of relationship are not regarded as unamenable to development. In a ward where morale is poor, or where there is a predominance of non-negotiable arbitrary rules, it can be difficult for a patient to experience relationships that are consistent, encouraging and responsive enough to allow growth towards more adult relationships. An expectation of obedience can often promote, in reaction, a culture of petulance and defiance – the only ways left to express individuality. As in adolescents, such behaviour is often an expression of the desire to move towards more equal adult relationships, without yet having the means or experience to be confident in them. Even where an acute in-patient unit is 'good enough' at promoting personal growth, the current obligation on patients to move on quickly from such settings can promote a paradoxical clinging to symptoms and to acting-out behaviours as a means of remaining attached to the hospital. This is especially true when those who have no prospect of their needs being met elsewhere have formed needy and intense attachments to staff or to other patients.

Working with intense attachments

So, by providing containment during crises and by taking on parental functions, in-patient wards and teams very often provoke intense, even pathological, attachments among their patients, especially those with borderline personality disorder, who are liable to relate to the team in ways that are both extreme and ambivalent. Threats of separation or perceived episodes of rejection or disapproval can result in a major psychological regression. This often reflects fears of abandonment and re-creations of earlier trauma – regression can become 'malignant' when both psychological progress or movement towards autonomy are seen as bringing with them the threat of discharge from hospital and loss of support. Many paradoxes arise when it is found that a patient is most likely to make progress and to leave hospital when the threat of being discharged, or being granted leave, is removed. If, for example, a woman who fears abandonment believes that her bed is still safe inside the hospital, it becomes much more possible for her to function outside knowing that her ownership of the bed is not threatened: the bed symbolises a safe place, which can be revisited at times of stress.

Case study 17.2
A 38-year-old woman with bipolar disorder who had been admitted for mania every year or two, was admitted yet again to hospital, under the Mental Health Act. A dynamic evaluation of her problems revealed profound difficulties in separating from her mother and a mutually dependent patho-logical relationship between mother and daughter. Further exploration revealed that the patient had an intense wish to separate from her mother but, equally, suffered from a fear of loneliness and inability to cope. Rather than arrange a rapid discharge, a long-term admission was agreed and a programme of family meetings and occupational therapy was set up as a prelude to residence in supported community accommodation. After successful periods of leave, the patient was discharged. She has had no relapses of illness for 5 years and is living independently.

Among the most vulnerable patients, who have no internalised benign figure of authority and cannot easily hold on to an attachment during its physical absence, there is a need, even when outside hospital, to check out the continued existence of those to whom they have become attached. Patients with such intense needs often develop a 'revolving door' relationship with the in-patient ward. Although many mental illnesses are characterised by their fluctuating nature, the apparent well-being of some patients once discharged from hospital does not always mean that their sense of attachment to the ward has dissipated. Even among patients who appear to be functioning well on the surface there is very often, at a deeper level, a continuing attachment to the setting in which the most vulnerable, most disturbed parts of themsel-ves are contained – an attachment that may take on hostile forms. Some interesting work, derived from a psychoanalytic model, has explored the use of 'partial hospitalisation' as a means of managing patents with severe borderline personality disorders: the patients have available to them a hierarchy of support mechanisms, which can be made sensitive to their varying levels of need (Bateman & Fonagy, 1999, 2001).

Team reviews

Plans for such matters as periods of leave, medication, strategies to solve practical problems and discharge packages are normally discussed during the weekly ward round or team review. These occasions can often, in their traditional forms, assume a hierarchical structure that has the potential to disempower both the patient and staff members. In order to 'flatten' the hierarchy, it is necessary to include the patient, as much as possible, in the decision-making process, as well as to give all staff members, especially those in closest contact with the patient, adequate time to express their views. One potentially successful way of achieving this is to emphasise, in the role of the keyworker or named nurse, the importance of the task of being an advocate for the patient. Under this model, the named nurse and patient will meet, often a day or two before the ward round, to agree a set of problems and proposals that can be presented to the multidisciplinary team during the review and to provide a basis for the team's discussion. These team reviews can be daunting, and the named nurse may attend on the patient's behalf if necessary. In this model, the multidisciplinary team is, in effect, a resource available to the patient that can help discuss what is possible and realistic, and how shared plans may be achieved. Aids such as an electronic whiteboard or a laptop computer with a printer can produce instant written documentation for later consideration and further discussion.

Giving users and carers a voice in the planning and running of the service

In the past, community meetings on the ward played an important role in allowing the group to explore its response to its environment and its members to share experiences (Clark *et al*, 1962) (For more thoughts on community meetings see Chapter 20). The movement that promotes the involvement of users can be seen as a rediscovery of older therapeutic community principles as applied to a more dispersed, community-based service incorporating day hospital and community services as well as in-patient wards. Given that, in any locality, each of these services will cater for several hundred patients at any given time, there are many practical difficulties in setting up a forum within the local mental health community that both represents the aspirations of the users as a group and allows each user expression as an individual. Using the ward community meeting as a paradigm, one of the main tasks in any comprehensive service is to set in motion a process whereby staff, patients and carers can together develop a representative forum where open, consistent dialogue and resolution of difficult conflicts becomes possible. Ideally, these meetings should take place in the community itself – where the service is being delivered. It is likely that the most vocal users at the early meetings will be those with the strongest feelings about their experiences of their illness or of the services. Although there may be resentment that some individuals appear too dominant and even destructive, it is important to recognise that such individuals may be carrying, indeed expressing, the feelings of many others, and that they are providing an opportunity for the meeting to help in working them through. Equally, it is important that all groups and individuals feel they can gain access to any power structures that will determine such important issues as, for example, the ward environment, the working conditions of staff and the resources available in the community. The same solution will not be applicable everywhere. The geography and demographic nature of each locality will determine the form that evolves. Meetings with other localities should be an integral part of the culture, so that ideas can be shared, productive dialogue can take place, and isolation and defensiveness avoided.

Such a consultation structure, which involves managers and carers, as well as front-line staff and users themselves, needs to be organised so that it does not have the feeling of being a 'free for all'. Patient and carer groups should be supported and funded by statutory agencies and independent advice should be available to ensure that active members do not feel isolated in their task of representing the views of their group. Very often, a group chaired by a senior manager, involving a variety of interest groups, with a balance of representation from each, will avoid the development of a 'them and us' feeling.

The necessity of helping patients to assume a sense of autonomy and to have a voice in the planning process is becoming more important at a time when the pendulum of public attitudes towards psychiatric care has swung away from the liberal consensus. The advent of consumerism and an emphasis on human rights provides some counterbalance to this tendency and, service wide, user groups have an increasing influence in planning and development. This holds out the prospect of consultative structures that will allow individual users to participate in the planning and running of the services provided to them and, not least, an increased opportunity for therapeutic encounters, and the working through of conflicts and problems.

Case study 17.3

A middle-aged man, in his forties, with no previous history of psychiatric contact, began to take a succession of overdoses leading to repeated admissions to hospital. In his childhood, he had been brought up in a series of children's homes, frequently being moved from one to the other, often with little warning. In early adult life, he had found a niche in the armed services, but had never settled to subsequent civilian life, especially when his children reached their rebellious teenage years. During his admissions to the psychiatric ward he became an adept chairman of community meetings and after discharge he became a valued 'users' representative' at planning and consultation meetings. His new role helped to restore his self-esteem and confidence to the extent that hospital admissions were no longer necessary and he remained well, with minimal follow-up necessary.

Future developments and challenges

The wish to create both consumer-friendly, locally accessible units and secure units closely linked to the criminal justice system suggests that the large, district general hospital units designed to cater for all types of problem will, in time, become obsolete. Future mental health settings are likely to be smaller units whose characteristics will be determined by staffing expertise, security and, in particular, the agencies that form their closest links – primary care, the criminal justice system or general hospitals. Although local units would support many patients, a centralised hospital site would still be necessary to support the dispersed services, to provide teaching facilities and to house the more highly specialised services. This model conforms to aspects of a medical/surgical paradigm, where patients are able to gain access to units with specific expertise in their particular problems, although in the case of mental health, the expertise will often be of an enabling rather than a providing nature.

Given the tendency of specialist units to develop a circumscribed view of their role, the presence of goodwill and a sense of common ownership will be vital to prevent unhelpful territorial and ownership disputes over patients. Also, management structures must allow time and space for the discussion of boundary problems between services, so that patients are not retained or moved on inappropriately. A patient who is ready to move from a setting that is primarily containing to one that is more exploratory and developmental should be encouraged to do so.

One of the problems with the 'care in the community' policy devised at the time of asylum closures in the UK is that it implied a disjunction between in-patient care and community care; indeed, it contained an implicit disapproval of in-patient care. In psychological terms, the model was predicated on the common notion that the solution to disturbance and vulnerability is simply to encourage the most positive functioning parts of the self to flourish, in the belief that negative parts will thereby atrophy. The current emphasis on improving in-patient services at last recognises that patients with serious mental illnesses require a comprehensive service that provides encouragement to the good, well-functioning self, care for the vulnerable self and containment of the disturbed, chaotic self.

References

Barton, R. (1976) *Institutional Neurosis*. Bristol: John Wright.
Bateman, A. & Fonagy, P. (1999) Effectiveness of partial hospitalisation in the treatment of borderline personality disorder: a randomised controlled trial. *American Journal of Psychiatry*, **156**, 1563–1569.

Bateman, A. & Fonagy, P. (2001) Treatment of borderline personality disorder with a psychoanalytically oriented partial hospitalisation: an 18-month follow up. *American Journal of Psychiatry*, **158**, 36–42.

Clark, D. H., Hooper, D. E. & Oram, E. G (1962) Creating a therapeutic community in a psychiatric ward. *Human Relations*, **15**, 123.

Department of Health (2001) *The Mental Health Policy Implementation Guide*. London: Department of Health.

Department of Health (2002) *Mental Health Policy Implementation Guide: Adult In-patient Care Provision*. London: Department of Health.

Goffman, E. (1961) *Asylums*. New York: Doubleday.

Kerr, D., Bevan, H., Gowland, B., *et al* (2002) Redesigning cancer care. *BMJ*, **4**, 164–166.

Mind (2000) *Environmentally Friendly? Patients' Views on Conditions in Psychiatric Wards* (Mind Report). London: Mind.

Royal College of Psychiatrists (1998) *Not Just Bricks and Mortar. Report of the Royal College of Psychiatrists Working Party on the Size, Structure, Siting, and Security of New Acute Adult Psychiatric In-Patient Units* (Council Report CR62). London: Royal College of Psychiatrists.

CHAPTER 18

Developing the workforce

Justine Faulkner

Editors' introduction   Justine Faulkner has a particular interest in training and development and the positive impact that these can have. Before moving to Bath, Justine was based with the Sainsbury Centre for Mental Health, where her role incorporated the development, delivery and management of training programmes designed specifically for staff within acute in-patients settings. In this chapter, Justine argues that in-patient care should be reframed as a specialty, with better trained and better rewarded staff. She describes a 'skills package' with this objective and identifies some important principles that should underpin any project to train and develop the workforce.

Current workforce issues

Workforce development has been described as the process of ensuring that the NHS has the right numbers of staff, with the right skills in the right place to deliver an effective service (Department of Health, 2002a). In the context of this definition, it is clear that workforce development within in-patient care is in need of urgent attention, particularly given that workforce and leadership issues are now seen as the key to restoring the fortunes of in-patient care (Department of Health, 2002b). Although there are still more staff employed within in-patient services than in other parts of the mental health system, the staffing situation is widely acknowledged to be deeply problematic and creative solutions are still in the development stage (Box 18.1).

The largest occupational group within in-patient services are nurses. Despite the stated commitment of services to deliver multidisciplinary

---

Box 18.1   The present situation

- In-patient work is poorly rewarded in terms of career structure and financial incentive
- In-patient wards are usually staffed by doctors and nurses; psychologists, occupational therapists and art therapists are in short supply and generally choose to work elsewhere
- Nursing staff on in-patient wards describe low morale, high levels of anxiety and burnout
- Recruitment and retention of nurses on acute wards is poor, and high numbers of agency staff are filling the gaps

---

in-patient care, this is rarely a reality for service users. In-patient care remains, by and large, the province of doctors and nurses (Sainsbury Centre for Mental Health, 1998). This appears in part to be due to shortages of occupational therapy and psychology staff and to their preference for working in settings other than in-patient care. The perception of in-patient care as unattractive work is not confined to occupational therapists and psychologists, as the majority of services are experiencing difficulties in recruiting and retaining nursing and medical staff. This is seen to be the result of a reduction in the quality of working life on the wards owing to increased levels of patient distress and disturbance, staff shortages and poor-quality clinical leadership and supervision (Department of Health, 1999a).

For nurses, the career structures and reward packages within in-patient care are significantly inferior to those offered within community services. This disparity in reward packages is historical and links to the perception of in-patient care as a training ground for novices. This perception still exists in many services and, as a result, the majority of the workforce are inexperienced practitioners, who rapidly move on to community-based services. This dependence on an inexperienced workforce contributes to negative perceptions of in-patient care. The least experienced practitioners are expected to provide for patients who have the most complex and acute problems.

The resulting work stress is compounded by a lack of leadership and supervision, and the workforce describe understandably high levels of anxiety and burnout. A number of ways forward have been proposed. Government policy suggests that reward packages for in-patient care are reconsidered (Department of Health, 2002b). There are also initiatives underway to recruit unqualified workers to in-patient wards. This could be seen, however, to replicate the problems presented by the already inexperienced staff group. It would seem in the short term that acute care is caught in a downward spiral in terms of workforce development.

Good-quality training and development offer a way of breaking into this spiral, as they are known to have a positive effect on staff morale and confidence. The development of a specific specialist 'skills-set' for in-patient care may result in the area being seen as a clinical specialty rather than a training ground for novice practitioners. Any moves in this direction, however, will require the development of support structures such as expanded career pathways and innovative workforce planning (Box 18.2).

In-patient staff may well lack the appropriate skills to deal with the change in composition of the patient group. Levels of disturbance and distress have increased, and services have experienced an increase in the numbers of hospitalised individuals presenting with complex needs such as diagnoses of borderline personality disorder and comorbid

---

Box 18.2 Breaking into the downward spiral

- Expand the career pathway
- Introduce innovative workforce planning
- Provide good-quality training and development
- Encourage the reframing of acute in-patient work as a clinical specialty by the development of a specific specialist skills-set

---

substance misuse, or severe mental illness. The reasons for this are complex. However, it is clear that the historical practice of excluding these two groups from in-patient services has resulted in a lack of opportunity for staff to develop skills in working with them.

It is also acknowledged that the inexperience of in-patient staff has a negative effect on clinical practice. Students have little exposure to psychiatric in-patients during their undergraduate training, and this results in a lack of confidence and competence in working with seriously unwell individuals. This lack of confidence and skill is perceived by some as the major contributing factor in the lack of contact between staff and patients in acute settings. Contact time is extremely limited, and clients frequently cite this as a deficit (Sainsbury Centre for Mental Health, 1998).

Despite concerns about the inadequate time that staff spend with patients and the widely reported lack of patient satisfaction with in-patient services, psychiatric nursing staff report high levels of activity, exhaustion and burnout. Their workload is substantial, but it could be argued that the majority of this is not focused directly on meeting the needs of patients, who are therefore not always aware of it. Working practices within in-patient care are often designed to provide a service to other professionals and other parts of the mental health system rather than to patients or their carers. Many examples of this can be found through analysing the activity of nursing staff on acute wards, which focuses on administration and liaison with other professionals, leaving little time available for patient contact (Higgins *et al*, 1998).

The policy direction

In response, the Department of Health has issued a number of recommendations regarding staff activity in in-patient care. A key recommendation has been that training should be developed, to enable hospital-based staff to deliver psychosocial interventions (Department of Health, 1999*a,b*). These are structured, interaction-based interventions informed by a biopsychosocial understanding of mental ill health. The components of a number of these interventions are explored later in this chapter. The appeal of psychosocial interventions is that they are supported by some degree of evidence, and are underpinned by collaboration between the client and the professional. They have been implemented with some success in a number of community services (Baker, 2000).

It would seem, therefore, that policy-makers assume that in-patient care will be substantially improved by the introduction of psychosocial interventions. However, this assumption conflicts with the views of a number of prominent user-commentators, who emphasise the need for sensitive and individualised interactions rather than systematic treatment approaches. Recent publications by authors with extensive experience of using in-patient services express scepticism regarding the benefits of 'evidence-based practice' for users. Campbell (2000) states that 'human warmth' is the approach that is valued by users and absent in in-patient care. Rose (2000) supports this, warning that professionals have a tendency to use technical language and professional behaviours in order to avoid a genuinely human interaction with patients. Arguably, a significant increase in the amount of psychosocial interventions may increase the professionalisation of interactions, thus worsening patients' experiences of hospital care.

The way forward

The lack of consensus as to the appropriate skills-set for in-patient staff may be due to differing assumptions about the role and function of in-patient care. It seems clear that the acute in-patient wards of today have changed radically from the 'therapeutic communities' of yesteryear, because of changes in service configuration that have emphasised community treatment for those able to receive it. Little thought, however, has been given to the role and function of in-patient care in response to this changing context, and attention has not been paid to the development needs of staff in adapting to this new care model.

To gain a clear view of the skills appropriate for in-patient units it is necessary to spend time considering the role and function of the in-patient service in the context of the rest of the local mental health system. Staff skills must be tailored to deliver the service that is required and may need to be adapted to the local context.

It is important to acknowledge that helping staff to develop and consolidate a range of in-patient care delivery skills will not in itself address the poor quality of patients' experience. It is necessary to work with staff to ensure that they develop, or reconnect with, positive and inclusive attitudes to patients. In order to achieve change, attitude development is as vital as skills training (Box 18.3).

Box 18.3 General skills, qualities and attitudes required for in-patient care

- A patient-focused understanding of mental distress, underpinned by empathy and a genuine understanding of these individuals' priorities, goals and concerns
- Active listening and sensitivity
- Demonstration of honesty, warmth and openness

A skills-set for in-patient care

For the purposes of developing training packages, the Sainsbury Centre for Mental Health has defined the role and function of in-patient care under the following headings: assessment and engagement, crisis management, symptom stabilisation, and reintegration with community services. These are outlined in Boxes 18.4 to 18.7. The skills identified

---

Box 18.4 Assessment and engagement

The initial contact with patients is very important and should include:
- space to listen to their fears
- information about the layout and routine of the ward, what is expected of them and who to ask for help

When gathering information about the patient:
- coordinate information-gathering within the multidisciplinary team: patients may feel distressed and frustrated if they are asked the same questions over and over again
- be aware of how the patient experiences being asked questions (they may feel battered and unhelpfully exposed)
- pace the questions: it is not necessary to gather all the information at one sitting

Do not focus exclusively on pathology: it is useful for patients to discuss how they function when they are well

The use of measures – a range of tools are available to assess symptoms, functioning and experience of medication; these provide a baseline for monitoring, and the information that is gained can be shared with the patient and carers, and result in an agreed and practical plan of care

Risk assessment:
- should be based on collaborative discourse with the patient and significant others and acknowledge their perception of risk
- should trigger the start of contingency planning

Carers:
- can make a valuable contribution to the team's assessment and management of the patient
- may have needs of their own (e.g. for support or information): these should also be assessed

---

Box 18.5   The key requirements of crisis management

- De-escalation and conflict-avoidance skills
- Negotiation skills
- Physical restraint
- Well-considered contingency planning: ensuring that all involved understand the expectations of them in a crisis situation can help to lower anxiety and prevent the escalation of incidents
- Repairing the damage: after the crisis, focus on rebuilding relationships that might have been damaged

---

within this model fall primarily into the area of psychosocial interventions, which have the potential to form the basis of good practice that can be fully evaluated to provide an evidence base for in-patient care.

In an evaluation of the impact of a training package in psychosocial interventions that I carried out using patient interviews, patients reported that their relationships with staff had improved after the training. The reported improvement might be due to increased clinical

---

Box 18.6   Stabilising the patient's symptoms

Medication management
- Develop a basic theoretical understanding of psychopharmacology and a grasp of user issues with regard to medication
- Monitor side-effects
- Develop strategies to enhance concordance (negotiation skills, psycho-educational skills, motivational interviewing techniques and lifestyle-friendly prescribing)

Early warning signs monitoring and relapse prevention
- Work collaboratively to develop an understanding of the circumstances and experiences that lead to relapse
- With the client, work out the individual's relapse signature
- Collaboratively identify strategies to avoid full-blown relapse or to minimise the negative impact of relapse (e.g. crisis planning, advance directives about medication and treatment)

Cognitive–behavioural approaches
- These provide a useful theoretical framework for understanding mental distress
- Low-key cognitive–behavioural approaches can be used, for example, to promote coping strategies and to teach diversional techniques to minimise distress

Family interventions
- Develop skills to engage carers
- Assess their knowledge of the client's problems
- Deliver customised education packages as appropriate

Box 18.7   Reintegration of patients into the community

• Develop a discharge plan in collaboration with the patient
• Communicate the plan to all relevant stakeholders
• Sensitively manage the transfer of relationships from the in-patient unit to the patient's community support with due consideration of the emotional bonds that may have developed during the hospital stay

---

skills, but it might also be a result of improved staff morale and confidence. This more generalised impact of training on morale and confidence may be as significant as enhanced skills when attempting to transform in-patient care.

The skills outlined in Boxes 18.3 to 18.7 are not exhaustive and individual services may wish to add or prioritise certain functions or activities, depending on the needs of their patients. The development of enhanced clinical skills and positive attitudes alone will not improve the therapeutic experience of in-patients. It is also necessary to develop effective leadership within the workforce.

Leadership skills

Effective leaders within in-patient care need a wealth of experience and expert clinical skills in order to manage and contain crises and drive forward clinical innovation. Key leadership tasks within the changing world of in-patient care will be the development of a vision of positive and inclusive services and the communication of this to others. In addition to inspiring and motivating the workforce to commit themselves to positive change, leaders will also need to support and nurture practitioners who have succumbed to exhaustion and burnout.

The skills required to carry out this challenging task include advanced verbal and written communication skills, creative problem-solving, coaching and supervision, negotiation and conflict resolution, and the ability to successfully manage change (see Chapter 11).

Practical strategies to enhance attitudes and skills

Achieving positive attitude change hinges on enabling practitioners to reassess their own attitudes and values within a contained and emotionally safe environment. This involves a comprehensive supervisory procedure and a culture in which self-reflection is encouraged on an everyday basis, for example in staff meetings and handovers.

Training workshops, delivered by users or carers, which focus on the subjective experience of hospitalisation and contact with services are extremely positively evaluated by practitioners as a means of broadening awareness and increasing empathy. This approach of exposing practitioners to user and carer testimony can also take place outside a formal training programme and can be achieved by the considered use of video or written material.

The skills-set described above comprises a range of psychosocial approaches, and there are fairly well-established methods of teaching these. Methods include classroom-based workshops, role-play and supervised practice. The challenge is not in teaching practitioners the skills, but in enabling them to carry these out within the in-patient setting. This involves, in the main, reducing the intensity and length of the intervention and teaching practitioners to apply it in a 'real-life' ad hoc manner, rather than through a formal session approach.

It is also important to maximise the support for practitioners in making changes to their practice and in reducing the number of barriers that they face. This can be achieved through whole-team training and by working formally with managers and lead clinicians to raise their awareness of contemporary practice in in-patient care.

The venue for training should be easily accessible for practitioners and, if possible, close to the clinical setting, as this will maximise the connections made between training and practice. There are practical disadvantages to holding training sessions on the wards themselves, however, owing to the numerous interruptions and the high levels of anxiety experienced by staff in the clinical setting.

The difficulties in releasing staff from the wards to attend training sessions have resulted in attempts to provide flexible e-learning packages, which can be accessed on the ward computers. Thus far, e-based initiatives within in-patient care have been evaluated poorly in terms of their impact on practice, owing to limited staff uptake of the packages. Whether this is due to limited IT skills, time constraints, or lack of motivation is unclear. Individuals wishing to develop e-based learning for ward staff would benefit from exploring the levels of IT skills, and the feasibility of staff accessing a programme during working hours, prior to developing training packages.

Carrying out a training-needs analysis

In order to develop a training programme for practitioners within in-patient care, an analysis of local need is required. Ideally, the initial step should be a consultation with all stakeholders, including users, carers and voluntary organisations, to develop a shared vision of the role and function of the in-patient service. The skills required to carry out these activities can then be mapped to provide a skills-set, which then becomes the template for curriculum development.

Organisational structures to support training initiatives

The aim of workforce development is provide services with sufficient people in the right place and with the right skills to deliver the right service. Training will help staff to develop skills and may improve recruitment and retention. However, training alone will not resolve the workforce issues within in-patient care. Once developed, any training programme should be underpinned by an examination of the structure of the working day within the in-patient unit, to ensure that it supports the transfer of skills into practice and maximises the delivery of therapeutic care. Changes in practice as a result of training should be supported by new policies and procedures and reflected in innovative workforce planning.

Conclusion

Successful attempts to address workforce development issues within in-patient care will require a multifaceted and comprehensive approach. The role, function and structure of in-patient services should be revisited, to ensure that they support training interventions. This is a time-consuming and lengthy process, but it is necessary if in-patient services are to develop and change sufficiently to take on a valuable role in the modern configuration of mental health services.

References

Baker, J. (2000) Developing psychosocial care: the development and evaluation of a short course which aims to introduce psychosocial interventions to in-patient staff. *Journal of Psychiatric and Mental Health Nursing*, 7, 477–481.

Campbell, P. (2000) Absence at the heart. *Openmind*, 104, July/August, 14–15.

Department of Health (1999a) *Addressing Acute Concerns*. London: Stationery Office.

Department of Health (1999b) *The National Service Framework – Mental Health*. London: Stationery Office.

Department of Health (2002a) *HR in the NHS Plan: More Staff Working Differently*. London: Stationery Office.

Department of Health (2002b) *Mental Health Policy Implementation Guide: Adult Acute In-patient Care Provision*. London: Stationery Office.

Higgins, R., Hurst, K., Wistow, G., et al (1998) *Psychiatric Nursing Revisited: The Care Provided for Acute Psychiatric Patients*. London: Whurr.

Rose, D. (2000) A year of care. *Openmind*, 106, Nov/Dec, 14–15.

Sainsbury Centre for Mental Health (1998) *Acute Problems*. London: Sainsbury Centre for Mental Health.

CHAPTER 19

Delivering psychological therapies in acute in-patient settings

Peter Kinderman

Editors' introduction Peter Kinderman is Reader in Clinical Psychology at the University of Liverpool. He discusses the impact that psychology could have on acute wards, both in terms of clinical interventions and as a profession. In particular, he describes a pilot study using psychology assistants, and the beneficial effects this had on the ward culture.

The importance of psychological therapies in mental health services is increasing rapidly. Services users repeatedly express a desire for psychological therapies, government policy such as the National Service Framework emphasises their importance and the evidence base, already strong, is growing rapidly. Recent guidelines from the National Institute for Clinical Excellence (NICE) stress the importance of cognitive–behavioural therapy and family therapy in the management of schizophrenia and recommend that these should be much more commonly offered to patients and families (National Institute for Clinical Excellence, 2002). More generally, psychological approaches are now recognised elements of care packages for all psychiatric disorders. Assessments should address psychological functioning as well as focus on medical diagnosis, and psychological formulations are of great value in informing multidisciplinary care planning. This chapter focuses on acute psychiatric services and, in particular, acute admission wards. The great majority of patients who have schizophrenia will experience an acute admission, and for many this will be their first contact with psychiatric services. This initial point of contact should be the place in which the foundations of further treatment are laid. This should include psychological assessment and the start of psychological therapies to be continued after discharge into the community.

The situation on acute wards, as described elsewhere in this book, is, however, far from conducive to the delivery of psychological therapies. A superficially attractive solution would be to increase the number of clinical psychologists working on acute admission wards, but the availability of qualified clinical psychologists is, unfortunately, low. There are several other possible solutions to the challenge of increasing the use of psychological approaches in acute psychiatric units. More clinical psychologists could be trained, nurses could be

Box 19.1   Service-user concerns that might be improved by a clinical psychologist

- The poor physical and psychological environment for care
- Insufficient information on their condition and treatment
- Lack of involvement and engagement in planning and review of their own care and in how the ward is run
- Inadequate staff contact, particularly one to one

trained in cognitive–behavioural therapy, and additional, psychological, training could be developed for other professionals. This chapter focuses on the potential role of assistant psychologists on acute psychiatry wards, describing the experience of introducing them on an acute admission unit in Manchester and their impact on the ward environment.

The problems of adult acute in-patient care provision are now well documented and recognised in the recent Department of Health (2002) guide to mental health policy implementation. The skills of clinical psychologists, although usually deployed in individual work with patients, seem ideally suited to assist with a number of the problem areas identified by service users and the key contributing factors included in the implementation guide (Boxes 19.1 and 19.2).

If clinical psychologists were integral members of the multi-disciplinary team on acute admission wards, working with the ward and the team as well as with individual patients, they could have a number of important roles. Specific individual therapies and psychological understandings of complex cases is an obvious area for their involvement, as are skills in clinical supervision. The scientific background and evidence base for psychological interventions should complement those for biological interventions such as drug treatments and should improve

Box 19.2   Key contributing factors that might be addressed with the help of a clincial psychologist

Over-pressured staff have difficulty in maintaining a consistent therapeutic engagement

Change in the patient profile, e.g. complex presentations involving substance misuse and personality disorder

Inability to identify, and therefore to respond to, early signs of individual or group disturbance

Lack of systematic, evidence-based approaches

Poor clinical supervision, staff support and professional development for ward staff

Lack of multidisciplinary professional input to treatment programmes for in-patients the use of evidence-based approaches in practice. Their most important role, however, is as champions for psychological thinking in the ward, making it a place more conducive to the delivery of psychological therapies and the making of therapeutic relationships.

The changing role of psychology in the National Health Service

National policy is increasingly stressing the importance of psychological interventions in mental health services and also suggests potentially massive changes in the roles of clinical psychologists. The National Framework for Mental Health (Department of Health, 1999) makes frequent reference to broadly psychological or psychosocial provision in acute mental health services. It states that 'Assessment should cover psychiatric, psychological and social functioning' (p. 44). The NICE guidelines quoted in the introduction reinforce these points, stating in their audit standards:

'Family interventions [should] be offered to 100% of families of individuals with schizophrenia who have experienced a recent relapse, are considered at risk of relapsing, or who have persisting symptoms, and are living with or in close contact with their family.
'... 100% of individuals with schizophrenia who are experiencing persisting psychotic symptoms should be offered CBT [cognitive–behavioural therapy]' (pp. 54 & 55).

Current government proposals to reform mental health legislation have potentially more fundamental implications for the roles of psychologists. As this chapter goes to press, the Government's proposals to reform the Mental Health Act 1983 are still under review. The current status of the proposed reforms is complex and fluid. Nevertheless, in a variety of documents there is a clear move from a 'diagnose and treat' model of care to an 'assessment and care plan' model. The Department of Health also seems minded to see the role of 'clinical supervisor' (the proposed replacement of the 'responsible medical officer'), who will oversee all care plans (including compulsory care) carried out by 'consultant psychologists'.

Individual therapies

The core of clinical psychology practice to date has been in delivering individual therapies. Recent academic publications (e.g. British Psychological Society Division of Clinical Psychology, 2000) have provided accessible but scientifically valid reviews of relevant research in these areas. More importantly, major grant-funded randomised controlled trials have repeatedly demonstrated the effectiveness of psychological approaches in a range of mental health problems (Hawton *et al*, 1989). Since a large number of people in acute psychiatric wards have psychotic problems, it is worth stressing the demonstrable effectiveness of psychological treatments – especially cognitive–behavioural therapy – in psychosis.

There are a number of cognitive–behavioural therapy 'treatment manuals' (detailed descriptions of the therapy) currently available. Most cognitive–behavioural therapy packages are offered to people who have, or have had, distressing experiences, but are well enough to attend out-patient appointments. There is evidence, however, that hospital in-patients with acute and severe psychiatric problems may also benefit from psychological interventions (Lewis *et al*, 2002). It is also apparent that relatively simple cognitive–behavioural approaches, conducted by general psychiatrists within conventional working arrangements, can be effective for patients with psychosis (Turkington & Kingdon, 2000). As many of these patients will experience a hospital admission, making this as supportive as possible to future treatment should be a priority.

In response to the kinds of evidence outlined above, there has been a rapid growth in training in psychosocial interventions in the UK. A wide range of staff receive training on specialist cognitive–behavioural therapy or psychosocial interventions courses: nursing assistants, social workers, occupational therapists and a variety of medical practitioners. Psychosocial interventions are widely used by staff in residential mental health settings, where they are included in the traditional approach to patient care (although not as specialist stand-alone therapies). Psycho-social interventions and training have been shown to benefit the outcomes of service users (Tarrier & Bobes, 2000).

Other psychological or psychosocial interventions include addressing medication compliance. Patients cease taking their medication for various reasons such as intolerance of side-effects, differences in conceptual frameworks between psychiatrist and patient, fears about stigma or dependence, or the natural tendency to stop taking medication when one feels well. Pure psychoeducational or didactic approaches have limited effectiveness here. Medication compliance therapy (or medication adherence therapy) is based on a combination of cognitive–behavioural techniques and motivational interviewing, and has been found to lead to significant improvements in attitudes to medication, insight and compliance.

By no means all patients on in-patient wards experience psychosis. A recent Department of Health guidance document examined the principle conditions that could usefully be addressed by psychological therapies (Department of Health, 2001). It concluded that psychological therapy should be routinely considered as an option when assessing mental health problems, and specifically recommended psychological interven-tions for the problems listed in Box 19.3.

> **Box 19.3** Possible targets for psychological interventions in acute or in-patient settings
>
> Psychosis
> Adjustment to life events, illnesses, disabilities or losses
> Post-traumatic stress symptoms or disorder
> Depression
> Anxiety disorders
> Eating disorders
> Personality disorders (skilled practitioners only)
> Substance misuse
> Interpersonal and relationship difficulties
> Anger management
> Assessing and treating cognitive deficits

The role of a clinical psychologist

Of course, clinical psychologists such as myself would claim that we do more than provide therapy. Although therapeutic interventions for individual patients are important, many psychologists would suggest that other roles are equally important. Thus, clinical psychologists are involved in teaching, training and supervising other staff members, in assessing patients as well as providing therapy, and in helping to manage complex teams.

Psychological assessment has many practical similarities with psychiatric assessment: assessment of current mental state; description and quantification of symptoms and syndromes; assessment of personal functioning; and clinical management issues. Assessment of psychosocial environments and mediating factors (family and social environment, service delivery setting, coping strategies and support) also receive considerable attention. A psychological approach may also assess the goals and aspirations of individual patients. Psychologists are increasingly stressing in assessments patients' biases in thinking styles, cognitive schemas and personality functioning. Finally, of course, assessment should address which treatments are available, their potential efficacy and the likely prognosis.

Psychological formulations attempt to explain why people are experiencing difficulties. They usually consist of a list of the individual's problems and possible psychological reasons for these. Clinical psychologists attempt to develop, in collaboration with the client, ideas about what things might have led to the development of these problems. For this reason, formulations are very individual, tailored for each person and relevant to their specific problems. Many psychologists stress the benefits of such a formulation-based approach over that of traditional diagnosis (Bentall, 1990).

Typically, a formulation will examine what events have happened in a person's life, and how they have interpreted and reacted to these. Formulations tend to change as the psychologists and their clients learn more about the problems. Formulations are designed to be 'best guesses' about the problems, and these guesses are tested out over time. The process of developing a formulation is collaborative. Psychologist and client work together to develop a picture of the problems and a joint theory as to what has caused them and what might help.

Psychological case formulations are complex. Clinical psychologists use a large variety of psychological theories, each drawing on scientific research. Although individual case formulation will not incorporate all this research, each person may have a range of interrelated psychological difficulties. Such an approach also provides an opportunity to influence the conceptual framework employed on a ward. Because of the complexity of formulations, experience, training and, most importantly, supervision are required.

Provision of psychologists

Implementing the delivery of psychosocial interventions in the psychiatric service generally, and in acute psychiatry in particular, has been problematic. The Department of Health itself foresees impediments to the implementation of the National Service Framework plans. In particular, difficulties are expected in the recruitment of National Health Service (NHS) mental health staff, including clinical psychologists. Moreover, it acknowledges that 'not all mental health service staff ... have the skills and competencies to deliver modern mental health services' (Department of Health, 1999: p. 108). Psychological interventions, including cognitive–behavioural therapy, are specifically mentioned.

Training of clinical psychologists and cognitive–behavioural therapists is expensive, difficult to obtain and lengthy. There are plans to increase markedly the number of clinical psychologists in training. Even if large numbers of were to be trained, it remains doubtful whether many would gravitate towards acute psychiatry, let alone towards work in in-patient settings. Another possible strategy is to train specialist nurses and others to deliver cognitive–behavioural therapy. The impact of such training on clinical practice has been questioned, and again there are doubts as to whether these individuals would return to working in acute and in-patient settings or, as with most clinical psychologists, end up in out-patient and community settings.

In addition, the inclusion of a psychological or psychosocial perspective in the assessment and care of people with serious or acute mental health problems does not equate to the provision of cognitive therapy. Authors typically refer to cognitive–behavioural therapy as one of a larger number of related psychological perspectives, conceptual frameworks, assessment procedures, formulation techniques and psychological interventions that can be useful (Tarrier & Bobes, 2000).

Challenges must therefore be overcome before National Service Framework aims can be met and before psychological and psychosocial approaches can be further incorporated into mental health teams. One possible solution to these challenges lies in the employment of a wide range of professionals who can use psychological approaches in their work. The rest of this chapter concentrates on the extent to which we can employ psychology assistants in acute in-patient psychiatry.

Assistant psychologists

Assistant psychologists are widely employed in the NHS. Clinical psychology remains a highly valued profession, and there is consequently a 'bottleneck' in training. Many highly qualified psychology graduates are currently attempting to gain clinically relevant experience work while applying for one of the relatively small number of places on post-graduate clinical psychology training courses. As their name suggests, they always (and vitally) work under the supervision of qualified clinical psychologists and assist in direct clinical work as well as research and training. An accurate figure for the number of assistant psychologists working in the NHS is hard to come by. Employment in community mental health trusts is not uncommon, but working on wards is.

Pilot initiatives

A pilot project has been undertaken to explore the benefits of employing assistant psychologists in acute psychiatric wards in central Manchester, in the UK. The Edale in-patient psychiatric unit has 41 beds across two wards, with a further 10 beds provided in a more secure environment. Before the initiative to employ assistant psychologists, the unit had received little input from clinical psychology services and no dedicated sessional time. Following a preliminary report into psychosocial needs, money from the psychiatric nursing budget was used to create a 1-year fixed-term post of assistant psychologist.

The post was intended as a pilot project and had relatively limited objectives. The initial expectations of the post holder were carefully defined to reflect the fact that assistant psychologists are relatively inexperienced. It was decided that the post holder would:

1   interview patients from a psychological perspective using standard-
     ised assessment tools;
2   provide a brief written formulation for the patients seen and feed
     back relevant information to the ward team;

3   facilitate therapeutic intervention, by making appropriate referrals and by carrying out simple interventions under supervision.

In her work on the ward, the assistant psychologist conducted a personal history-taking interview of each patient, identifying their particular psychological needs, and then wrote a preliminary psychological formulation and made recommendations for psychological interventions. After initial assessment, she continued to see each patient at least once a week. A variety of assessment tools were used within a cognitive–behavioural paradigm to aid a psychological formulation.

Suitable referrals for the clinical psychology service were identified and, under supervision, the assistant psychologist carried out simple interventions that were felt appropriate for her level of skill. These interventions were in conjunction with work being done by qualified clinical psychologists. The results of assessments were discussed with the supervisor before the developing formulation was presented and discussed with other members of the care team. Supervision of the assistant psychologist's work took place in two 1-hour sessions per week, conducted by a senior clinical psychologist. This was seen as the minimum necessary. Feedback on formulations, assessments and interventions was given at the weekly ward rounds. The continued contact that the assistant psychologist had with patients enabled her to articulate patients' points of view at ward rounds, which it was recognised could sometimes intimidate patients and make it difficult for them to express themselves.

In conjunction with the unit's occupational therapist, the assistant psychologist worked on developing and promoting an in-patient activity scheme. A budget was provided for the scheme and this was used to fund the purchase of items for a variety of activities. Together they also organised and delivered training for clinical support workers both on the targeted ward and wider, for trust employees. This included training on client-centred approaches and anxiety management techniques, and the offer of additional supervision. The assistant psychologist also held sessions for medical students on psychological models in severe and enduring mental illness.

Finally, the assistant psychologist implemented the practice of community meetings. These were held once a week and all patients were encouraged to attend. The meetings gave patients a forum in which they were able to express their opinions about their care, discuss their worries and make requests for change. The minutes from these meetings were distributed to the consultant psychiatrists and the management involved in the running of the unit. A patients' council and a relatives' support group were set up in conjunction with a local charity, and these met in the unit once a month, in the evening. Transport was arranged for those relatives who required it.

Audit

A semi-independent audit was conducted on the project. This examined whether the post met the original criteria, the eventual structure of the post, changes in ward practice implemented as a direct result of the post and the overall impact the post had had on ward culture. On the basis of semi-structured interviews with key staff, it was agreed that the post had not simply met the initial expectations and objectives of the role, but had actually exceeded them (see Box 19.4).

The audit suggested that the assessments carried out by the assistant psychologist were appropriate and thorough, and provided a detailed, objective analysis of patients' mental state from which the team could work. The feedback given at ward rounds was considered 'excellent' and 'an extremely helpful addition to psychiatric formulations'. The assistant psychologist was reported to be a constant and reliable source of information about a patient's mental state.

The audit did recognise limitations on an assistant psychologist's ability to carry out psychological interventions. The simple interventions undertaken were believed to have been helpful, but it was felt that more skilled intervention by a qualified clinical psychologist would have been of greater benefit in some cases.

Interviewees agreed strongly that an assistant psychologist has a definite contribution to make to the care of mentally ill patients in an in-patient environment. The different perspective that the role provides was identified as one of the most valuable contributions. Overall, interviewees felt that the assistant psychologist had a significant impact on ward culture and the treatment that the patients received.

Interviewees also commented on the fact that the assistant psychologist was seen as a valued member of the ward team. They reported that they valued her advice on the day-to-day care of patients and collaborated

---

Box 19.4 Roles of the assistant psychologist in the pilot scheme

- Interview patients from a psychological perspective, using standard assessment tools
- Provide a brief written formulation for the patients interviewed
- Feed back the relevant information to the team
- Contribute to ward rounds and discussions
- Make appropriate referrals of assessed patients
- Under supervision, plan, design, execute and evaluate interventions
- Develop and promote in-patient activity
- Develop and promote community meetings (meetings of patients faciliated by a staff member, to share issues of mutual concern)
- Teach and train clinical support workers, students and qualified staff
- Participate in research

with her in simple interventions. The fact that this collaboration and cooperation occurred in conjunction with a continuing request for greater qualified clinical psychology input suggests that interviewees saw a role for psychology both at a consultant level (visiting for ward rounds and communicating mainly with the senior team members) and within the team, as a member of it. The presence of an assistant psychologist as a junior colleague, perhaps more approachable and less threatening, may have had a different but arguably greater impact on ward culture than would the visits of a consultant.

Discussion

The potential role for psychology in acute psychiatry, both as a discipline and as a profession, is immense. Psychological approaches to therapy and understanding have scientific credibility – even for severe illnesses and even for patients in acute distress. The challenge is how to fulfil this role. There are many parts to a solution. This chapter does not attempt to address them all. Clinical psychologists welcome apparent commitments to the additional funding of more clinical psychologists, but this alone may not have much impact on acute psychiatric wards. Initiatives in training nurses, occupational therapists, social workers and medical practitioners in cognitive–behavioural therapy or slightly broader psychosocial interventions will pay dividends. Staff teams will, progressively, see an increase in their collective expertise and understanding of psychological issues.

There will, however, remain a need for the specialist input of psychologists. Central to a psychologist's approach is case formulation. Good formulations are scientifically valid and make reference to causal psychological processes. This involves a good academic understanding of the processes that guide and shape our thoughts and emotions – psychology.

The optimum would be for acute psychiatry to employ the skills of increasing numbers of qualified clinical psychologists. Experience to date has shown that assistant psychologists can be beneficially employed. Although assistant psychologists are often thought of as unskilled and unqualified, they have completed degree-level education in psychology. Assistant psychologists should not be seen as a replacement for qualified staff. On the basis of the successful pilot projects in Manchester and Liverpool, I would recommend the employment of assistant psychologists in acute psychiatry. An assistant psychologist as a member of each ward-based team would ensure appropriate avenues for feedback and communication.

In this chapter, I have tried to outline some of the difficulties encountered in adapting national policy – in this case, the involvement of psychologists on acute in-patient psychiatric wards – to real-world services. There is increasing emphasis on a psychological perspective in mental health care, and increasing calls for psychological services. However, even if clinical psychologists are seen as wise and skilled, they are also frequently seen as remote and inaccessible. If appropriate conditions of employment – most especially, appropriate supervision – are in place, assistant psychologists have much to offer. Although assistant psychologists will not be able to meet all of the increasing expectations for psychological perspectives and interventions, they could make an important contribution.

References

Bentall, R. P. (1990) *Reconstructing Schizophrenia*. London: Routledge.

British Psychological Society Division of Clinical Psychology (2000) *Understanding Mental Illness and Psychotic Experiences: A Report by the British Psychological Society Division of Clinical Psychology*. Leicester: British Psychological Society.

Department of Health (1999) *A National Service Framework for Mental Health*. London: Department of Health.

Department of Health (2001) *Treatment CHOICE in Psychological Therapies and Counselling: Evidence-Based Clinical Practice Guidelines*. London: Department of Health.

Department of Health (2002) *Adult Acute In-patient Care Provision: Mental Health Policy Implementation Guide*. London: Department of Health.

Hawton, K., Salkovskis, P. M., Kirk, J., *et al* (eds.) (1989) *Cognitive Behaviour Therapy for Psychiatric Problems: A Practical Guide*. Oxford: Oxford University Press.

Lewis, S. W., Tarrier, N., Haddock, G., *et al* (2002) Randomised controlled trial of cognitive–behavioural therapy in early schizophrenia: acute-phase outcomes. *British Journal of Psychiatry*, **181** (suppl. 43), s91–s97.

National Institute for Clinical Excellence (2002) *Schizophrenia: Core Interventions in the Treatment and Management of Schizophrenia in Primary and Secondary Care (NICE Guideline)*. London: NICE. http://www.nice.org.uk/pdf/CG1NICEguideline.pdf

Tarrier, N. & Bobes, J. (2000) The importance of psychosocial interventions and patient involvement in the treatment of schizophrenia. *International Journal of Psychiatry in Clinical Practice*, **4**, 1, s35–s51.

Turkington, D. & Kingdon, D. (2000) Cognitive–behavioural techniques for general psychiatrists in the management of patients with psychoses. *British Journal of Psychiatry*, **177**, 101–106.

CHAPTER 20

What can psychotherapy contribute to improving the culture on acute psychiatric wards?

Jeremy Holmes

Editors' introduction   Jeremy Holmes is renowned for creatively combining the role of general psychiatrist and psychotherapist. He is also passionate about research and particularly well known for his work on attachment theory. In this chapter, he makes a convincing argument for the importance of psychotherapy on acute wards and describes how he thinks this should be implemented.

The past few decades have seen a curious linguistic shift in the use of the word 'community' in mental health. In the 1950s and early '60s 'community psychiatry' was synonymous with milieu therapy and the 'therapeutic community' – i.e. the attempt to create a vibrant community of patients and staff, in a shared space, working actively together to overcome disability, illness and stigma. The contrast was with institutional psychiatry, caricatured as the silent, soulless and at times abusive wards of the Victorian mental hospital. The two main therapeutic tools of the therapeutic community were psychotherapeutic: group therapy and creative therapies such as art therapy and psychodrama. These approaches were pioneered in specialist units such as the Henderson Hospital in Surrey, but progressive acute wards more generally emphasised the use of ward groups and the importance of patients playing an active part in decision-making.

With 'decarceration' (i.e. the emptying of the institutions) and the replacement of large mental hospitals nearly complete, those idealistic days seem far away. User surveys tend to be highly critical of in-patient care. In one survey, 57% of patients said that they would have liked more contact with staff, and 82% reported less than 15 minutes per day in face-to-face contact with staff (Mind, 2000). Indeed, today's acute wards run the risk of being not so much un-therapeutic as anti-therapeutic (c.f. Fagin, 2001), as a result of poor staff morale, just as acute medical and surgical wards can be toxic to patients if they are infected with antibiotic-resistant organisms.

Acute wards tend to be seen by staff as unattractive places to work compared with community settings. There is often rapid staff turnover and, especially in the inner cities, extensive use of agency staff to make up numbers, with consequent barriers to strategic development of the in-patient environment. Lack of continuity and commitment tend to mean that custodial rather than therapeutic mores prevail, especially as avoidance of risk is seen as the overriding principle guiding in-patient work.

One way to survive the chaos and mental pain which are the raw materials of mental health work is to batten down the hatches and to retreat into a defensive world of cynicism and mild paranoia, in which exploration of feelings and meanings is seen as potentially disruptive and dangerous. Pragmatism, safety and control become ends in themselves rather than means to enable an in-patient stay to be a potential turning point in the course of a psychiatric illness.

From a psychotherapeutic perspective, *containment* is an essential precondition for psychological growth, in that it creates a potential space within which feelings can be safely explored. But if psychotherapeutic commitment and skill is lacking, containment can easily be perceived as controlling and constricting. Indeed, psychotherapy can seem disruptive rather than facilitative, while psychotherapists are seen as woolly-minded idealists who have no idea about the reality of acute psychiatric work or, worse still, as sinister figures bent on disabling staff by laying bare their weaknesses for managers and colleagues to exploit.

The case for psychological therapies

Hard evidence that psychological therapies can play a significant role in in-patient care is far from robust, perhaps because the attention of the research community has been focused elsewhere. Nevertheless, the research literature does provide some grounds for thinking that psychological approaches might play an important role in improving quality of care in the in-patient setting (Box 20.1).

Box 20.1   Important concepts to think about

- High expressed emotion implies overinvolvement and critical comments and is linked to relapse in patients with schizophrenia

- The ward atmosphere can be measured (see Chapter 14)

- The therapeutic alliance is the best predictor of good outcome in therapy

- Attachment needs are fundamental and linked to the idea of the acute ward as a secure base

- Malignant alienation (increasing emotional distance and hostility in the staff–patient relationship) is a significant predictor of in-patient suicide

---

First, there is the overwhelming evidence that psychosocial factors are relevant to the course of schizophrenia. In the home setting, high expressed emotion (overinvolvement and critical comments) in carers is associated with increased risk of relapse (Leff & Vaughn, 1985). Similar findings apply to professional carers of patients living in hostels (Ball *et al*, 1992). Although expressed emotion studies have not thus far been performed in the in-patient setting, it seems likely that low levels of criticism and hostility in staff would be associated with better outcomes in acute wards too. This view is supported by studies using the Ward Atmosphere Scale (see Chapter 14), which suggest that patient satisfaction and reduced readmission rates in schizophrenia are correlated with a ward atmosphere that strikes an appropriate balance between structure and spontaneity (Middelboe *et al*, 2001).

Second, there is the consistent finding in the psychotherapy research literature that the quality of the therapeutic alliance is the best predictor of good outcome in therapy (Roth & Fonagy, 1996). A positive view of the therapist and therapy setting by patients predicts low drop-out and significant reduction in symptomatology. Again, this finding is based mainly on out-patient settings, but if translated into in-patient care would suggest that skill in establishing a therapeutic alliance among ward staff would improve outcomes.

This links with extrapolations from the attachment literature (Holmes, 2001), which suggest that a prime function of mental health services is to provide a 'secure base' for patients. In an in-patient context, a secure base would represent a familiar person in a familiar place to which the mentally ill sufferer can turn at times of threat or illness, characterised by a combination of responsiveness and sensitivity with the capacity to set limits and help cope with separation. Doubtless, acute in-patient wards are sometimes used by patients and their carers in this way. Under favourable circumstances the quality of attachment to such wards is secure, in the ways described above. At other times typical insecure patterns of rejection or inconsistent overprotection may prevail, fuelled partly by the patient's psychopathology, partly by the insecure states of mind in staff teams.

Third, there is evidence that the quality of the staff–patient relationship is a significant predictor of in-patient suicide. Watts & Morgan (1994) found that prior to suicide there is a marked deterioration in relationships between patient and staff, characterised by increasing emotional distance and hostility, a condition they dub 'malignant alienation' (see also Chapter 3). A psychotherapeutic approach has the capacity to contain and detoxify the difficult feelings that disturbed patients inevitably arouse in those who work with them, mainly through individual supervision and staff group meetings.

Fourth, there is the burgeoning literature on the efficacy of psychological methods in psychosis and other major psychiatric disorders.

Cognitive–behavioural approaches to delusions, self-management of hallucinations and other techniques have mainly been delivered in out-patient settings, but equipping ward staff with these psychological skills can strengthen the therapeutic alliance and provide a first step in a psychotherapeutic approach which can then be continued after discharge (see also Chapters 18 and 19). Hostility and withdrawal on the part of staff are often a manifestation of a sense of being deskilled and unable to cope. Training in psychological therapy can help overcome this.

Finally, the role of personality disorder in the make-up of many patients who find themselves in the acute in-patient setting must be mentioned (National Institute for Mental Health Effectiveness, 2003). Most studies suggest that at least 50% of in-patients have a personality disorder in addition to a DSM Axis I condition. There is increasing evidence for the efficacy of psychotherapeutic approaches in the treatment of personality disorder. Although these are usually delivered in a community setting, an educational programme that raises awareness about treatment possibilities, decreases prejudice and generally empowers staff in their dealings with such patients can have a significant part in making acute in-patient work more effective and satisfying.

Practical measures

How can these general principles be translated into practical improvements in the in-patient environment? Given the rapid turnover and nature of clinical disturbance on most in-patient wards it would be unrealistic and inappropriate to suggest that specific psychological therapies become the mainstay of work of the ward – those are needed later in the care programme, in the day hospital or out-patient setting. Three key sets of skills are vital, however. First, there is the capacity to build a therapeutic alliance with patients and their relatives. Second, the development of self-awareness and reflective practice both at the level of individual practitioner and for the staff team as a whole, thereby reducing projection and so lowering expressed emotion and the likelihood of malignant alienation. Third, specific skills are needed in the management of personality disorder, eating disorders and psychological approaches to psychosis in the in-patient setting. The first two are requirements for all who work on an in-patient ward; the third can be developed in selected staff members, who can then act as mentors for the staff team as a whole.

Ongoing training and detailed supervision of clinical work are integral to psychologically informed practice; in the in-patient setting these are probably more important than any specific programmes. Regular supervision and staff support are the crucial ingredients in improving the quality of psychological care on acute wards.

Box 20.2 What needs to be implemented

Level 1 A weekly or fortnightly staff supervision group facilitated by a member of the psychological therapies team (there is evidence that such groups reduce the number of violent incidents)

Level 2 A small group therapy programme and community meetings, with strong emphasis on monitoring ward events

Level 3 Skills in specific psychological therapy techniques and their application to in-patient settings

Three levels of psychological input into acute care can be envisaged, each of which adds to the preceding level. These are summarised in Box 20.2.

Level 1

As a bare minimum, a weekly or fortnightly multidisciplinary staff support group is essential, ideally facilitated by a psychotherapist with training in group dynamics, actively supported and attended by senior staff, including consultant psychiatrists and ward managers. These are multi-function groups in which the impact of difficult cases can be discussed and staff tensions can be explored in a safe and confidential setting. There is some evidence (Kho *et al*, 1998) that the existence of such a group serves to reduce the number of violent episodes on a ward, presumably by reducing expressed emotion and enhancing staff group cohesion. Experience would suggest, however, that without the active support and regular attendance of senior nursing and medical staff such groups tend to founder.

Level 2

In addition to the above, there is a need for an active programme of group therapy for patients, run by ward staff (including psychiatrists) and supervised by psychotherapists trained in group work. This may include a weekly or twice-weekly community meeting (or 'large group') for all patients and staff, and/or regular small groups for selected patients depending on level of function and diagnosis. The purpose of such group work is to foster awareness of the life of the ward as a whole, and to begin to make connections between clinical events such as exacerbation of symptoms, episodes of attempted suicide, violent outbursts, deepened depression, alcoholic relapse and so on in an interpersonal context. There is inevitably a two-way relationship between the impact on patients and that on staff of such events. First, they will in themselves affect the overall atmosphere on the ward, and second, 'what is going on' on the ward (staff and patient arrivals and departures; sexual attraction between patients; unresolved conflict over territory; boredom; unsatisfactory experiences on ward rounds, etc.) can trigger untoward episodes.

An acute ward is potentially such a chaotic place, with rapid turnover and intensity of psychotic behaviour, that all this is no mean task. Not to address this, however, is to neglect an important way of understanding or engaging closely with 'madness'. For mental health workers, this is at best a lost opportunity and at worst a dereliction of a primary duty.

Ward groups, however 'sticky' or apparently mundane, can become an integral part of ward life, and are able to deal with the inevitable resistance, usually manifesting itself by non-attendance, they arouse in patients and some staff. Developing an appropriate here-and-now, systemic, relevant and dynamic style for such groups represents a major clinical and research challenge. Mace (2002) has argued that techniques borrowed from family therapy are more appropriate to such groups than those derived primarily from group analysis. A ward has many of the characteristics of a 'family', with its unavoidable hierarchical relationship between patients and staff, sibling rivalry between patients, blocked and clear communication channels and so on, all of which can be explored in a group context. This, Mace argues, is a more appropriate focus than, say, historical reconstruction of individual patients' difficulties that would be advocated by more traditional group methods.

Level 3

In addition to the above, there needs to be specific expertise in and provision of psychological therapies for in-patients suffering from psychosis, eating disorders and personality disorders. Staff members often do acquire additional training in psychological therapies, for example by attending a course in cognitive–behavioural therapy; however, the skills often atrophy in the traditional ward setting. Not enough thought is currently given to providing training that is appropriate to the in-patient setting and to the management structures that are needed to support it (see Chapter 18). Selected staff members who have had training in cognitive–behavioural approaches in psychosis need to become part of a managed clinical network for psychosis services and take the lead in supervising keyworkers in helping their clients to cope with hallucinations and to challenge delusional ideas. Others are conversant with behavioural and interpersonal approaches to severe eating disorders and can take the lead with such difficult patients when admitted. Patients with personality disorder are among the most problematic of in-patient cases, invariably arousing strong feelings among staff. Expertise in the combination of responsiveness and limit-setting that is most appropriate for this group does not come without training and support. Here too having one or more staff members who are part of a managed clinical network for personality disorder and have received training in appropriate psychotherapy skills can make a significant difference to outcomes (Holmes, 1999).

Conclusion

Fostering a psychological approach to in-patient care will require a shift in culture, management and training. There has to be a determined commitment from senior medical, nursing and management staff to create change. An in-patient psychological therapies implementation group with representatives from psychiatry (with one member of the consultant group taking the lead in acute care), psychotherapy, nursing, psychology, occupational therapy and management is needed. Each professional grouping needs to think through the implications for its own particular discipline.

Despite the important moves towards community care, the work of the consultant psychiatrist could, in theory, centre on the in-patient ward. That is where the most ill patients at any one time tend to be, and the greatest efforts of the consultants should be concentrated there. Sadly, this is often not the case. All too often, the consultant will come onto a ward, usually shared with several other consultants, see 'his' or 'her' patients, and depart. Maintenance of the ward culture and management of the ward as a whole is left by default to the nurses, rather than being a collaborative therapeutic enterprise. Too often the ward appears to have the characteristics of a one-parent family in which survival is the main consideration, as opposed to a mutually supportive 'combined parent' of medical and nursing staff, with greater opportunities for experiment and growth.

The contention of this chapter is that the rediscovery of a psychological culture on the acute unit can produce improved clinical outcomes, a reduction in untoward events, and increased staff and patient satisfaction. The acute ward can become a place of creativity and change rather than of burden and threat. For this to happen, a sustained research and management effort will be required, but if this is successful, the positive impact on morale could be significant and rejuvenating.

References

Ball, R. A., Moore, E. & Kuipers, L. (1992) Expressed emotion in community care staff. A comparison of patient outcome in a nine month follow-up of two hostels. *Social Psychiatry and Psychiatric Epidemiology*, **27**, 35–39.

Fagin, L. (2001) Therapeutic and counter-therapeutic factors in acute ward settings. *Psychoanalytic Psychotherapy*, **15**, 99–120.

Holmes, J. (1999) Psychodynamic approaches to the management and treatment of severe personality disorder in general psychiatric settings. *CPD Psychiatry*, **1**, 53–57.

Holmes, J. (2001) *The Search for the Secure Base: Attachment and Psychotherapy*. London: Routledge.

Kho, K., Sensky, T., Mortimer, A., *et al* (1998) Prospective study into factors associated with aggressive incidents in psychiatric acute admission wards. *British Journal of Psychiatry*, **172**, 38–43.

Leff, J. & Vaughn, C. (1985) *Expressed Emotion in Families*. London; Guilford.

Leiberman, P. & Strauss, J. (1986) Brief hospitalisation: what are its effects? *American Journal of Psychiatry*, **143**, 1557–1562.

Mace, C. (2002) Groups and integration in psychotherapy. In *Integration in Psychotherapy: Models and Methods* (eds J. Holmes & A. Bateman), pp. 69–86. Oxford: Oxford University Press.

Middelboe, T., Schedt, T., Byrsting, K., *et al* (2001) Ward atmosphere in acute psychiatric in-patient care. *Acta Scandinavica Psychiatrica*, **103**, 212–219.

Mind (2000) *Environmentally Friendly? Patients Views on Conditions in Psychiatric Wards*. London: Mind.

National Institute for Mental Health Effectiveness (2003) *Personality Disorder: No Longer a Diagnosis of Exclusion*. London: Department of Health.

Roth, A. & Fonagy, P. (1996) *What Works for Whom?* London: Guilford.

Watts, D. & Morgan, G. (1994) Malignant alienation. Dangers for patients who are hard to like. *British Journal of Psychiatry*, **164**, 11–15.

Part IV

Specialist settings

CHAPTER 21

The residential care and treatment of adolescents

Jim Rose

Editors' introduction Jim Rose has worked in various residential and community-based projects with young people for over 25 years. In this chapter, he conveys something of what he has learned about the nature of the organisational dynamics that exist in institutions looking after disturbed adolescents and the ways in which these may be understood and used to inform treatment.

Although many of the principles developed throughout this book about how therapeutic environments are created and sustained are the same, residential work with adolescents has important differences and has its own unique opportunities and challenges. At the heart of these differences are the young people themselves, who bring into the residential setting all those qualities of youth that can be at once very appealing and utterly frustrating. A group of adolescents produces a particular impact on the adults charged with their care and treatment. Although many of the processes that are found in other therapeutic settings and that describe the relationships between staff and patients are readily identifiable, in an adolescent group they take on distinctive qualities that must be understood and specifically addressed if any benefit is to be gained. Once more these processes arise directly from the adolescent nature of the group and the ways in which relationships between adolescent and adult groups are shaped and formed.

The manner, therefore, in which a residential environment for young people is created and sustained has to accommodate these characteristic features if the overall experience is going to be genuinely therapeutic. This applies in equal measure to the design and robustness of the building and its furniture as to the organisation and delivery of necessary social and educational functions. In addition, the ways in which the highly charged emotional content of daily life in the residential setting is processed and managed by the staff will similarly determine to what extent the adolescents feel cared for and able to respond to the interventions offered.

Context and settings

There are a variety of reasons why young people find themselves living in a group environment for a period of time and there are a number of settings in which this may occur. There are also distinct legal frameworks that apply to the different circumstances of young people living away from home and that may directly affect the nature of the treatments offered.

The circumstances of young people living away from home are regulated by a number of separate pieces of legislation that may apply singly or through a combination of orders. For example, a young person may be looked after by the local authority under the Children Act 1989, but also be subject to a detention and training order under the Crime and Disorder Act 1998 and placed in a young offender institution. The same sort of thing may be true for a young person in an adolescent unit in a hospital who is detained under Mental Health Act 1983 legislation, but at the same time is also in the care of a local authority under the Children Act. Young people in residential schools are usually there under the conditions of a special educational needs statement initiated by the local authority education department, but some are 'looked after' children placed by social services departments in a children's home during holidays.

The settings in which mental health professionals come into contact and work with young people include: open and secure adolescent units within a hospital setting; local authority and independently managed children's homes; residential special schools; and local authority secure units, secure training centres and young offender institutions. The term 'children's home' covers both small two- to six-bed units and much larger establishments and includes those offering a more clearly articulated therapeutic approach to the care and treatment of the young people, as for example the Charterhouse Group of Therapeutic Communities (http://www.charterhousegroup.org.uk).

Regardless of the type of residential unit in which they are placed, all young people will have a number of workers from a variety of agencies involved in the planning and management of their care and treatment. The relationship between professional workers outside of the residential unit and the staff groups involved in the daily care of, and programmes for, the young person inside the unit is critical to the overall success of a placement. The design and implementation of a therapeutic regime in a residential setting must take into account the expectations of the external agencies involved with the young people and include them as part of any monitoring or review of the programme. The same is also the case with regard to the families of the young people.

It is a key task of managers to manage the boundary between the external and internal worlds of their establishment. The internal dynamics of institutions looking after young people are extremely complex and varied, as are the feelings that are generated in the staff. In fact, in any given case involving a young person, gaining an understanding of how the relationships between professional agencies, family members and staff groups in the residential unit function may offer important clues about the nature of the difficulties and problems experienced by the young person and so become the key to more effective interventions.

The young people

The overall national decline in the number of residential placements for young people who, for whatever reason, cannot live with their natural parents has resulted in a population in children's homes made up of a more concentrated and transient group of difficult-to-place adolescents. These individuals present a wide range of antisocial behaviours, have long-standing emotional and behavioural problems often linked to earlier abusive and disrupted family experiences and include a worryingly high number who have diagnosable mental health problems. In addition, these are likely to be disaffected with or have disengaged from education services and, as a result of their antisocial behaviour, may have been formally excluded from school. Also within this group are individuals who have had thoughts of self-harm or suicide, some of whom will have acted on those feelings, and who continue to be a worry to the staff who have to manage their behaviour. A similar profile of histories and behaviours is characteristic of young people in secure units and young offender institutions. Although young people in adolescent units that are part of mental health services usually have clearer diagnoses of mental illness, a percentage of them share the background, personal histories and experiences of the young people in social care or secure settings.

In talking to any group of staff working with young people in a residential unit there are always a number of common issues that crop up, whatever the particular setting. In the main these revolve around how difficult the young people are to manage and the effect that working with them has on individual staff members. However, despite the particular nature of their problems and the specific focus of intervention or treatment programmes, they also present the characteristic behaviours of adolescence (Box 21.1).

Box 21.1 Adolescent issues that affect the residential environment

- The transition from childhood dependence into adult independence
- Restructuring of relationships with parental figures
- Changes to the body, which heighten sexual awareness
- Increased interest in peer group attitudes and relationships

---

However, for the majority of young people in residential units the processes of adolescence are complicated by the quality and nature of their earlier experiences. These experiences often have a particular influence on their ability to make and sustain relationships with members of their peer group as well as with the adults with whom they come into contact, especially those who have some responsibility for their management and care.

One of the difficulties for staff in these situations is distinguishing between what might be considered 'normal' adolescent behaviour and behaviour that is clearly a function of disturbance and requires intervention. Working with young people can, of course, also arouse in members of staff issues from their own adolescence. Many staff in residential units are not so far removed from the age group with whom they are working and this can lead to overidentification. On the other hand, older staff are not immune from the pressures produced by an adolescent group and may find themselves reliving the past through the experiences of the young people in their care (and perhaps envying them).

In a therapeutic community setting for adults, a central principle of the way in which a community works is that both staff and patients take responsibility for the safety of the community as a whole and use the vehicles of community or small-group meetings to monitor and regulate this. In a setting for adolescents, although the principle of 'community' may be a goal, the issue of the nature of the authority taken by the adult staff will figure more sharply. From time to time the adults will find themselves in situations in which they have to assert their authority as adults over an immature and acting-out group of adolescents. Although the aim is always to be working, both in group terms as well as in individual cases, towards the young people's increased management and ordering of their own affairs, for many of them this will be their first experience of adults using appropriate authority in demonstrably fair and non-abusive ways. If nothing else is achieved, to have provided a young person with a different kind of experience of the behaviour of adults towards them is of therapeutic benefit.

The demands made by a group of adolescents on their adult carers are both physical and emotional. Working with young people is physically demanding, as their energy levels tend to be high, but it is the overwhelming emotional demands that are often the hardest to tolerate. Young people crave adult attention and, although it may not always be sought in the most socially adroit of ways, it is a constant pressure on the staff. Often, these demands are an important source of information about the nature of the young person's earlier attachment experiences. They can also be an attempt to recreate and perhaps punish the failures of their early carers or to compensate for their inadequacy. Knowledge essential for staff working with adolescents is shown in Box 21.2.

> **Box 21.2** Staff working with adolescents
>
> Understanding of the following is essential:
> - The importance of ideas associated with attachment theory
> - The symbolic meaning to the individual of what might appear to be just routine, ordinary events
> - The relationship between professional agencies, family members and the residential unit staff, and the way this offers important clues about the nature of a young person's difficulties

Therapy with the radio on

Despite differences in the legal frameworks governing the placement of young people in residential settings and the varying management arrangements under which these institutions are operated, many similarities and common themes emerge when planning a therapeutic programme or regime for them. As mentioned above, much of this is to do with the nature of adolescence and the impact that working in an environment with young people has on the adult staff. It is one of the ironies in considering residential work with children and young people that the staff who are in most direct and immediate contact with them are at the same time most likely to be the least trained and unqualified. And yet, as we shall see, these are the people who are crucial for ensuring that the core routines and daily activities are consistently and reliably delivered.

It is this routine of daily activity that provides the framework of group life in a residential unit; getting up in the morning, mealtimes, education, activities, small group meetings and bedtimes are the cornerstones of day-to-day life, and delivering these in a consistent and reliable way is a key contributing factor in providing the containment that an adolescent group needs. The significance of these routines may be understood at a number of different levels. Above all, they provide a structure to the day that young people whose lives may previously have been chaotic can respond to and feel held by. At another level they are important vehicles enabling the adult staff to engage with the young people and get to know them. They are also important opportunities for learning new skills and, with carefully directed feedback, can provide young people with fresh insight into their behaviour and the impact of this on others. The experiences of mealtimes, of night-time, and of adults entering into personal space and time can arouse deeply painful memories that, if sensitively used, can become an important part of treatment. Enabling staff to understand the symbolic meanings of what may appear to be just routine, ordinary events and to carry them out each day in a consistent but fresh way and in a manner that responds to the individual need of each young person is a foremost part of therapeutic residential work.

Within the framework provided by the daily routine, an adolescent group should be involved in as wide a choice of stimulating and interesting activities as possible. Although formal group meetings, group work and some individual therapeutic work may be achievable, most of the work with this age group is undertaken in the context of 'other' activities, both formal and informal and with usually more than one thing happening at the same time. Although these young people's experiences of school and education might be negative, if they can be re-engaged in any aspect of learning while in a residential unit, it is an important step forward and may become a building block for other areas of personal development. Art, music and drama are important vehicles through which young people are able to learn about themselves and others, and these form part of a broader range of media that play a significant part in adolescent culture generally. Harnessing these interests and directing them towards opportunities for reflecting on more personal issues is part of the skill of residential work.

Within the structure of daily routines and activities it is the relationship of the adults to them that provides the most containing experience for the adolescents. This is true not just at group level, however, for although the fundamental experience of a residential setting is gained in the group, it is also imperative that each young person knows that at some level they are being thought about by significant adults in the unit, particularly those involved in their immediate care, and that their individual needs are understood and are being attended to.

Adolescent groups may be characterised by high levels of acting-out behaviour that can border on the self-destructive or become extremely hostile. The delivery of a well-planned and full daily programme offers containment not just in terms of occupying time usefully, but also in providing the necessary spaces for relationships with staff and residents that allow opportunities for growth and development. The underlying therapeutic aim of all activity is to reduce or prevent acting out and to stimulate individuals' potential for thinking and talking about their emotions and behaviour or how they might respond more appropriately and creatively to their difficulties. Of course, many of the adolescents in residential settings are only at the beginning of the road to thinking. Although they are very aware of the immediate feelings of their own acute distress, they have often buried the causes too deep to be retrieved in words. This is why the adult staff have enormous responsibility for them, by providing immediate safety and by thinking for them until they can begin to engage in thinking for themselves (see Box 21.3). The ability of an adult group to hold on to the material

---

Box 21.3 Some thoughts about thinking

- All residents need to feel that they are being thought about by adults in the unit and that their needs are understood and are being addressed
- Residents have often buried the causes of their distress too deep for words
- The staff often have to think for the young people until they are ready to think for themselves
- Opportunities for reflection on personal issues often appear during informal activities and while other things are happening
- An interest in adolescent culture (e.g. art, music and drama) can be harnessed to help young people learn about themselves and others
- Disturbed young people frequently attack (directly or indirectly) the process of thinking that is fundamental to the therapeutic task

---

metaphorically thrown at it by the young people, to process it and give it back in digestible form is a critical part of the therapeutic experience.

The young people in a residential unit may be very resistant to this process and, individually and in groups, seek ways of sabotaging the therapeutic endeavour. Adolescents use the same psychological mechanisms of defence as adults, including projection, splitting and denial (see Chapter 4). Staff teams can find themselves holding strong and differing views about individual residents, and individual members of staff can experience unfamiliar and strange feelings, perhaps of a violent or sexual nature, and be uncertain as to where such emotions come from. Young residents can also directly attack the process of thinking that is fundamental to the therapeutic task. Staff meetings, handovers and supervision sessions are regularly put in jeopardy by an ever-demanding group of young people, and the office door is often quite literally an object of attack when staff are gathered behind it for a private meeting.

Residential units for young people are inevitably busy and frenetic places. Events happen in quick succession, small and seemingly irrelevant incidents or exchanges take on a significance that can occupy hours of staff's and residents' time and minor details of life acquire disproportionate meaning. And yet within this maelstrom the central task of thinking has to be preserved. For this reason, a therapeutic environment can be created and sustained only if the needs of the staff are acknowledged and addressed as carefully as those of the residents. Making time for supervision, team meetings and training is not a luxury. Within these structures it is important that staff are given opportunities not just to reflect on the practical content of their work, but also to process the material with which they are confronted in a way that allows space for discussion about its emotional content as well.

Conclusion

Providing a therapeutic environment for young people in a residential setting is complex and difficult. It requires a strong and focused management that can maintain the boundaries between the external and internal pressures generated in such settings and support the daily work of the staff teams in delivering a reliable and consistent programme of routines and activities. Above all, the staff must be able to resist the fierce projections of the adolescent residents and withstand their hostility and anger, while at the same time responding to the high levels of distress and neediness that this group also presents. Energy, resilience and humour are essential qualities for staff in these settings, as is the ability to be flexible while maintaining boundaries around acceptable and unacceptable behaviour. Group-living with adolescents involves a tricky combination of routine and spontaneity; using opportunities for communication and learning as they arise in the course of daily life, but at the same time putting in place more formal structures within which to engage the young people in the processes of change and development. As someone (I forget who) wisely put it:

'When young people are being like children it's OK because you can nurture them. When they are being like adults it's OK because you can talk to them. When they are being adolescents it's impossible!'

Helping make the impossible a little easier is quite a good way of describing the task of residential work with young people.

Further reading

Brown, E., Bullock, R., Hobson, C., et al (1998) Making Residential Care Work: Structure and Culture in Children's Homes. Aldershot: Ashgate Publishing.

Howe, D., Brandon, M., Hinings, D., et al (1999) Attachment Theory, Child Maltreatment and Family Support. London: Macmillan.

Kahan, B. (1994) Growing Up in Groups. London: HMSO.

Rose, J. (2002) Working with Young People in Secure Accommodation – From Chaos to Culture. Hove: Brunner-Routledge.

Rose, M. (1990) Healing Hurt Minds: The Peper Harow Experience. London: Tavistock/Routledge.

Sinclair, I. & Gibbs, I. (1996) Quality of Care in Children's Homes. York: University of York Social Work Research and Development Unit.

Wheal, A. (1998) Adolescence. Positive Approaches for Working with Young People. Lyme Regis: Russell House Publishing.

CHAPTER 22

The ideal home and community for people with learning disabilities

Valerie Sinason and Sheila Hollins

Editors' introduction   Valerie Sinason and Sheila Hollins work in the Department of Mental Health at St George's Hospital Medical School, London. They are particularly well known for psychotherapeutic work with survivors of abuse who also have a learning disability, and they have written extensively on this subject. Their response to our request to write a chapter for this book was to take the request to their various patient groups. The result is a chapter that vividly conveys the trials and struggle and courage that may be needed to establish a place that is home.

When does a house, flat, room, hospital bed or space become a home? People with learning disabilities have for centuries been allocated spaces to exist in without any choice. As with other stigmatised groups, there can be an underlying assumption that those in need do not merit any choice and can be provided with the least optimum space available. However, being allocated any space, even without a choice, can be seen as historically representing a progression from the infanticide and abandonment of previous eras (Box 22.1).

For the purposes of this chapter we asked our men's group and various other patients for their ideas on what constituted a home and a community. The timing of our request was shortly before Christmas, when, regardless of religious belief or lack of it, the theme of a non-disabled baby who was born to die was predominant.

One middle-aged man, Mr A, who has a speech defect, spoke of the therapy room as the therapy womb. The womb is our first home, even though we are not conscious of it. In many countries, unborn babies

---

Box 22.1   Some important principles

- There is no ideal living situation; rather, it is about fitting the home to the individual
- A sense of choice and meaningfulness is all-important
- A home needs to reflect the individual and include personal possessions and objects of emotional importance
- The concept of home includes the circle of support

with disabilities can have their lives terminated, and in England universal screening for Down's syndrome is being introduced, with the expectation at the Department of Health that people with Down's syndrome will be eliminated before birth. The very first living and breathing space is not necessarily a home when you have a disability: the 'inside' space is as hard as the 'outside' one:

'Jesus did not have a learning disability but he still died and nobody wanted him at the Inn. He had to sleep with animals in the barn and people call me an animal because I wet myself, and they do not want me to have a house' – *Mary, aged 20.*

For those not entrapped by political upheaval or poverty, what are the chosen places to live? In the current period in Western Europe it is possible for some people with learning disabilities to consider the home or community of their choice. It is possible to choose to live close to the ground, in a bungalow, a ground-floor flat or a ground-floor room in a house. It is possible to live in an attic or a top-floor flat. It is possible to live near the sea, or the countryside or the shops. It is possible to live in a quiet area or a noisy area, with other people or alone. These are choices that lucky people have who might be unaware of the emotional experience that faces those who are 'moved in' with the same lack of care that led to previous generations of unwanted people being 'moved on'.

Vignette 22.1: A ready-made 'home'

Christine, aged 35, was moved 'into the community', to a beautifully modernised terraced home with three other women from her long-stay hospital. She did not choose these women to live with, nor did she choose where to live. As it happened, she was provided with a showcase room and kitchen. When we made a home visit the support worker opened the door. 'You must see Christine's new home. It is so amazing. Just look at the kitchen – it has everything in it'.

Christine sat smiling vacantly in her luxury kitchen while the support worker pointed to the microwave oven and all the plates and saucers in styles and design that we ourselves would have liked to have had. 'Show them your lovely home and room', exhorted the worker. Christine stood up slowly. She was now the tourist guide to 'care in the community'. She pointed out the shiny doorknobs, the thick carpet, the new armchairs. In her room she pointed disinterestedly to the curtains, the bed, the wardrobe. Then her eyes alighted on a dirty broken vase. She smiled with genuine enthusiasm and said 'Broken. Mine'. We commented that everything was so new and beautiful in the house that it did not feel hers or like her; whereas that vase was part of her history, it was old and had some damage and some beauty. It represented her.

Unfortunately, communities often come ready-made, and people are moved into living spaces without choice and without any memento of their own past lives.

Vignette 22.2 A hospital bed as home

When John, aged 54, was moved into a long-stay hospital he was frightened at being somewhere new. His experience was made harder by the lack of friendship shown him by all the other members of the ward. They seemed either afraid of him or angry with him. It emerged that his bed in the ward had for years been the unacknowledged 'home' of Peter, who had died the week before, at the age of 64. The lack of attention to bereavement issues and loss meant that someone else had been moved into Peter's home with no thought for those still mourning for Peter. A hospital bed can be a home as much as can a doorway or an institution. Bereavement issues and homes are very much interwoven for those with learning disabilities.

Loss of home and parent: a double loss

Often the death of a parent means facing not only that loss, but also the loss of the parental home. Many people referred for violence or disturbed behaviour have lost their parent and their home at the same moment, and no emotional allowance has been made for the double grief this has caused. Within the Western tradition, children leave the parental home as a sign of individuation and maturity, to move into their own homes, whether shared or not. In times of economic difficulty, but also as a result of good relationships, some young people stay in the parental home. However, for learning-disabled young people with severe or profound disabilities there is no point of emotional individuation when they could initiate a move to live on their own. For them, the concept of 'home' incorporates a circle of support, which may include an informal network of local community members and relatives, as well as skilled professionals.

Who do people with learning disabilities wish to live with? What is their good-enough peer group or community? There are, of course, many different views, as each person is different. However, certain themes emerge that we hear regularly; some of these are outlined below.

Dreams of home and community

Belonging to a family

'I want to live with my sister. But she is married and she has children and she does not want me to live with her. I like her house and she does not get tired like my Mum and Dad. When they die she will have to look after me' – *Myra, aged 26.*

'I want to live with my Mum for always. She is 65 now and getting older. I am afraid about what to do when she gets old. I hope I get older and die first' – *Nita, aged 40.*

Rare memories

'I want a house in Blackpool near the sea. We'd walk by the sea. Curry to eat. Shows. A pub near it. People you can talk to in the pub. Once I went in a pub in Blackpool and people were singing and they gave me a £5 note' – *Steven, aged 44.*

'Home is baked beans, sausages, eggs, tomatoes, cake, Coke, choc-ice and cheesecake' – *Tony, aged 50.*

A representation of choice

'Where I live people shout all the time. One man hits staff and he breaks furniture. I called the police. All I want is a quiet place. Somewhere quiet. I would like bed, furniture, TV and a kitchen. I want a bucket and mop. Disinfectant, bathroom, sink and garden. I want to live near a police station, far away from children. A house for another man and me. I don't mind if he is young or old or what colour he is. I just want someone quiet like me who likes TV, football and cooking. I would like Blackpool or Brighton for holidays. I'd like a staff member to take me to football matches. I would like my own key' – *Brian, aged 46.*

'I want a wireless, television, cupboards, my own bike and a new hat. I want a telephone. Paint a room blue. A table, I want. I like laying a table. No staff. Just a friend, Dan. Just him. I want a boyfriend and not a girlfriend. My own key and a telephone. And Dan. Just him' – *Chris, aged 32.*

'I just want night staff. Not in the daytime. The hospital needs new furniture to make it nicer, new kitchen and pictures for the walls. A new locker. No pets are allowed. That is sad. I would like my own key to my own bedroom' – *Eric, aged 46.*

Community

A large hospital for people with learning disabilities is closing (all long-stay hospitals in England are due to close by 2004). People are being moved 'into the community'. But what does this mean? Sometimes, when attachments are strong, an institution can truly be a home, within its own 'community', whereas a beautiful 'home in the community' might just be a house in a hostile environment. Jerry and Joan were both moved into terraced homes a bus-ride away from their former hospital. Jerry was depressed by the move, whereas Joan was elated. Jerry, aged 25, told us,

'In the hospital you could walk anywhere and nobody laughed at you. They all knew you. You could visit friends every day. You did not need a telephone. You did not need a bus or escort. Now I can't see anyone. I don't know how to use a phone and I can't go on a bus. It is very sad here. No one wants to talk to me'.

Joan, who was 36, made very different comments:

'In the hospital if I wanted tea I had to wait for tea-time. But here I have a kettle. My own kettle. I can have tea as often as I like. [She giggled.] I could have tea all day if I wanted. No I couldn't. Because if I had it all day I would not have any teabags left and they cost money and I have to go to the shop to buy more. I like having tea whenever I like'.

The community into which people are moved is not always welcoming of them: there have been protests and petitions against the idea of people with learning disabilities moving into the area. However, as the following vignette shows, sometimes the 'disabled' individuals have greater insight than the 'normal' community into which they are placed.

Vignette 22.3 Standing up to hostility

Susan, aged 42, was moved into a low-morale council estate with a high rate of crime. She was immediately stigmatised. However, she was a courageous woman and had worked through issues about her learning disability in therapy. One day she came to therapy with the following salutary tale: 'Boys on my estate laughed at me, threw stones at me, called me "spastic, spastic!" I told them I was spastic and they were lucky they were not. But they were rude boys and I am not rude". She had the emotional ability to see how she represented a frightening 'other' to the disturbed boys on the estate and was able to stand up for herself in difficult circumstances.

In other cases, support workers have made good liaison with neighbours.

Vignette 22.4 A warm welcome

When John moved into his new home at the age of 25 he received a warm welcome from his next-door neighbours, who had been sensitively briefed by his social worker. The local shopkeeper expanded this welcome into the neighbourhood, giving John a part-time job that gave him a sense of value and purpose, and his keyworker arranged transport to a club that John had belonged to while in hospital. In return, John was able to provide physical help for an elderly neighbour as well as being an active member of his neighbourhood watch scheme. John is now happily settled.

A village community

There are a small number of purpose-built villages for people with learning disabilities that do their best to create a concept of community. Some parents welcome the apparent sense of protection and security offered by such segregated communities. However, these still face the problems of being truly democratic places where people can make meaningful choices. For example, one community took pride in making all its own food – or, rather, the non-disabled staff did. However, one resident told us 'I hate cheese. We made it. We have the animals too and I don't like looking after them. They smell. I want to live in a town with shops and buy food and not make it'. Another resident, however, said, 'When my mum and dad come I give them food I made. They are proud of me. I like living in the country here'.

Conclusion

People with a learning disability are citizens with a right to a home. If they are given adequate help in working out their dreams and needs, most can become full members of a community. Some, because of the level of their disability, are not able to participate in mainstream community life, and require a 'virtual community' of professionals and volunteers.

The key issue, of course, is one of choice. As with all other people, those with learning disabilities do not form a homogeneous group. They have many different needs and wishes. The attitudes of social workers and learning disability specialist staff play a central role in the provision of real choice. If low expectations are the norm, individual dreams may simply not be heard.

Further reading

Hollins, S. & Hutchinson, D. (1993) *A New Home in the Community* (Books Beyond Words). London: St George's Mental Health Library.

Hollins, S. & Hutchinson, D. (1993) *Peter's New Home* (Books Beyond Words). London: St George's Mental Health Library.

Hollins, S. & Esterhuyzen, A. (1997) Bereavement and grief in adults with learning disabilities. *British Journal of Psychiatry*, **170**, 497–501.

Sinason.,V. (1992) *Mental Handicap and the Human Condition. New Approaches from The Tavistock*. London: Free Association Books.

Sinason, V. (2002) Treating people with learning disabilities after physical or sexual abuse. *Advances in Psychiatric Treatment*, **8**, 424–431.

CHAPTER 23

Secure psychiatric services

Steffan Davies

Editors' introduction In this chapter Steffan Davies gives an overview of secure psychiatric services in the UK. He argues that increasing specialisation will allow therapeutic environments to be better fitted for particular patient groups and describes two units that illustrate this.

The aim of secure psychiatric services is to treat and rehabilitate patients so that they can safely function again in the community. For a small number of patients, this is not possible. For this group, humane containment in the least restrictive environment compatible with safety becomes the aim. The majority of patients admitted to secure psychiatric services, even those convicted of very serious offences, eventually move to open services or into the community, albeit with intensive support at times. However, a small number of patients live out the remainder of their lives in secure units.

Chapter 3 used examples from secure psychiatric services, in particular the high-security hospitals, to illustrate some of the problems of large, and what are now the closest approximations to 'total', institutions (see Chapter 3, p. 21) in the National Health Service (NHS). Here, in addition to looking at the specific characteristics of secure services, I include examples of units, including the one in which I work (Cedars Community), that consciously use the therapeutic environment as an essential part of the treatment they offer.

Secure psychiatric services in the UK predominantly treat men with schizophrenia. The next largest group is men with personality disorder. Other groups include women with various psychiatric disorders and people with learning difficulties. These last two groups are considered specifically in other chapters in this book, albeit not specifically in a forensic context. For the sake of clarity and economy of space, this chapter focuses on men with schizophrenia and personality disorder. In reality there are high degrees of comorbidity or dual diagnosis between the two, particularly in the high-security hospitals, and rates of substance misuse problems are also high, often in excess of 80%.

One of the main challenges for secure services is maintaining the difficult balance between security and therapy. Too little or the wrong type of security leads to problems such as assault, absconding and undermining of therapeutic activities (for example, through trading in illicit drugs). Too much or the wrong type leads to undue restrictions on patients, arguably breeching their human rights, and exposes patients to the potential dangers of institutionalisation and abuse. Either can contribute to the problems outlined in Chapter 3. The inability to take therapeutic risks is an increasing problem for secure psychiatric services in a risk-averse society, particularly in high security. This leads to the danger either of detaining patients longer than is necessary or of risks having to be taken in less secure settings where they may be more difficult to contain.

Security

Security is traditionally thought of as combining three elements: the physical, the procedural and the relational (Box 23.1). The first, physical security, includes walls, fences, doors and the fabric of the unit. These are often the most obvious aspects of security seen by visitors to a unit and they are sometimes designed specifically to reassure the public. The second, procedural security, includes the procedures in place to ensure the safe running of the unit, for example searching, controlled access to materials that could be used as weapons or ignition sources and control of external communications. These day-to-day aspects of the internal regime are often the most intrusive on patients' lives, but they can become so much part of the ward routine as to be little noticed by visitors who spend short periods on the ward. The third – and in secure psychiatric services the most important – aspect of security is relational security. This involves the therapeutic relationship between staff and patients as well as factors such as staff numbers and their disciplinary mix and specialist skills (e.g. in managing violence and aggression (see Chapter 13) or in specific treatments such as anger management).

Secure services are traditionally thought of as being at three levels: low, medium and high. Some open wards act as forensic units, usually with enhanced staffing levels and forensic experience and skills. Low secure services are usually local to a health district, designed to contain disturbed behaviour but not so secure as to prevent determined absconsion attempts. They often have some form of perimeter fence, locked doors and aspects of procedural and relational security. Recent

---

Box 23.1 Aspects of security

Physical   Walls, fences, doors, locks

Procedural   Searching, controlling entry and exit, access to potential weapons

Relational   Staff numbers, skills, experience, ability to maintain a therapeutic alliance

---

Department of Health guidance (Department of Health, 2002) defines low secure services as those able to:

'deliver intensive, comprehensive, multidisciplinary treatment and care by qualified staff for patients who demonstrate disturbed behaviour in the context of a serious mental disorder and who require the provision of security'.

It further recommends that these units

'aim to provide a homely, secure environment, which has occupational and recreational opportunities linked with community facilities'.

The former Director General of the Prison Service, Sir Richard Tilt (see Chapter 3), recently reviewed security at the high secure hospitals. He made numerous recommendations to increase security to the level of a category B prison. This has involved the spending of tens of millions of pounds on new double fences around the hospitals, improved reception and control facilities and an increase in specialist security staff. There have also been draconian directives on procedural security, including the searching of staff and visitors on entry to the hospitals, banning the bringing in of virtually all food and drink for patients and stopping incoming phone calls. The Tilt report said little about relational security but the staff:patient ratios at a high-security hospital are around five times those at a category B prison, large numbers of staff have professional qualifications and the reduction of risk by the treatment of mental disorder is the hospitals' primary aim.

This security review was requested in response to security lapses at Ashworth Hospital. The resulting recommendations seem designed to deal with a small minority of highly dangerous and inventive psycho-pathically disordered patients and are unnecessarily restrictive on patients with mental illness, learning disability and female patients (see Chapter 3, p. 27). Security in the three high-security hospitals in England and Wales is now much more standardised than ever before, largely as codified in the Tilt Report and following procedures generated by its implementation.

Medium secure services lie between the local low secure services and the high secure hospitals. The Department of Health has produced a design guide for standards of physical security in medium secure units (NHS Estates, 1993), but these guidelines are not always adhered to. They were last updated in 1993 and are in some respects out of date: for example, there is no reference to closed-circuit television (CCTV). Standards of security are very variable, but are likely to increase in response to the tightening of security in the high-security hospitals. An illustration of the variability of security guidance is the contrast between the NHS Estates' recommendation that fences in medium secure units be 5.8 m high and that in a recent article on therapeutic uses of security (Kennedy, 2002), which suggests that 3 m high is appropriate.

There is currently a great deal of overlap between low and medium secure services in many aspects of security provision. This has some advantages in terms of movement of patients between the two. A more obvious difference is the time patients spend in the different levels of security. Generally admissions to high security, where there are extensive facilities within the secure area, are measured in years, even decades; in medium security, admissions generally range from a few months to 2 or 3 years; and in low security, admissions are more often measured in weeks and months. Medium secure units tend to be larger and have some degree of functional division between wards, for example admission and assessment, ongoing treatment, pre-discharge and intensive care. The increasing realisation that a significant minority of patients require prolonged, possibly life-long, admissions, but do not need a high-security environment has led to the development of long-term secure services. Most of these are in the private sector, but they are becoming increasingly common in the NHS. These require either more treatment facilities within the secure area, or the ability to safely escort patients to occupational or leisure facilities in open units or the community.

Although prison is not often thought of as a treatment environment, there are very high rates of mental disorder among prisoners, both sentenced and remand. The responsibility for delivering treatment has rested with the prison medical service, but government policy increasingly is to transfer this responsibility to the NHS. Standards of psychiatric care in the prison service have often been criticised, but there are examples of good practice such as the services provided at HMP Nottingham and HMP Belmarsh in London, which both have NHS 'beacon status'. As discussed below, there are also a number of therapeutic communities operating within the prison service for inmates with personality disorder. There is a great deal of overlap between the populations of prisons and of secure psychiatric services, with around two-thirds of admissions being transferred from penal settings.

Example 23.1: HMP Gartree therapeutic community

HMP Gartree is a category B prison serving a population of life-sentenced prisoners near Market Harborough in Leicestershire (Woodward, 1999). The prison has a 21-place separate wing that runs as a democratic therapeutic community. All community residents join voluntarily and current residents are involved in decisions on acceptance of new residents and discharge of existing ones. The therapeutic programme consists of community and small group meetings in the mornings and the 'living and learning' experience of being part of the community. Residents are encouraged to take a major part in the programme, for example chairing community meetings. They participate in the normal prison regime in the afternoons. The length of stay in the Gartree therapeutic community is often longer than the 18–24 months common at other prison therapeutic communities such as that in HMP Grendon. This is because many Gartree residents have killed friends or people they loved, which can leave them with prolonged and complicated grief issues to be worked through.

Treatments

The treatment of patients in secure psychiatric settings has much in common with that in general settings. Drug treatment is the mainstay of treatment for schizophrenia, although there is increasing interest in psychological therapies such as cognitive–behavioural therapy. In addition to treatments for mental illness, offending behaviours and other problem areas such as substance misuse also need to be addressed. Depending on the unit and its resources, these are usually addressed by individual or group treatments such as anger management or modified prison service programmes such as sex offender treatment programmes (SOTPs). Forensic patients are often from socially deprived backgrounds with poor educational records and adverse experiences in childhood. There are consequently needs for basic education and more formal psychotherapies, if patients are able to engage.

The treatment of personality disorder has also traditionally been an area of interest for forensic psychiatry, particularly in high security. However, treatment programmes were often poorly developed and at times seemed to rely on unspecified milieus and a process of maturation. Recent years have seen an increasing reluctance to admit patients with personality disorder into secure services, and less than 5% of restricted patients admitted for treatment have a Mental Health Act classification of psychopathic disorder (Johnson & Taylor, 2002). Problems in the personality disorder services at Ashworth Hospital led to the Fallon Enquiry (see Chapter 3) and to the Tilt Report. Treatment for personality disorder is usually felt to require specific psychologically based programmes, with a clear rationale and opportunities to confront and challenge aberrant behaviours. This type of treatment environment would be contraindicated for patients with persisting psychotic symptoms.

Forensic services often serve large catchment areas such as NHS regions with populations of several million. The admission criteria are therefore usually based on area of residence (within the catchment area), the need for hospital treatment under the Mental Health Act, and risk commensurate with the level of security. This leads to very heterogeneous patient groups, containing for example both men and women with treatment-responsive schizophrenia, affective disorders and comorbid personality disorder. There are therefore difficulties in aligning therapeutic programmes to patient characteristics.

Therapeutic environments

There are obvious problems in creating therapeutic environments within secure psychiatric services. Almost all patients are detained in such services and their cooperation is likely to be lacking from the outset or to be withdrawn during treatment. There is a constant risk of physical violence to staff and, more commonly, to other patients, and at times physical intervention by staff is necessary. Lengths of stay, particularly in medium and high security, are usually measured in years, leading to frustration among patients. Physical space is often lacking and the provision of appropriate structured daytime activity, even in the larger units, is often inadequate. Security needs to be maintained at the level of the highest-risk patient, often to the detriment of others. Treatments for personality disorder would be very different to those for patients with chronic psychosis or with treatment-responsive psychosis without significant underlying personality disturbance. Many of the features of therapeutic environments described in this book – the physical environment, staff skills and training, managing violence and aggression, effective team working and cultural issues – are as important, or even more important, in secure psychiatric services as in general psychiatric and rehabilitation services. The majority of patients in secure services have schizophrenia and a prolonged admission, at least by acute psychiatric standards. There should therefore be a greater potential to think about therapeutic environments for specific patient groups, particularly those with psychosis and personality disorder.

There is a small literature focusing on environmental approaches to psychosis. These include the British tradition of the therapeutic community approach (Clark, 1999), which traces its origin to Tukes' 'moral treatment' at The Retreat in the late-18th century. Another approach is the use of a token economy, which has never been popular in the UK, despite its adoption by a number of units at times, although it continues to have supporters in the USA (Paul *et al*, 1997). A more recent approach, arising from the literature on family work in schizophrenia, looks at negative expressed emotion, which is related to risk of relapse in psychotic illness. This has also contributed to the adaptation to in-patient settings of the psychosocial interventions model, which draws on family interventions and cognitive–behavioural therapy. A recent systematic review of the psychiatric literature (Smith, 2000) using the search terms SCHIZOPHRENIA or PSYCHOSIS and TREATMENT ENVIRONMENT or MILIEU or THERAPEUTIC COMMUNITY or WARD ATMOSPHERE yielded 25 articles published between 1978 and 1998. Smith concluded that

'In brief such an environment should be highly supportive, with an emphasis on relationships and orientated toward individual needs. There should be little expression of anger and aggression, a relaxed, non-restrictive regime of care and opportunities for user involvement … A therapeutic community model, modified to provide high levels of emotional support and individual care, may help ... patients [with psychosis]'.

For psychopathic disorder the literature is larger, and although there is still very little on behavioural and cognitive–behavioural treatment environments, there is an increasing amount on the use of programmes based on cognitive–behavioural therapy to reduce reoffending. 'Milieu therapy' and hospital admission in its widest sense may have some effect on the outcome, in terms of reconviction, for patients with psychopathic disorders, but the literature is small and uncontrolled (Dolan & Coid, 1993). There is a much larger literature on therapeutic community treatment of personality disorder, and this has been subject to a systematic review by Lees *et al* (1999). The authors examined 8160 articles on therapeutic communities. They found 113 outcome studies, including 10 randomised controlled trials, 10 cross-institutional studies and a further 32 using some kind of control group. A meta-analysis of the 29 suitable studies found 'very strong support to the effectiveness of therapeutic community treatment' (p. 3). This provided type 1 evidence for the effectiveness of therapeutic communities according to the UK NHS National Service Framework (Department of Health, 1999) criteria: at least one good systematic review including at least one randomised controlled trial. Although therapeutic communities are found in a number of prisons, in UK secure services only one unit operates as a therapeutic community; this is Woodstock Ward, for patients with personality disorder at Broadmoor Hospital.

More recently there has been interest in the use of dialectical behavioural therapy, developed with female out-patients with borderline personality disorders (discussed in Winston, 2000), for psychopathic disorders in the special hospitals.

What literature there is seems to emphasise the value of low levels of expressed negative emotion and high levels of individual support and individual care for patients with psychosis. In contrast, for those with personality disorder the emphasis is on emotionally challenging environments where feedback and peer pressure play a major role in modifying offending behaviour. The differences in environment are very important, as the qualities that are therapeutic for personality disordered patients are contraindicated for those with psychosis.

Security regimes

In general terms, the security regimes required for different diagnostic groups are distinct. This was in part illustrated in Chapter 3, where the liberalisation of an over-punitive regime was felt to benefit patients with mental illness or learning disabilities. This, however, led to problems in providing adequate internal controls on the personality disorder unit. The resulting enquiry made sweeping security recommendations that are now being criticised for their negative impact on other patient groups, particularly women and individuals with mental illness or learning disabilities. Security regimes need to be more tailored to patients' characteristics. In simple terms, the control of disorganised episodic violence in response to psychotic symptoms needs a very different approach to the planned violence, concerted action and active subversion of security seen at the Ashworth personality disorder unit. There are, of course, degrees of comorbidity in the patient groups, but the development of more specialist-focused services should enable security regimes as well as therapeutic milieus to be designed around patient needs.

Specialism *v.* generalism

The implications of specialism as opposed to generalism were in part explored in Chapter 3. If environments are to be therapeutic, there must be careful attention paid to the patient group treated in them. Other advantages of units specialising in a particular type of patient are the development of staff skills that can be put into practice in psychotherapy, occupational rehabilitation programmes and medication regimes as well as in environmental treatments (Box 23.2).

There is an increasing move towards specialisation within secure services, with the development of women-only services, specialist personality disorder services, forensic rehabilitation in special hospitals (see Example 3.1 in Chapter 3 and Example 23.2 below), and a national high-security service for deaf patients at Rampton Hospital. The disadvantages of specialisation, particularly for less common conditions, is the

---

Box 23.2   Advantages of specialism and generalism

Specialism	*Generalism*
Easier to focus therapeutic environment on needs of patient group	Better able to serve a geographical area and maintain community links
Easier to develop and use specific therapeutic skills	Less likely to exclude patients as not fitting admission criteria
More homogeneous patient group reduces risks of victimisation	Heterogeneous patient group more representative of real life
Homogeneous patient group allows security regime to be tailored to specific risks of group	Heterogeneous group allows more opportunities for acting out and thus aids risk assessment

tension between proximity to family and community and often geo-graphically distant specialist units. There is also the risk that patients may fall between different specialist services and be rejected by all.

Example 23.2   Cedars Community, Rampton Hospital

Cedars Community is a 14-bedded unit sited in a self-contained villa within the high secure perimeter at Rampton Hospital. Patients all have psychotic illnesses that have not responded to treatment with anti-psychotic medication, usually including clozapine. All patients are male and have been referred by consultants in the hospital. Patients are severely disabled by positive and or negative symptoms of psychosis and engage poorly with the daytime activity programmes within the hospital. Exclusion criteria are: being too disturbed to be managed in the villa; the presence of significant learning disability or acquired brain injury; or functioning at too high a level. The patient numbers are lower than in the other villas and staff numbers are higher. There is a greater need for relational security and less need for elaborate physical and procedural security with this patient group, a point that is difficult to make in the current security regime.

Treatments fall into three broad areas: drug, psychological and milieu. All patients receive psychotropic medication, often combinations of neuroleptics and/or mood stabilisers. Individual therapies, including art therapy, speech and language therapy and individual work on mental health and offence-related issues, are conducted by psychologists, named nurses and occupational therapists. Other activities focus on basic skills such as self-care, motivation, social and communication skills and engagement with treatment. Very few patients are able to access other activities in the hospital, such as workshops and offending-behaviour programmes, because of the level of their disability (for example, a limited concentration span).

The ward milieu is specifically designed to be supportive, relaxed and gently facilitative, encouraging engagement of patients with their peers and staff. The unit is run using a therapeutic community approach. In practical terms this includes daily community meetings, usually around 15 minutes in length and informal. Patients are encouraged to participate in democratic decision-making wherever possible, for example in planning activities and ward décor. Attempts have been made to flatten the hierarchy in the multi-disciplinary team. There are a number of ongoing audit and research projects planned or underway designed to monitor progress and promote a spirit of enquiry. The Ward Atmosphere Scale is used to monitor the therapeutic environment created and to modify it when necessary. Future staff training and supervision is planned to heighten awareness of group processes and dynamics.

Example 23.3   The personality disorder unit at Arnold Lodge

Arnold Lodge is a medium secure unit in Leicester and it is part of Notting-hamshire Healthcare NHS Trust (further details are available at http://pdu.arnoldlodge.co.uk). Its 12-bedded personality disorder unit takes patients for a maximum of 2 years. It is the only medium secure unit in the NHS specifically designed to treat individuals with a personality disorder. It serves the Trent Region, which has a population of about 4.5 million and contains the cities of Derby, Leicester, Nottingham and Sheffield. To be eligible for admission patients must: be male; have a diagnosable personality disorder; require treatment in medium security; be motivated to engage in treatment; not be sexually sadistic; not have a psychosis; and have a referrer prepared to accept them back at the end of treatment, or if they drop out or are discharged prematurely.

The treatment programme is skills-based and broadly cognitive–behavioural in orientation. There is an emphasis on improving deficits in impulsivity and on anger management and learning how to stop and think before acting (D'Silva & Duggan, 2002).

The ward milieu is a major part of treatment. The patients' day is very structured, being timetabled between 08.00 h and 18.00 h. There are clear rules and expectations, including no physical violence and that people be civil to one another. Patients are expected to participate and engage, the regime is described as challenging and, in some respects, 'stricter than prison'. There is an interest in what happens during informal time and how this can relate to treatment planning and monitoring progress. Patients are expected to use the principles of the formal treatment programme, with its emphasis on nego-tiation, in resolving interpersonal conflicts with staff and peers. All staff need to be familiar with the programme and to adopt a consistent approach, giving feedback to patients and subsequently to the clinical team. There is a strong emphasis on multidisciplinary working, which has significant training implic-ations, particularly for maintaining the unit culture as staff change over time. A professor of forensic mental health heads the unit and there is an active programme of research and evaluation.

Both of the units described in Examples 23.2 and 23.3 are explicit in their attention to the ward environment. They are both specialist units with clear inclusion and exclusion criteria. The patient groups are very different: Cedars Community deals with treatment-resistant psychosis and people with long histories of institutionalisation, whereas the Arnold Lodge personality disorder unit predominantly houses young men with personality disorder transferred from prison. The environments created are very different. Cedars is described as supportive, relaxed and gently facilitative, the personality disorder unit as challenging and 'stricter than prison'. Both encourage the use of psychological therapies, in their broadest sense, as integral parts of their treatment programmes. The ward environments are designed around the patient group and its problems and are intended to support the use of individual psychological therapies in addition to being therapeutic in their own right.

Conclusion

Forensic psychiatric services operate at different levels of security, from open wards to high-security hospitals. The need to be aware of the risk of violence and the security measures needed to manage it are in a constant, and hopefully creative, tension with therapeutic activities.

The development of increasing sub-specialisation within forensic psychiatry (e.g. personality disorder, severe enduring mental illness, women's services) has allowed the development of more homogeneous patient groups. This should in turn lead to the development of more focused therapeutic milieus, as illustrated by the examples in this chapter.

References

Clark, D. (1999) Social psychiatry: the therapeutic community approach. In *Therapeutic Communities: Past Present and Future* (eds P. Campling & R. Haigh), pp. 32–38. London: Jessica Kingsley.

Department of Health (1999) *National Service Framework for Mental Health: Modern Standards and Service Models*. London: Stationery Office.

Department of Health (2002) *Mental Health Policy Implementation Guide: National Minimum Standards for General Adult Services in Psychiatric Intensive Care Units (PICU) and Low Secure Environments*. London: Department of Health. http://www.nimhe.org.uk/whatshapp/item_display_publications.asp?id=339

Dolan, B. & Coid, J. (1993) *Psychopathic and Antisocial Personality Disorders: Treatment and Research Issues*. London: Gaskell.

D'Silva, K. & Duggan, C. (2002) Service innovations: development of a psychoeducational programme for patients with personality disorder. *Psychiatric Bulletin*, **26**, 268–271.

Johnson, S. & Taylor, R. (2002) *Statistics of Mentally Disordered Offenders 2001*. London: Office for National Statistics. http://www.homeoffice.gov.uk/rds/pdfs2/hosb1302.pdf

Kennedy, H. (2002) Therapeutic uses of security: mapping forensic mental health services by stratifying risk. *Advances in Psychiatric Treatment*, **8**, 433–443.

Lees, J., Manning, N. & Rawlings, B. (1999) *Therapeutic Community Effectiveness: A Systematic International Review of Therapeutic Community Treatment for People with Personality Disorders and Mentally Disordered Offenders*. York: NHS Centre for Reviews and Dissemination, University of York.

Mental Health Act Commission (2001) *The Mental Health Act Commission 9th Biennial Report 1999–2001*. London: Stationery Office.

NHS Estates (1993) *Design Guide: Medium Secure Psychiatric Units*. London: Department of Health.

Paul, G. L., Stuve, P. & Menditto, A. A. (1997) Social-learning programme (with token economy) for adult psychiatric in-patients. *Clinical Psychologist*, **50**, 14–17.

Smith, J. (2000) The healing elements of an environment for those with chronic psychosis. *Therapeutic Communities*, **21**, 37–46.

Winston, A. P. (2000) Recent developments in borderline personality disorder. *Advances in Psychiatric Treatment*, **6**, 211–218.

Woodward, R. (1999) The prison communities. In *Therapeutic Communities: Past Present and Future* (eds P. Campling & R. Haigh), pp. 162–173. London: Jessica Kingsley.

CHAPTER 24

A nurturing environment for older adults

Wendy Ferguson, Shelley Hammersley and Lin Burton

Editors' introduction This chapter compassionately describes the needs of older people with dementia and outlines ways we could develop services to be more responsive. Wendy Ferguson, Shelley Hammersley and Lin Burton are occupational therapists working either in community health teams or day hospital services for older people. They have a particular interest in person-centred care and the use of activity to maintain skills and well-being within dementia care. We hope that those with a general as well as a specific interest will read this chapter, as the principles outlined are ingredients for all those who aspire to create environments that are empathetic and nurturing.

An 80-year-old woman has just been admitted to an in-patient facility. She looks frail and has fallen at home; she has a history of depression and now has a diagnosis of Alzheimer's disease. Those facts are written in her notes and the plan of care built around them. But who is she? She is Mabel, who was married to Jack for 60 years, whom she last remembers dying in a hospital bed. She doesn't like hospitals and did not want to come. She was qualified as a teacher and worked until retirement. She likes sugar but not milk in her tea and when at home she always lies on her bed for an hour after lunch. There is so much more to know. How much of this information is sought and reflected in assessments and care planning?

Carlson *et al* (1998), when researching successful ageing, said:

'nonagenarians are not time travellers who suddenly appear at 90 years of age with no past. Rather, they have undertaken a long journey through life and have been profoundly shaped by the particular joys, sorrows, triumphs, and cuts and bruises that they have experienced along the way'.

Dewing (2000) writes that a man who had Alzheimer's disease said:

'Help me to be strong and free until my self no longer exists ... most people expect to die some day, but whoever expected to lose their self first?'.

The challenge for staff in all facilities, whether in hospitals or residential/nursing homes, is to look beyond the diagnosis and presenting behaviour, past the medical model of care and the task-driven culture to truly know the people they are caring for. Only then can they begin to understand what life is like for those people and create environments that provide individualised therapeutic care.

This chapter is written by occupational therapists and therefore from the perspective of that profession. However, the theories and practices examined encompass all who work with older people with mental health problems.

Maslow (1954), who was a leading theorist in the development of humanistic psychology, proposed a model for classifying human motives, which he called the hierarchy of needs. This formed an interesting insight into the relationship between motivation and the opportunities afforded by the environment. In ascending order, the hierarchy consisted of: physiological needs (hunger, thirst); safety needs (feelings of security); the need for the sense of belonging and love (to be accepted and belong); esteem needs (to achieve and gain recognition); cognitive needs (to know and explore); aesthetic needs (order and beauty); and finally the need for self-actualisation (to find self-fulfilment and realise one's potential). He proposed that the needs at one level need to be at least partially met before those at the next level up become important and are therefore determinants for action. The aim for all therapeutic environments must be to encourage people to attain their highest possible potential regardless of disability. Unfortunately, this does not always occur. Frequently, we expect patients and residents to adapt to our routines and service needs, to step into our picture, rather than adapting ourselves to meet their individual needs and stepping into theirs.

Kitwood (1997) developed a model of 'person-centred care'. Although his work specifically looked at care provision for people with dementia, the principles that underpin person-centred care follow Maslow's theoretical ideals and are relevant to all, whatever the diagnosis. In her article for nurses, Dewing (2000) supports Kitwood's theories of creating caring environments, which are based on the psychosocial model of care, when she says,

'the medical model takes nurses down a "dead end". There is no point in being therapeutic or focusing on the future because everything is already determined by the disease process; the person is already lost or dead. The focus of care is on the physical body and containment of problems... In contrast, the psychosocial model takes nurses and older people down an open-ended path that says death of the self is not inevitable. It also means that therapeutic care (interactions and interventions) and therapies are essential to prevent death of the self'.

Settings that provide care for older people who have mental illnesses other than dementia are equally challenged. The World Health Organization in 1947 attempted to define health as not simply an absence of illness, but the state of complete physical, mental and social well-being. Consequently, true therapeutic environments should offer more than a place of safety and medication. They should, through collaborative, active, individualised assessments, also attempt to address those psychological, spiritual and social aspects of the person that gives them that sense of completeness or wholeness.

Supporting this, Kitwood (1997) maintained that caring for older people is more than just meeting their physical needs such as feeding and watering, keeping them clean and safe, and more than just reacting to presenting behaviours or dispensing medication. It is about creating a nurturing environment which values and supports the belief that everyone, whatever their disability, has basic needs for identity, attachment, inclusion, occupation and comfort, and that these needs must be met to enable them to maintain their sense of well-being. These are described in turn below.

The need for identity

Identity involves a sense of who we are and of our continuity with our past. In practice this means, for example, staff addressing patients and residents by the name they prefer and allowing them always to wear clothes that belong to them, not 'community clothing' (Box 24.1). We have already met Mabel. On her admission information it states that her name is Gladys Mabel, and staff automatically call her Gladys, to which she doesn't respond. If she had been asked what she wished to be called she would have said her name was Mabel. What we wear and the possessions that surround us make statements about us as individuals. To have photographs available of family and friends and personal belongings that remind patients of who they are is therefore of great importance: without these things, they appear anonymous, just another in a long line of people who have occupied the lounge.

One of us (W.F.) worked with a person with dementia who was having difficulty settling into residential care. To help this process we made a life-story collage for him to put on his bedroom wall. This enabled the staff to find out about him and it encouraged communication. He became a person with a past. Giving residents time to acknowledge their past

---

Box 24.1   Retaining a sense of identity

The following factors help patients to keep a sense of their own identity:

- Staff addressing them by the name they prefer
- Wearing their own clothes
- Having personal possessions with them, including photographs of family and friends
- Participating in life-story work

---

experiences and encouraging staff to recognise these are both important when developing care plans and observing behaviour. Life-story work is invaluable in helping patients to retain that sense of identity and some facilities have adopted the creation of these on admission as standard practice. At Merevale House in Cardiff (Cardiff Community Healthcare NHS Trust, 1998), a residential unit for people with dementia, each resident, together with their keyworker and relatives, completes a life-story book. This helps staff to see the person as a whole with his or her unique personal history. Achievements and work, loves and life experiences, likes and dislikes are all recorded, along with photographs and memorabilia. The staff use this information in all their communication with residents, and as a basis for appropriate care.

The need for attachment

Attachment enables us to feel that we are important to another person in some way. In practice this means that the care environment requires staffing structures and expertise that give staff the time and ability to create meaningful relationships with patients or residents (Box 24.2). This is often overlooked in busy task-oriented settings where facilities are understaffed, or staffed by frequently changing agency personnel; where time and emphasis are put on detailed record-keeping in a system more mindful of litigation; where tasks have to be done, measured and audited. Staffing groups need to creatively consider the way they spend time and ask themselves questions such as which times of the day are less busy and can be more effectively used and do they make the most of opportunities available to have one-to-one contact with people.

Allan (2001) explored ways of drawing out the views of people with dementia by using a variety of communication methods, including pictorial and word cues. The researchers trained staff to use time more effectively for communication. They also found that those times when staff were assisting with essential tasks such as bathing or dressing were not always recognised as offering potential therapeutic value,

---

Box 24.2   Facilitating attachment

- Institutions should acknowledge the importance of meaningful one-to-one relationships between staff and residents and should implement staffing structures conducive to their creation
- Staff should make the most of opportunities to have one-to-one contact with residents, e.g. while doing essential tasks such as bathing and preparing for bed
- Communication may be aided by using pictures and word cues

---

although they provided opportunities to create an atmosphere of intimacy and sharing that aided communication and helped build relationships. The staff also shared with patients routine tasks such as laundry-sorting and laying tables, to provide opportunities to talk, to gain opinions and to discover delights or concerns.

An environment in which people feel comfortable and at ease will always aid communication. Listening to people's opinions about the environment in which they find themselves, whatever their disability, is essential to meeting their needs in a therapeutic way. Some facilities, on recognising the shortage of trained nursing staff, are finding it beneficial not only for each resident to have a key nurse but also to have an assigned health care assistant who potentially has the time to develop a more consistent one-to-one relationship.

During a recent visit to a day hospital, W.F. was interested to watch a person who was physically frail and had spent some time shuffling aimlessly around his chair and not engaging with his surroundings at all. Suddenly, on seeing a particular member of staff come into the room, he walked purposefully up to her at some speed, with a large smile on his face and touched her on the arm to attract attention. She acknowledged him with conversation and laughter with which he engaged. This person had an obvious attachment to that member of staff, which motivated his actions and created a sense of well-being.

The need for inclusion

Inclusion describes the need to feel that we belong and are part of a social group (Box 24.3). Often we see large lounges with people in chairs seated around the edges, with no interaction, the television or radio creating noise, each individual sitting alone yet among others. The way environments are designed have an effect on the way people feel and behave, and if right can help to create all manner of positive

---

Box 24.3   Creating a sense of inclusion

- Encourage individuals to make their own space within public rooms
- Arrange furniture into small groups to enable people to easily talk with each other
- Encourage a shared focus of interest
- Use colour creatively (e.g. paint toilet doors in a bright colour) to help orientation and mastery of the environment
- Encourage activities with a shared goal or activities that contribute to the environment as a whole
- Maintain an environment and create routines as much like the older person's home life as possible

---

feelings. A nursing home in Leicestershire ensured that residents could have 'their space' within public rooms, in the same way as many older people would have a favourite chair at home. Joyce, who had been discharged to this facility having experienced a period of depression, was able to sit in her own chair, hang her footballers' pin-up calendar on the wall and have her table beside her with her books, sweets and papers. She chose to sit next to people who had similar interests and with whom she could share. That group arranged the flowers for the room and knitted blankets for the chairs. She felt included and made a successful transition to establish it as her home.

Design changes can be made to create a therapeutic environment: organising lounge or dining room furniture into small groups to enable people to talk with each other easily; being more creative with decorative colour to create a particular atmosphere; or using colour to help orientation. Kirklands, a residential home in Cumbria, took the opportunity when refurbishing to paint toilet door frames a single bright colour throughout the building, in order to help residents locate the toilets. They also employed a local artist to paint a mural, which featured surrounding areas and images relevant to the residents. This brightened the environment, encouraged reminiscence and a sense of belonging (Innes, 1998). Encouraging activity, particularly that which requires a shared goal or makes a contribution to the facility as a whole, helps people feel they belong. Burton (1997), while evaluating a project that introduced activities to wards for dementia care, reported the following carers' comments:

'[activities] helped him in mixing with others – activities have drawn them together, used to sit on his own, now socialises more' and 'activities allowed her to interact with people, never really been a person to join in, but this really helped her to settle on the ward'.

One large company that runs homes for older people with dementia across the country bases its care on maintaining an environment and creating routines as much like the older person's home life as possible. If residents wish to wash the dishes after the meal they do so; if that requires dishes to be put into the dishwasher to be rewashed, that is acceptable. If, like Mabel at the start of this chapter, a resident's routine is to return to bed after lunch, that too is acceptable. Residents are encouraged to make hot drinks for themselves, if this is thought to be safe. In this way people contribute to their care environment, interact with other residents and feel included.

The need for occupation

This has been much researched, particularly through occupational science, which is the study of the human as an occupational being. It also underpins the profession of occupational therapy, which was founded on a belief that there is a relationship between how health affects and is affected by engagement in purposeful, meaningful occupation (Box 24.4). Wilcock (2001) wrote that occupation

'is the biological mechanism for human health and survival, and therefore people have inbuilt needs to engage in occupation. We are in fact all occupational beings'.

Yet, although some facilities have taken on board this basic need to 'do', the need for activity continues to be poorly recognised within care systems as a whole and few have designated activity organisers whose sole role is to meet this occupational requirement. The culture in hospital settings, predominantly influenced by the medical model, gives priority to a staffing profile that provides a safe environment, delivers physical care and medication and responds to problems. Although these are important, Kitwood (1997) argues that caring should be concerned primarily with the maintenance and enhancement of 'personhood'. To that end, occupation needs to be an essential part of every environment, with suitably trained staff to enable this to happen.

Perrin (1995) stated that, in her experience,

'although most settings have some understanding that activities are "a good thing", in practice most activities are carried out by unqualified staff … very few of whom have been trained in the appropriate use of occupation'.

Occupational therapists, whose core skills lie within the field of meeting occupational needs, goal-planning and adaptation, should be employed within such environments. Training is essential for the planning of goals appropriate to needs, for appreciating the value of occupation to health, for engaging people sensitively with the right approach and for identifying its therapeutic effect.

An example of an assessment that can be used within dementia care by all is the Pool Activity Level (PAL) instrument (Pool, 1999), which uses observation to describe a person's ability to engage in activities. It

---

Box 24.4 Providing occupation

- Occupation is an important component of being human and should be offered in every care environment
- Occupational therapists are appropriately skilled to take a lead in identifying occupational needs, goal-planning and adaptation, and in sharing their specialist knowledge with the multidisciplinary team to enable others to work in a similar way
- Each individual's ability to engage in activities should be assessed (e.g. using the Pool Activity Level instrument) and activities should be adapted and individualised as appropriate

covers four activity levels: planned, exploratory, sensory and reflex. Once the activity level is identified, by completing the observational checklist, planning can be done in conjunction with personal history, to engage the individual in appropriate activity. For example, a facility might think it a good idea to have newspapers available: residents functioning at a planned level would enjoy reading and sharing information from them; those at an exploratory level might enjoy holding them and turning the pages, but would not necessarily read them; those at the sensory level might enjoy the feel and sound of the paper and scrunch it up into a ball; and those at the reflex level might smile as they feel the air on their faces from a newspaper used by a carer as a fan. There are activities that meet all needs if training, time, creativity and a broader vision are present. The alternative is occupational deprivation: lethargy, low mood, loss of skills and 'ill-being', which may lead to behaviours often labelled as problem or challenging, such as wandering and shouting.

The need for comfort

The final need that Kitwood referred to is comfort (Box 24.5). In practice it is about the way staff relate to the people in their care. The skills and attributes required when responding to this need are sometimes inherent in staff, but these skills may not be explicitly acknowledged, recognised or developed. A good awareness of ourselves, including the way we as individuals work, and our own attitudes or prejudices, will enable us to establish nurturing environments and successful one-to-one contacts.

Such awareness also challenges our views on ageing. Carlson *et al* (1998), in their work on successful ageing, wrote

'we must view ageing as a complex interplay of mostly controllable factors, and not as the pathological offspring of some irreversible and inevitable decline'.

Box 24.5   Creating a sense of comfort

Comfort:

- is associated with tenderness, closeness and warmth
- requires self-aware staff in order to overcome unhelpful attitudes and prejudice
- links with a sense of reassurance and control which can be encouraged, for example, by structuring routines to include personally treasured occupations and encounters

---

They argued that the key to successful ageing is not necessarily good physical or mental health, but it is the feeling within older people that they have or can regain a sense of control over their lives. For example, although physically frail older people may have fewer activity options available to them, they can still function within these limitations to compose a rich and joyful life by structuring their routine to include personally treasured occupations and encounters. In the same way, people who know that they are in the early stages of dementia might gain reassurance and a sense of control if engaged in memory-training work that enables them to help themselves.

Conclusion

This chapter does not offer an exhaustive list of instructions on how to create and maintain an environment in which therapeutic practice is best achieved (although some key points are listed in Box 24.6). In mental health care for older people facilities vary greatly, from hospital in-patient settings that serve people with depression and aim at short-term intervention to residential units that people with dementia call 'home'. They are all as unique as the people they serve. However, we hope that this chapter encourages health care staff to think outside the

---

Box 24.6   Some practical requirements for a therapeutic environment

- Communication, both within a multidisciplinary team and with the people in its care
- A staffing profile diverse and skilled enough to address all levels of Maslow's hierarchy of needs, to help patients or residents to reach their maximum potential
- A thorough understanding of the principles of person-centred care, so that assessment and intervention are based on each individual's unique story and experiences
- A care plan working towards each resident's personal objectives and goals, not those of the service
- Giving residents a sense of security in a comfortable environment
- An environment that does not create dependency but respects the value of activity, encouraging residents to retain some control through collaborative care planning and to retain feelings of self-worth and competency by using their skills and achievements
- An environment that allows those who struggle to meet cognitive needs to explore, to take risks and to participate, however 'inefficiently', in order to make sense of the world around them
- An emotionally safe environment with skilled staff to help people (both staff and residents) to explore their inner selves and embark on changes
- Enabling residents to maintain their dignity, their identity and a feeling of belonging

---

Box 24.7 Questions to ask ourselves

- What should we prioritise?
- Which times of the day are less busy and can be more effectively utilised?
- Do we make the most of opportunities available to have one-to-one contact with residents?
- Could we communicate (with colleagues and with residents) more effectively?

---

box, beyond what they immediately know or observe, and to view each elderly person as a whole person who has a unique place in the environment just as they have a unique contribution to make to the places where they work (Box 24.7).

References

Allan, K. (2001) Drawing out the views on services: meeting the many challenges. *Journal of Dementia Care*, March/April, 26–29.

Burton, L. (1997) *Ward Activities Pilot Project Organic Wards Evaluation.* Leicester: Leicestershire Partnership NHS Trust.

Cardiff Community Healthcare NHS Trust (1998) *Signpost to Older People and Mental Health Matters: 3.* Cardiff: Cardiff Community Healthcare NHS Trust

Carlson, M., Clark, F. & Young, B. (1998) Practical contributions of occupational science to the art of successful ageing: how to sculpt a meaningful life in older adulthood. *Journal of Occupational Science*, **5**, 107–118.

Dewing, J. (2000) Promoting well-being in older people with cognitive impairment. *Elderly Care*, **12**, 19–22.

Innes, A. (1998) A sea-change at Kirklands. *Journal of Dementia Care*, Nov/Dec, 21–23.

Kitwood, T. (1997) *Dementia Reconsidered.* Buckingham: Open University Press.

Maslow, A. (1954) *Motivation and Personality.* New York: Harper and Row.

Perrin, T. (1995) A new pattern of life: re-assessing the role of occupation and activities. In *The New Culture of Dementia Care* (eds T. Kitwood & S. Benson), pp. 66–69. London: Hawker Publications.

Pool, J. (1999) *The Pool Activity Level (PAL) Instrument. A Practical Resource for Carers of People with Dementia, Bradford Dementia Group.* London: Jessica Kingsley.

Wilcock, A. (2001) Occupational science: the key to broadening horizons. *British Journal of Occupational Therapy*, **64**, 8.

CHAPTER 25

Therapeutic communities

Sandra Kelly, Judith Hill, Heather Boardman and Ian Overton

Editors' introduction   Sandra Kelly (lead nurse), Judith Hill, Heather Boardman and Ian Overton (staff nurse) are all part of the NHS therapeutic community at Francis Dixon Lodge in Leicester. This chapter is about their subjective experiences and describes very vividly what it feels like to live and work in a therapeutic community.

A staff member's journey

By Sandra Kelly

I am the lead nurse at Francis Dixon Lodge, and have been in post for 2 years. I have worked in the unit for 10 years. I have a background of general nursing training and belong to the generation of nurses that moved away from the task-oriented care of patients' physical needs to a more holistic approach that also catered for patients' emotional well-being. However, when I qualified, I became disenchanted by the lack of confidence within general nursing about addressing emotional distress within the everyday working structure. There are numerous accounts that I could give where I felt emotional pain had been neglected.

One in particular comes to mind, when I was working on a busy surgical assessment ward. I was giving a woman a postoperative wash; she had come in the day before knowing that the doctors were going to have a look at her stomach, and she was uncomfortable and weak from the operation. At the same time, a ward round had begun. A doctor in his white coat popped his head through the curtains and asked to have a word. It was the consultant. As I was a junior nurse at the time, I went to finish up and get out of the way. The doctor asked me to stay. He sat for a moment and told the woman she had inoperable cancer of the stomach. He then got up and left us. She and I remained silent. I did not know what to say. I was overwhelmed with the impact of her news. What would she say to her family? Who would help her with this? I remember feeling consumed with anger. How could the consultant just tell her like that and go. I continued with tending to her, both of us in silence. I finished what I was doing, went away somewhere and cried.

I was not aware of anyone talking to that woman about what she needed to do before she died. She had the very best of physical care, everything to keep her from increasing physical pain, but was left to struggle with the emotional journey on her own. I felt ill equipped to manage the distress of the patient. My general training had taught me a lot but clearly not enough. I wondered if I could ever get the balance right, between physical and emotional care, so that I could attend to such a level of distress, both mine and the patient's, without it overwhelming me. I decided to train as a mental health nurse, with the intention of going back to general nursing with the skills to deal with the emotional distress – but I have not made it back yet!

During my training as a mental health nurse, once again I became frustrated by the dependence on drug therapy and the reliance on the Mental Health Act as a container for emotional distress. In addition, there were unhelpful inconsistencies of care from one unit to another. Interestingly, the whole atmosphere of the ward seemed to depend more on the personality of the leader than on the particular therapeutic framework employed.

I became particularly interested in the group of patients who do not have a mental illness but express their very high levels of emotional distress through impulsive, destructive behaviours – particularly self-harm. Once the admission crisis was over, I would wonder what had really brought this person into hospital. Frequently these patients would elicit concern in some staff, irritation and impatience in others. What struck me was that the patient often looked rather like myself, 20 something and as harmless as the next person. However, when discharge was mentioned to the patient, the drama and acting out began again. This is because the patient was fearful about the withdrawal of the care and containment provided by the acute ward.

The relationship between the patient and the keyworker often quickly became emotionally overloaded. The keyworker was frequently changed without proper consultation or a sufficient attempt to understand the relationship between the keyworker and the patient. I asked myself what the problem was that meant that the patient could talk to the keyworker freely, but remained mute when seen in the ward round by the consultant psychiatrist? I can remember as a student nurse that patients disclosed some of their most powerful thoughts to me at times. However, I was never asked about my contact with patients. It was left very much up to me to divulge what I knew, and to decide what I thought was relevant for the ward team to hear. I assumed as a student that information that you had been given by a patient had also been talked about with other staff. For example, I could sit in the coffee room with a patient, listening to an outpouring of sadness, anger, sometimes even hatred towards the consultant psychiatrist, but I never knew whether this information was generally known or not.

Once again I was faced with the same struggles as when tending to the woman who was told in such a matter-of-fact way that she had cancer. I had to just get on and tend to physical needs, while emotional needs could not be acknowledged. In mental health nursing, I was faced with the same dilemma of patients expressing overwhelming feelings of distress that appeared to come from nowhere, but were not directly dealt with – rather they were avoided or ignored. Medication appeared to be the answer to everything.

I know now that physical cuts to the skin, or overdoses, are an attempt to communicate emotional distress. However, back then, cutting one's own skin created such hostile and angry feelings in the staff team and, I suspect, in other patients too. More often than not, the whole team would feel hatred and intolerance for the person who had carried out self-harm. Sometimes, someone would empathise with a patient's feelings and distress, often much to other staff's irritation. On the whole, medication was usually prescribed to calm the person down if the staff noted any agitation or distress. I again felt helpless in this situation.

I came across therapeutic community work (Box 25.1) by accident. My tutors at university certainly knew little about it. Francis Dixon Lodge was the first psychiatric unit I had seen that did not rely on medication and had a structured day, with a treatment philosophy.

After my arrival at Francis Dixon Lodge, and once over my initial fear of the structure, the timetable and the amount of participation in the programme that was required of me as a student nurse, I was relatively comfortable in the community. However, I naturally felt uncomfortable with the disturbing psychological content of the community meetings and psychotherapy groups. I wondered how these could be helping the patients. I was thankful for the weekly student supervision group, which helped me to understand the psychodynamic processes within

---

Box 25.1 What are therapeutic communities?

- Therapeutic communities provide intensive psychosocial treatment that may include a variety of therapies but where the therapeutic environment itself is seen as the primary agent of change
- The community (staff and users) work collaboratively to create a 'safe frame' within which problems can be explored and understood – in residential or day units or a combination of both
- Members of the community are seen as bringing strengths and creativity to the therapeutic environment and are encouraged to develop a sense of agency by taking a significant role in decision-making and the everyday running of the unit

For further information contact: The Association of Therapeutic Communities, Barns Centre, Church Lane, Toddington, near Cheltenham, Gloucestershire GL54 5DQ. Tel/fax: 01242 620077; e-mail: past@therapeuticcommunities.org; website: www.therapeuticcommunities.org

even at times felt a bit crazy. I have been comforted by the following words by someone in a similar position:

'As a leader one must be manager, teacher, supervisor, therapist, friend, carer, advocate and guru. One must inspire, lead, motivate, criticise, support, comfort, confront, praise and reassure. Moreover, one must move from one role to another often in quick succession and more often than not under extreme pressure from other factors threatening to engulf one's own identity and position' (S. Paget, personal communication, 2001).

I am a Black woman and well used to having to manage stereotypical projections, which I attract because of the colour of my skin. 'Are you reacting to me like this because I am Black?' is such a difficult question to ask and seems to attract such defensiveness, even aggression. Yet, I know I have the right to struggle with this question and establish that I am being treated fairly and equally.

I feel I cannot write more, for I am in the middle of my journey. It is a painfully intense and familiar place, but there is always a sense of learning about myself and moving forwards.

A living–learning experience

By Judith Hill

I have struggled with depression, anxiety and problems with relationships since the age of about 9. I am now 27 and have been a resident at Francis Dixon Lodge therapeutic community for just over 6 months. Previously I have had a small amount of cognitive–behavioural therapy, seen counsellors for short periods of time, seen GPs, psychiatrists, and tried to help myself by reading the numerous self-help books that are available.

Before arriving at Francis Dixon Lodge, I knew little about what living in a therapeutic community would entail or how it could help me. I knew that it was essentially a 'living–learning' experience and that there would be group psychotherapy and that as much of the work or help would come from the other people I would be living with as from the staff that work there. I had never experienced group therapy before and was apprehensive about this new approach.

Living and working in a therapeutic community is hard. It is challenging, confrontational and tends to recreate the same difficulties and problems that you experienced in the 'outside world.' The difference is that you get a chance to look at them in depth, attempt to work through them and understand them in a 'safe' environment. Rather than analysing problems in isolation (as in one-to-one therapy), residents living in the community often relate to one another, and can work through these problems together, guided by staff (Box 25.2).

> **Box 25.2** Important therapeutic community concepts
>
> - The living–learning experience – all aspects of community living contribute to the therapeutic process
> - The culture of inquiry – all involved are encouraged to be curious and to ask questions
> - Communalism – a culture of shared tasks, rolling your sleeves up and joining in
> - A flattened hierarchy – all are encouraged to have a voice and authority has to be earned rather than simply assumed because of one's role

The residents are involved in much of what goes on in the community, in the day-to-day running of the place, cooking and cleaning, chairing the twice-daily community meetings or helping in assessments of potential new residents. Residents can question how certain things are done and are encouraged to take responsibility for themselves and their actions, to try to come to their own conclusions and evaluate their own progress. Sometimes I have found this overwhelming and frustrating. There appear to be no 'answers', and it is easy to feel lost among all the chaos that there sometimes is in the community, especially if a number of residents are struggling with difficult feelings at the same time. There are no quick-fix solutions, and it is a long, slow and often painful process to change destructive or unhelpful behaviour. However, the therapeutic community can be extremely supportive, and it helps residents to question their thoughts, patterns of behaviour and the degree of control or power they have over their own lives, in order to manage difficulties in a more productive way.

A powerful experience

By Heather Boardman

I entered the acute ward for the fourth time in one year. For the first time in my life I left all responsibility for myself at the door. An unusual position for me, a person who has felt an overwhelming amount of responsibility for myself and others for over 30 years. I left my baggage of responsibility at the door.

My stay was like a deconstruction of my personality, my abilities and my worth. I continued the path that awaited me on the acute ward and fully entered the self-destruction, no one cares anyway. Obviously the psychiatrist and nursing staff in partnership had to contain me, this was done via large amounts of medication in addition to ECT [electroconvulsive therapy]. The whole process was destructive to my mind and soul but it enabled me to stay alive.

Eventually I entered into the therapeutic community. What a shock to the system after a lengthy stay on an acute ward. This difference has been sobering to say the least. I entered the door and collected the responsibility for me at the door. Heavily laden after a long time at first felt somewhat disabling. I limped around for 3 months, giving feedback to members of the community and pushing all issues relating to me as far away as possible – in addition to trying to keep people away from me. At 3 months, through evaluation and a care plan, I was able to see that the movement I had made was not in distance but in depth. I was now a part of other people's lives and like it or not (which I don't) they were part of me. I've struggled a great deal with accepting support from others. I give support and I am in a battle to accept support. I'm not alone here, there are many members of the community who have survived our experiences alone and that has been the safest way we could have survived, expect nothing from no one and there's no disappointment.

The responsibility to manage a better future is now mine again. I've tried this for many years the only way I know how but this time it's different: we live together, work together and grieve together. I would imagine you are thinking that it all sounds rather 'airy-fairy'. It's not. It's powerful work, more powerful than any other experience of life itself. The community will challenge destructive behaviour; they will express their anger in a safe way when anyone behaves destructively. We are all fighting our destructive behaviour so why should one person think it's OK to go back? Easily we could all join in, but that doesn't happen as we are all at different stages within the therapeutic process. The culture of enquiry is at first alarming, you don't want people asking you why you bath four times a day or why you don't want to eat with the community each night. Therefore at first you do the norm to avoid the questions and what your behaviour relates to. You can't behave 'just so' for very long, what's really happening catches up with you. This leads to you doing the most intense work and you are able to question yourself also. The relationships that develop are like no others you have ever had and I would suggest like no others you ever have again, unique, that's what they are. You can be challenged by other members of the community, that's safe, they are not going to hate you, and it's your actions and behaviour that someone is angry about, not you as a person. Anyone is challenged within the community: nursing staff, clinical consultant, psychotherapist, SHO [senior house officer], community member. They call it flattened hierarchy. Of course, they are only flattened to a certain extent. We have to remember at certain points the staff decision is final.

The relationships that develop with staff can be extremely intense and potentially traumatic. You can battle with transference, not wanting to feel it. Sometimes you get to a point and everyone else can see that they represent certain figures in your past but your skilled avoidance clouds what is really going on.

Sometimes you feel like your head is going to explode, so much is going on. You direct every interaction you have, every glance that anyone gives. You want to run from the feelings of self-harm/ parasuicide to get some relief from the pressure. The responsibility for oneself and the potential anger you invoke enable a certain level of containment. The difference is on an acute ward you would be sectioned, watched, the door locked. In a therapeutic community you sign up for an unwritten emotional section. The emotional section is more powerful and progressive, unlike the Mental Health Act section that gives you something to fight against, something to blame for your destructive activities.

As time progresses within the therapeutic community, you begin to recognise how another member's behaviour angers you. You can also unravel that anger and see what it relates to. I have gone through a period not acknowledging that anger and not daring to express what it relates to, but eventually you have to otherwise your head would 'pop'. The fallout is far too hard to bear; therefore, eventually you bring up the issues as they arrive.

Self-evaluation is a valuable part of the process. Sometimes I think I'm not making any movement but, however small, the movement is a reminder that the emotional roller coaster has to be better than being locked in and medicated until you rattle.

The relationships I've built while at the therapeutic community are unique, no one will ever know me in the way the residents here do. The relationships are often full of conflict; the difference is this conflict is safe. The community support each other all the way. I never want to cross the doorstep of an acute ward again. My experience of an acute ward is of a psychiatric facility which maintains life, unlike a therapeutic community that promotes managing your life and a future. The majority of us who get through the therapeutic community experience can manage a future ... I'm hopeful I'm one of these people.

A nurse's perspective

By Ian Overton

I came to Francis Dixon Lodge a year after qualifying as a nurse. Something about the visit I had made earlier that year had impressed me. Seeing residents 'own' their community and taking a lead in decisions about their therapy felt empowering and I applied for a position as soon as one became vacant. It had long been a wish of mine to work in a place where responsibility and, moreover, decisions should as much as possible be in the hands of the residents. I wondered if the reality of working in a therapeutic community would match my initial impression.

To enter a therapeutic community is to start a journey of learning and personal development. To begin with, there were a bewildering number of rules and residents would happily remind me if I transgressed or forgot some. It was also apparent that I could not so easily hide behind my role, as there was a greater expectation to be open and genuine. It was also surprising to me how overt staff conflict was. With staff days and sensitivity groups, issues within the team regularly get aired with strength of feelings. Often this mirrors dynamics within the resident group.

The nurses have an important role in a therapeutic community in that they are present day and night and are privy to not only structured time but also unstructured social time. A great deal of work is generated from observing and interacting with residents at mealtimes, in the evenings or during activities. Such communication can tap into personal dynamics that can then be brought into a community meeting for further explanation. Seemingly minor interactions may lead to much deeper feelings from formative experiences. At Francis Dixon Lodge, which is self-catering, work groups for shopping, cleaning and meal preparation allow staff to participate daily in community life. This inclusion breaks down distinctions between staff and residents and empowers residents by giving them responsibility.

Working in a therapeutic community is very much about teamwork, not only within the multidisciplinary team but also within the whole community. Communication is vital so that clinical decisions are known to residents, but also, when appropriate, it can be put out for discussion among the residents. For example, it was felt important to involve residents in health and safety. So a dialogue was initiated with them and we jointly produced a residents' job description. Now residents actively participate in inspections and raise issues relating to our environment.

Of great importance is the ability to offer and receive constructive criticism or comment. Very often one's self-awareness does not catch up with one's actions, and other staff may observe and comment on this. Group supervision allows such issues to be discussed and explored sensitively. Reflection and peer feedback facilitate personal growth and I have particularly noticed that my responses are more genuine and honest since starting at Francis Dixon Lodge.

In a therapeutic community it is important to share responsibility for rules and boundaries rather than relying on a hierarchy, which can foster dependency and rebelliousness. Sometimes it is even necessary to remind other staff, for example of the importance of starting on time. Very often it is the residents group who reinforce and police the boundaries. Many residents' personal boundaries are poor or very limited, often because of neglectful or abusive childhood experience. The therapeutic community may be the first environment in which the resident has ever felt held or contained, and maintaining firm but flexible boundaries enables this. Boundary-pushing is not infrequent and I remember being particularly vulnerable to this when I first started. For example, participation in group activities can be problematic with some individuals struggling to attend regularly. Various excuses may be offered but these need to be challenged in community meetings. With time I grew more confident with challenging such infringements. One aspect that is difficult to manage is that of overinvolvement and the temptation to get drawn into one-to-one work with residents. It is important to persuade the resident that they need to return to their feelings in a meeting, otherwise staff can be left holding onto secrets and difficult material, which over time can cause paranoia, with residents wondering who knows what, misunderstandings and splits within the staff team and the community.

Inevitably, residents will some times reach crisis point. If appropriate, it may be necessary to call a crisis meeting and rally the support of other residents. It cannot be emphasised enough how important it is to utilise all support possible, and one major source not to be under-estimated is that of the residents themselves. Senior residents provide an experienced group of individuals who can often be highly supportive of their struggling colleagues. A common scenario might involve a resident acting out and taking an overdose. A crisis meeting is called and the group offers to support the individual in crisis by sending a couple of residents with her to the casualty department as support. Generally, there are always some residents who are struggling less or managing to cope better at the moment, and these will often volunteer to assist. In another situation a phone call might be received from a day resident struggling at home. After offering some time on the phone to support and ground that individual, it may be felt necessary to inform other residents. Together the staff and residents can work out a plan to support the absent resident, calling them back or sometimes travelling in their own cars to offer direct support. Ultimately the nurse needs to make an assessment of risk. In some instances if risk of suicide or serious self-harm are great, it may be necessary to coordinate outside agencies such as an ambulance or the police.

Another area of importance is that of transference and counter-transference. Because nurses tend to be on duty on a range of shifts transference can be particularly problematic. Duties such as handing out medication or involvement in work groups or being around at bedtime can cause distress to both resident and nurse. It is important that the nurse is aware of their own feelings and behaviour and can utilise supervision and 'after groups' (reflective staff meetings held after all therapeutic groups). Growing self-awareness may also enable the nurse to perceive their own countertransference and work through this with other staff. I vividly remember on my first day a female resident cringing and making a rapid exit at her first sight of me. With time, sensitivity and patience the transference was explored and understood. Now we both have an understanding and I have developed a productive therapeutic alliance with her.

The most rewarding aspect of therapeutic communities is the empowerment of residents. At Francis Dixon Lodge residents often lead or completely own aspects of the clinical programme. An example is the care plan group. When it was first suggested that residents would write their own care plans and evaluate them every 2 weeks, there was an outcry that staff were shirking their responsibility. However, over time this has become part of the culture, with a weekly care plan meeting that breaks into small working groups. We have recently changed the name 'care plan' to 'progress plan', which seems more congruent with our philosophy. Whatever the name, it is the fact that residents own these plans and engage in the thinking that matters.

Standing back sometimes can be important, as it is tempting to go rushing in and rescue residents. But this can be unhelpful, actually repeating pathological dynamics from the past. It is tempting to rescue residents who appear vulnerable, but this may be driven by our own needs to feel liked and depended upon. It can sometimes feel that in order to earn our pay packet we have to say lots of clever things, but in reality, being there is as much a part of a nurse's role as intervening; it is about knowing when to offer support or feedback and when to sit back. It is important not to foster unhelpful dependence in the residents, which will often have been a problem for them in other settings.

The importance of the nurse's role cannot be overstated. Being there at mealtimes, at bedtime and first thing in the morning may give some residents their first experience of having someone there. The simple act of being around, watching a TV 'soap' in the evening or peeling potatoes together can be very supportive and grounding. Residents, past and present, often report that when they phone in seeking reassurance, a familiar voice at the end of the phone can be sufficient to ground them.

Some nurses are undergoing an introductory training in psychodynamic therapy, but few have formal training in specialist group psychotherapy despite the fact that facilitating group work is part of the job. However, many nurses have a breadth of experience gained during training, post-registration and life in general that they bring to therapeutic communities. Yet there is never time to remain complacent. I have found working in a therapeutic community very stimulating because I am constantly learning things about the residents and myself. After a year working at Francis Dixon Lodge, I still have a sense of wonder at the courage some people show, a sense of admiration at the changes people make, and feel privileged to be part of such an experience.

Further reading

Campling, P. (2001) Therapeutic communities. *Advances in Psychiatric Treatment, 7,* 365–372.

Campling, P. M. & Haigh, R. (1999) *Therapeutic Communities Past, Present and Future.* London: Jessica Kingsley.

Dooher, J. & Byrt, R. (2003) *Empowerment and the Health Service User.* Salisbury: Quay Books, Mark Allen Publishing. (Chapter 10 is written by various staff and residents from Francis Dixon Lodge.)

Kennard, D. (1998) *An Introduction to Therapeutic Communities.* London: Jessica Kingsley.

Lees, J., Manning, N. & Rawlings, B. (1999) *Therapeutic Community Effectiveness: A Systematic Review of Therapeutic Community Treatment for People with Personality Disorder and Mentally Disordered Offenders.* York: University of York, NHS Centre for Review and Dissemination.

CHAPTER 26

Rehabilitation and continuing care

John Howat

Editors' introduction John Howat has been a consultant in rehabilitation psychiatry in Nottingham for over 20 years. During this time he has been involved in the closure of four mental hospitals and the reprovision of services in the community. Through participation in the process he became aware of the paradox between the neo-institutionalised and compartmentalised nature of much provision with little change in community attitudes while at the same time witnessing some people experience major transformations in their self-belief and sense of mastery over their illnesses and the negative aspects of the care system. In this chapter John looks at therapeutic environments in their widest context and towards an exciting future for rehabilitation informed by a recovery philosophy, social inclusion and the better meeting of individuals' needs.

Psychiatric rehabilitation

Psychiatric rehabilitation has been described as the systematic application of interventions to reduce impairments, disabilities and handicaps. The aim is to

'ensure that the person with psychiatric disability can perform those physical, emotional and intellectual skills needed to live, learn and work in his or her own community, given the least amount of intervention necessary from agents of the helping profession' (Anthony & Liberman, 1986).

In a review of the evidence, Mueser *et al* (1997) identified five key factors across a range of rehabilitative activities, including case management, supported employment and family intervention (Box 26.1).

Box 26.1 Five characteristics of successful rehabilitation programmes (Mueser *et al*, 1997)

- Effective interventions tend to be direct and behavioural
- Rehabilitation programmes have specific effects on related outcomes, with limited generalisation to other domains
- Short-term interventions are less effective than long-term ones
- Interventions need to be delivered close to the patient's usual environment
- Effective programmes often combine skills-training and environmental support

---

The shift in the locus of care away from hospital into the community has led to the development of a network of rehabilitation service provision – with a progressively shifting emphasis from residential to day care and further to the use of normal community settings such as ordinary housing, community education, leisure and open employment.

This has been paralleled by a movement away from a care philosophy that emphasised placement at an appropriate level of provided support and relatively passive acquisition of new or relearned skills. In the past, needs assessment tended to be standardised and care planning programmatic. Now, the emphasis is on individual choices of objective, paths and strategies.

The concept of recovery

Interest in recovery as a concept and potential paradigm for services dates from the early 1990s in the USA (Warner, 2000) and recovery now features as a core element of the National Service Framework for Mental Health in England. Although the term has been used in very different ways, common features that convey the quintessence of the concept are summarised in Box 26.2.

Effective recovery-oriented services will need to explore the external environmental factors that encourage or stultify the process, together with their interaction with internal factors specific to the individual. The greatest challenge will be establishing an approach that is able to transfer the aggregate of the individual experience into a framework and set of values and skills for services and workers (Anthony, 2000).

Rehabilitation and the National Service Framework

Recent mental health policy in England has attempted to address inconsistencies, gaps and ineffective practices in the post-institutional

---

Box 26.2 Common features inherent in the concept of recovery (Ridgeway, 2001)

- The reawakening of hope after despair
- Breaking through denial and achieving understanding and acceptance
- Moving from withdrawal to engagement and active participation in life
- Active coping rather than passive adjustment
- No longer viewing oneself primarily as a mental patient and reclaiming a positive sense of self
- A journey from alienation to purpose
- A complex journey not accomplished alone – it involves support and partnership

national patchwork of services. The main mechanism for implementation is the National Service Framework for Mental Health. Early intervention in psychosis services are envisaged as a model treatment for the first 3 years for people following the onset of a psychotic illness, if required. There is an emphasis on optimising medication and deploying mainly behavioural psychological interventions on an individual and family basis. Less specifically, each person's employment, educational, financial and housing needs should be assessed and plans made to meet them.

Those with ongoing needs will graduate to the care of generic local community mental health teams or, possibly, more specialised continuing care teams known as rehabilitation and recovery teams. The assumption is that these teams will deliver support and supervision and also foster change and the promotion of independence through a mixture of direct intervention and brokerage.

Those who do not engage with such programmes will be eligible for open-ended care from assertive outreach teams.

Different types of residential housing and support services

The National Service Framework and policy position on residential services, other than from acute and intensive in-patient care, has been much less clear than that on the new, more modular, community team structures and functions. There appears to have been a reluctance to commit to any model or planned volume of provision of non-acute residential care except for those deemed to require secure provision. The only central guidance on the subject, on 24-hour nursed care for people with severe and enduring mental illness (National Health Service Executive, 1996), appeared rather late in the epoch of institutional closure but before the appearance of the National Service Framework, from which it appears to be detached.

Despite the massive relocation and reconfiguration of services in the closure era, there has been no systematic review of residential rehabilitation and continuing care with respect to numbers of units, defined functions, resources or therapeutic regime. There is uncertainty about policy; and an evidence base for deciding on how many beds and of what kind is lacking.

Available figures (known to be incomplete) recorded 6032 non-acute beds in England in 2002 (see http://www.dur.ac.uk/service.mapping/amh2002/), of which approximately half were in National Health Service (NHS) residential rehabilitation units and the remainder in 24-hour staffed care, both NHS and independent sector. A few of these units are long-stay wards within the remaining psychiatric hospitals. The remainder are community based and almost all were opened during the active phase of institutional closure – the final 15 years of the 20th century. In the main they were created to fulfil a resettlement function for long-stay hospital residents, funded from closure savings and frequently staffed by displaced hospital staff. The evidence suggests that these residential units did that job well, but their essentially supportive approach and associated staff skills have not suited the needs of the newer more assertive and frequently chaotic group of potential residents.

The second major category of residential rehabilitation and continuing care provision is the registered residential care home sector. In 2002, there were a 9480 people with mental health problems under the age of 65 in such homes and the number was increasing for this client group (see http://www.dur.ac.uk/service.mapping/amh2002/). There has been little guidance on the role and appropriate care regimes for care homes and how they should fit with other parts of the mental health system. Historically, the guidance for homes has been generic and appears to have been driven predominantly by the needs of older people, with an emphasis on physical care needs and support rather than rehabilitation or the fostering of independence.

Recent care standard regulations have dealt specifically with homes for younger people and there is more emphasis on residents' rights and participation in community activities, but there remains little about their overall role and their place within networks of care.

Many of the care homes were either established, or had their occupancy topped up, as stopgap outsourced elements of reprovision during institutional closure. In practice, they frequently provide regimented care with a lack of individual space or programmes. They are isolated physically and culturally from the mainstream of services and the wider community.

The ostensible distinction between these care types (and their different agency responsibilities for commissioning) revolves around the need for 'nursing care', but in practice the health care resource is more likely to be the service of last resort. Although there are moves to integrate the commissioning and provision of both health and social residential care, the distinction is still made with respect to funding responsibility and the different frameworks of standards and inspection that apply. In the absence of central policy guidance and evidence of effective models of care it has proved difficult to move on, either through evolution or closure and reprovision.

As a rule, individual community staff from a community mental health team or rehabilitation and recovery team visit care homes to monitor progress and to conduct care reviews. These visits may represent the only regular intrusion of the outside world into homes apart from inspection staff from the National Care Standards Commission. Some rehabilitation and recovery teams have taken on a development role, often working with local National Care Standards Commission staff and home managers to provide external help and support for the home's care team and to develop practice, clarify roles and responsibilities, and manage the processes of new referral and aftercare on moving on.

For individuals who prefer shared living for peer support and to combat loneliness, the main alternatives are group homes and adult (typically family) placements. There are difficulties inherent in such artificially generated social units in terms of reasonable limits on the accountability of an individual for others. Such schemes need clear preparation and support arrangements. Nevertheless, they add to the range and choice of supported living arrangements in any locality.

Supported ordinary living arrangements have in the past been through individual projects using funding from a variety of sources. They represent an ideal from the point of view of normalisation, independence and greater flexibility in adjusting and tailoring support to meet the specific type and level of each person's needs at any time (Carling, 1993). The Government's Supporting People programme (http://www.spkweb.org.uk/), which is being introduced at the time of writing, will establish clearer arrangements for the planning, commissioning and development of supported housing and also of 'floating support' available to individuals regardless of housing tenure. This should enable the more systematic creation of flexible support arrangements, including packages offering a higher intensity of support. There is a need to develop service models for mental health that will enable the health and social care elements to be delivered effectively together and to integrate supported housing with other residential care and rehabilitation services. Possibilities include the use of integrated or managed care networks.

All local authorities are exhorted to make use of direct payments, which give direct control of some care planning and commissioning to the individual service user, with appropriate support. The aim is empowerment and the creation of natural and less formal supports. For example, a service user might pay a friend to accompany them to a rehabilitation activity rather than rely on professional input. In mental health the uptake has thus far been negligible. It is unclear how much this is due to particular factors in the way care can be delivered or to the greater conservatism of mental health systems by comparison with those serving other disabled client groups.

The therapeutic milieu

There are few sustained examples in the UK of the implementation of programmatic behaviour management approaches such as the token economy. The evidence suggests that any gains are difficult to sustain and do not generalise well beyond the treatment setting and that there are daunting technical difficulties in achieving and maintaining a consistent system of measurement and reinforcement – particularly when tailored to individual needs. Nevertheless, many rehabilitation units have adopted elements of a behavioural approach within a social learning environment model, especially for the management of target problem behaviours or for specific tasks such as social skills training.

Fully fledged therapeutic communities are also rare, although more would identify milieu therapy as a core element in their approach. Key elements are a philosophy and practices that attempt to maximise the responsibility of individual residents for their behaviour, the development of positive social interaction and the use of individual and group sessions and programmes to develop insight and change.

There is ample evidence from empirical studies and personal accounts of the importance of exploration of personal coping strategies for psychotic experiences such as auditory hallucinations and ideas of reference. An example from popular culture would be the film *A Beautiful Mind*, about John Nash, the Nobel Prize winner who also suffered from mental illness.

The rehabilitation environment must allow space for personal discovery. It must also provide psychological containment for the anxiety that can attend the process. In a treatment-oriented environment the emergence of new, unpredictable behaviour may cause apprehension and be labelled by default as pathology in need of treatment. The aim is not stabilisation but occupation of the 'edge' zone of creative tension between stability and change. This can be an uncomfortable place and be anxiety provoking and overwhelming for staff (Foster & Roberts, 1998). Primitive psychological processes such as splitting and projective identification are common (see Chapter 4). Individual residents may become scapegoats within the staff and fellow-resident culture. There is evidence that high expressed emotion and critical comments have the same impact within residential units as in families (see Chapter 20). Some skilled external support for the team is essential in managing these processes.

There are also longer-term fluctuations of optimism and pessimism and internal orientation and external focus that have been recognised since the earliest institutional studies (see Chapter 2). Managing the unpredictability of psychosis also generates anxiety at the organisational level. The current predominance of a more paternalistic medical treatment model, short-termism and a culture of blame encourage return to an institutional ethos. An effective shared risk management strategy is important. Engaging managers, users and relatives in this as well as in ownership of the process of running and developing services helps to avoid polarisation. User-led service monitoring and research also have this effect, as well as providing valuable insights and encouraging empowerment.

> **Box 26.3**   The functions of residential rehabilitation and continuing care units
>
> - Extended assessment
> - Intensive rehabilitation programmes
> - Residential element of early intervention in psychosis programmes
> - Respite care
> - Crisis readmission in the course of care in a community setting
> - Continuing care where high levels of supervision and support are thought to be required for the foreseeable future
> - Step-down care for those moving from high and medium secure care

The functions of residential rehabilitation units are outlined in Box 26.3. In a locality with several such units different teams may take on special responsibility for some of these functions. Alternatively, they may be stratified in relation to some combination of challenging behaviour, risk, social disability and assumed likelihood of future independence. A few services have specialised units for women, as women typically form about a quarter of the client group and many are survivors of past abuse.

The dynamics of the unit is affected by the range of sources of referral: new arrivals coming from the community or via acute wards often feel reluctance and a sense of failure or loss of hope, whereas those coming from higher conditions of restriction in forensic and secure services usually experience greater physical freedom and more implicit and explicit demands for autonomy and responsibility.

Engaging in partnership working and developing a permeable boundary are helpful in breaking down the closed culture of residential units. This includes the use of facilities and programmes outside the unit but also running activities within the unit open to others. An example of this would be a Hearing Voices Group created in response to a high rate of persistent auditory hallucinations among residents. Staff and users acquired particular knowledge and skills that were shared with other service users from other parts of the rehabilitation services.

The development of satellite ordinary supported housing in a core and cluster model may enable more disabled people to test the water and move on gradually. The care and support required can be provided by a mixture of outreach from the host unit and social support through supported living arrangements and respite care in the base unit.

Smaller community-based units will frequently have experienced difficulties in obtaining planning permission and be very aware of their relationship with the immediate neighbourhood. It is much more common for higher-frequency socially embarrassing behaviour to be a cause of friction and a retreat into caution than the occasional instance of real threat. Helpful public relations includes prior planning by meeting the neighbours before the unit opens; mental health awareness training; participation in community activities; encouraging visits; and mutual practical help such as gardening.

Assertive outreach and case management

Assertive outreach teams are now the prescribed standard for the delivery of care to people with severe and enduring mental illness who do not engage well with services. The majority of the new teams being formed have grown out of existing community rehabilitation services. Teams vary in their model and ethos, but all share the following basic characteristics: delivering care directly rather than acting primarily as care coordinators; using natural settings in the community; employing a team held rather than individual caseworker approach; and providing care for as long as required (Stein & Santos, 1998). One part of the rationale is the management of transference on a shared basis, so that individual staff members are not overwhelmed by a patient's strong feelings of, for example, dependency or hostility.

In case management, the strengths model focuses on assets and their development rather than symptoms or problems (Rapp, 1998).

Employment

Since the earliest asylum-based studies on the influence of environmental factors on the course and outcome of psychosis, one of the most consistent findings has been that engagement in meaningful occupation is positive.

As with housing and other activities, there has been a move away from sheltered, congregated provision – to 'place and train' instead of 'train and place'. A number of studies have shown better outcomes in all respects using the individual placement and support model, which involves a minimal preparatory period and the use of normal jobs with support provided through job coaching which can be tailored to meet the individual's needs and tapered off or reintroduced as required. Further advantages of this approach are the enhanced self-esteem of 'real' work and socialisation outside the mental health system.

Individual placement and support schemes may take an opportunistic approach to developing niche placements, but they can also undertake preparatory work with employers. This can consist of mental health awareness training to reduce stigma and increase understanding, and liaison with personnel staff, occupational health and line management. This puts employment rehabilitation on a rights basis, strengthening the position of employees under the Disability Discrimination Act. Employers' increasing knowledge and interest may lead to joint preventive work tackling stress and other mental problems in the workplace.

Health and social care agencies are themselves large employers and can act as in-house development sites and exemplars of good practice. Standard One of the National Service Framework identifies the establishment of such schemes as an essential responsibility of all mental health care provider agencies. Successful projects such as that pioneered by the former Pathfinder Trust have found that, where user employment schemes have reached critical mass, there have been major secondary gains within the mental health workplace. Many staff have revealed personal histories of mental health problems and there has been a shift in the culture, with a reduction in polarisation of attitude between staff and service users. It has enabled non-tokenistic welcoming of job applications from those with experience of mental illness and positive target-setting for a proportion of the workforce with the same. Recognition of the value of the personal experience of illness and the process of recovery is endorsed by the establishment of posts such as 'experts by experience'. This breaks down barriers, adds valuable insights to the care process and puts a positive value on what has been regarded as a negative or shameful experience.

For those not aiming for open employment, social firms, which are cooperatives, often with a social purpose or aim, can provide a tolerant and supportive vehicle. They also offer possibilities as 'new mutuals' to develop as paid care provider services.

Social inclusion and the community as a therapeutic environment

The increasing importance of social inclusion within rehabilitation services requires a change in thinking about therapeutic environments. From the 1950s, day centres represented the first step of rehabilitation services outside the hospital setting, and as many were commissioned or run by social services departments they featured an emphasis on social therapies rather than a treatment model. Some emphasise structure and specific programmed activities, whereas others have a flexible drop-in approach.

The first alternatives to the established day care model grew from efforts to empower service users by encouraging staff to retreat into a background, facilitating role particularly in providing psychological containment and ensuring safety. The best-known example of this is the clubhouse model, which remains popular. Common features of the clubhouse are an emphasis on group decision-making and transitional employment provision through outside contracted work carried out by clubhouse members on a cooperative basis.

Providing meaningful daytime activities and rehabilitation in segregated and congregated environments has been criticised as stigmatising and disabling. Alternatives are based on a person-centred care plan driven by the dreams and aspirations of the individual, with input to support, enable and sustain their achievement. The shift is to the normal loci of such activities in the community. Success depends not only on the individual's preparedness, in terms of confidence and skills, to handle this but on setting up systems to influence the environment itself (Bates, 2002).

The community connections model divides the environment into a number of 'role spaces', typically employment; volunteering; education; arts and leisure; and faith. In each domain, a 'bridgebuilder' is responsible for developing relationships with host agencies in the community by working with them in schemes to develop social capital, asserting rights and negotiating access to normal programmes. This can include health promotion through mental health awareness training. The latter has more impact in changing public attitude when associated with active access through direct contact and demystification. Within this framework the individual user is supported by a 'connector', who may accompany them, or provide more distant support and encouragement as needed and desired. This support may be faded out as they gain familiarity and confidence and increased at times of stress or challenge.

Genuine progress towards social inclusion and supported living in the mainstream community and away from segregated care depends not only on the sum of rehabilitation endeavours with individuals, but on their impact on community attitudes and acceptance.

This chapter has mapped out the way recovery services might develop in the future and challenges the reader to think radically about what might constitute a therapeutic environment and where this could be. There is still, however, a place for the in-patient rehabilitation unit – although policy-makers may be reluctant to acknowledge it. This is as an alternative to acute or secure in-patient care, which would otherwise be the only options. Specialist rehabilitation units provide the opportunity to develop the kind of therapeutic environment that would not be possible on acute wards. Used flexibly within a well-managed integrated network of care they can act as a source of social support and psychological containment that helps to enable the start of the recovery journey.

References

Anthony, W. A. (2000) A recovery-oriented service system: setting some system level standards. *Psychiatric Rehabilitation Journal*, **24**, 159–168.

Anthony, W. A. & Liberman, R. P. (1986) The practice of psychiatric rehabilitation. Historical, conceptual and research base. *Schizophrenia Bulletin*, **12**, 542–545.

Bates, P. (2002) (ed.) *Working for Inclusion*. London: Sainsbury Centre for Mental Health.

Carling, P. J. (1993) Housing and supports for persons with mental illness. Emerging approaches to research and practice. *Hospital and Community Psychiatry*, **44**, 439–449.

Foster, A. & Roberts, V. Z. (1998) (ed.) *Managing Mental Health in the Community*. London: Routledge.

Mueser, K. T., Drake, R. E. & Bond, G. R. (1997) Recent advances in psychiatric rehabilitation for patients with severe mental illness. *Harvard Review of Psychiatry*, **5**, 123–137.

National Health Service Executive (1996) *24-Hour Nursed Care for People with Severe and Enduring Mental Illness*. Leeds: NHS Executive.

Rapp, C. A. (1998) *The Strengths Model: Case Management with People Suffering from Severe and Persistent Mental Illness*. New York: Oxford University Press.

Ridgeway, P. (2001) ReStorying psychiatric disability. Learning from first person accounts of recovery. *Psychiatric Rehabilitation Journal*, **24**, 335–343.

Stein, L. I. & Santos, A. B. (1998) *Assertive Community Treatment of Persons with Severe Mental Illness*. New York: Norton.

Warner, R. (2000) *The Environment of Schizophrenia*. London: Brunner-Routledge.

Index

Compiled by Linda English